CONTENTS

GW00536996

Editor
Guy Thomas
guy.thomas@mytimemedia.com

Consultant Editor
Richard West

Art Director
Alexandra Bourdelon

Advertisement Manager
Jay Jones
jay.jones@mytimemedia.com

Advertisement Production
Nik Harber

Publishers
MyTimeMedia Ltd,
Suite 25,
Eden House,
Enterprise Way,
Edenbridge,
Kent TN8 6HF.

Copyright MyTimeMedia Ltd.
Published in 2016

ISBN 978 1 907063848

print & digital media publishers

This guide is produced by
the team which brings you
Stamp Magazine

www.stampmagazine.co.uk

ADVICE &

MARKET PRICES

PURPOSE OF THIS BOOK

The objective of this guide is to give collectors accurate market
values of Great Britain stamps: the selling prices of most
dealers, as opposed to the inflated prices quoted by some
catalogues. The publisher of *British Stamp Market Values* is not
a dealer and is not affiliated to any dealer.

HOW TO USE THIS BOOK

The prices we quote and the abbreviations we use

This guide offers independent price information about all Great Britain stamps issued from 1840 to date, to help you budget for the items you require.

It quotes not the inflated prices that some catalogues give, but realistic market prices: the selling prices of most dealers.

The publisher of *British Stamp Market Values* is not affiliated to any dealer.

ABBREVIATIONS
The following abbreviations are used:
Des: designer
Perf: perforation
Wmk: watermark

GENERAL NOTES
■ Used prices quoted are for fine examples with full perforations or reasonable margins as applicable, and with either a light duplex cancellation (pre–1880) or a clear steel datestamp (post–1880).

■ Unused prices assume stamps are se–tenant where applicable.

■ As modern GB special stamps are usually sold only in sets, the price for a full set may be given instead of individual prices.

■ When a dash (–) appears in a price column it means that the stamp doesn't exist in that particular state, or that it is impracticable to price it.

EXPERTS WE CONSULTED OVER PRICING

RUSHSTAMPS
PO Box 1, Lyndhurst, Hampshire SO43 7PP
Rushstamps, run by Allan Grant, deals primarily in Great Britain. It publishes a bulging catalogue offering a wide range of material, which is available upon request.

BB STAMPS
PO Box 6277, Overton, Basingstoke, Hampshire RG25 3RN
Run by Brian Bayford, BB Stamps deals in GB stamps from Queen Victoria to Wildings.

MARK BLOXHAM
PO Box 204, Morpeth NE61 9AA
Mark Bloxham is a specialist in classic British stamps at the top end of the market.

PACKS & CARDS
Oaklands House, Reading Road North, Fleet, Hampshire GU51 4AB
Packs & Cards specialises in presentation packs and PHQ cards, selling by mail order, from its website and via eBay. It also supplies unusual items such as Post Office posters.

DON STADDON
Stamp Magazine contributor
Don Staddon is one of the leading authorities on Machin definitives.

IAN HARVEY
Member of the RPSL Expert Committee
Ian Harvey is a leading specialist collector of booklets from Edward VII to Elizabeth II.

STAMP PRINTERS

A quick guide to who printed what, and when

A relatively small number of security printers has dominated the production of British stamps since 1840. Here are their details.

PERKINS BACON 1840–1879
American inventor Jacob Perkins developed intaglio printing, and his son-in-law Joshua Bacon joined him in business in London.
First issue: 1840 1d black
Last issue: 1870–79 1½d rose-red

SOMERSET HOUSE 1847–1926
The Stamp Office at Somerset House in London had been printing revenue stamps since 1694, and was familiar with embossing technique required for the first high-value postage stamps.
First issue: 1847–54 1/- green
Last issue: 1924–26 definitive series

DE LA RUE 1855 to date
Guernseyman Thomas De La Rue came to prominence by offering surface-printing, which was ideal for stamps requiring perforation.
First issue: 1855–57 4d carmine

HARRISON & SONS 1911–1998
After initially printing by typography, this firm became synonymous with the photogravure technique from 1934 and remained the dominant printer of British stamps for many years. It was taken over by De La Rue in 1997.
First issue: 1911–13 definitive series
Last issue: 1998 The Queen's Beasts set

WATERLOW & SONS 1913–1955
There were two different Waterlow firms until 1920, after a family feud. The business was taken over by De La Rue in 1960.
First issue: 1913 'Seahorses' high-value series
Last issue:1955 'Castles' high-value series

BRADBURY WILKINSON 1918–1973
A producer of colonial stamps since 1875, this company was owned by the American Banknote Company from 1903 and was acquired by De La Rue in 1986.
First issue: 1918-19 'Seahorses' high-value series
Last issue: 1973 Parliamentary Conference set

ENSCHEDÉ 1979 to date
The Dutch company founded in 1703 became a back-up for Harrisons because of its capability of printing by photogravure.
First issue: 1979 8p red definitive

WADDINGTONS 1980–1981
This firm produced stamps under its own name only briefly, before acquiring House of Questa.
First issue: 1980 4p greenish-blue definitive
Last issue: 1981 4p and 20p definitives

HOUSE OF QUESTA 1980–2003
Initially independent, the company was owned by Waddingtons from 1984, MDC from 1996 and De La Rue from 2002.
First issue: 1980 75p grey definitive
Last issue: 2003 Extreme Endeavours set

WALSALL/ISP 1989 to date
The company initially promoted itself as an expert in self-adhesive printing, but has also printed gummed issues by litho and gravure.
It was fully rebranded as International Security Printers in 2014.
First issue: 1989 14p and 19p definitives (booklet)

CARTOR/ISP 2005 to date
The French company known for litho production and special printing techniques has been owned by Walsall since 2004.
First issue: 2004 customised Smilers sheets

GUIDE TO WATERMARKS

Identify the watermarks referred to in the price listings

Small crown	Large crown	Half penny	VR
Emblems	Small garter	Medium garter	Large garter
Spray of rose	Maltese cross	Large anchor	Small anchor
Orb	Imperial crown	Simple royal cypher GVR	Multiple royal cypher GVR
Single crown & script GVR	Multiple crowns/block GVR	Large crown & script GVR	Multiple crowns & E8R
Multiple crowns & GVIR	Single crown & GVIR	Tudor crown & E2R	St Edward's crown & E2R
Multiple St Edward's crown	Loops		

Watermarked paper was used to print most British stamps from 1840 until the later 1960s, as a security measure to make forgery difficult

QUEEN VICTORIA

For this reign prices are given for lightly mounted unused (left) and fine used (right). The exception is for the 1840–1841 issues, where fine used prices are subdivided into stamps with four margins (centre) and three margins (right).

Take care when buying unmounted mint because there are known cases of regumming.

LINE–ENGRAVED ISSUES

2d blue

1d black

◼ 1840, May 6. Penny Black

Engraved by Charles and Frederick Heath. Printed in recess by Perkins, Bacon. Wmk: Small Crown. Imperforate. Letters in lower corners only.

1d black	£11,000	£250	78.00
1d intense black	£15,000	£275	90.00
1d grey black	£14,000	£275	90.00
Plate 1a	£14,000	£300	90.00
Plate 1b	£11,000	£225	80.00
Plate 2	£11,000	£225	80.00
Plate 3	£14,000	£250	85.00
Plate 4	£11,000	£225	80.00
Plate 5	£11,000	£225	80.00
Plate 6	£11,000	£225	80.00
Plate 7	£12,000	£275	90.00
Plate 8	£14,000	£300	95.00
Plate 9	£14,000	£350	£125
Plate 10	£24,000	£600	£175
Plate 11	£16,000	£3,500	£750
Wmk inverted	£32,000	£2,200	£600
Bleute paper	£15,000	£500	£150
Red Maltese cross cancel	–	£250	90.00
Black Maltese cross cancel	–	£225	78.00
Blue Maltese cross cancel	–	£8,000	£2,000
Magenta Maltese cross cancel	–	£2,200	£400
Ruby Maltese cross cancel	–	£750	£225
Violet Maltese cross cancel	–	£12,000	£3,000
Number in cross (1–12)	–	£10,000	£3,000
Penny Post cancel only	–	£2,600	£600
Town datestamp only	–	£2,750	£600
1844 cancel	–	£1,000	£200

◼ 1840, May 8. Twopenny Blue

Engraved by Charles and Frederick Heath. Printed in recess by Perkins, Bacon. Wmk: Small Crown. Imperforate. Letters in lower corners only.

2d blue	£32,000	£550	£140
2d deep full blue	£36,000	£650	£170
2d pale blue	£36,000	£600	£150
Plate 1	£30,000	£550	£140
Plate 2	£40,000	£650	£170
Wmk Inverted	£60,000	£5,000	£2,800
Red Maltese cross cancel (Plate 1)	–	£600	£150
Red Maltese cross cancel (Plate 2)	–	£1,100	£225
Black Maltese cross cancel	–	£550	£140
Blue Maltese cross cancel	–	£6,000	£1,250
Magenta Maltese cross cancel	–	£4,000	£850
Ruby Maltese cross cancel	–	£2,000	£500
Number in cross (1–12)	–	£11,000	£3,000
Penny Post cancel only	–	£5,000	£1,200
Town datestamp only	–	£3,750	£800
1844 cancel	–	£1,250	£250

1d red

◼ 1841, February 10. Penny Red

Engraved by Charles and Frederick Heath. Printed in recess by Perkins, Bacon. Wmk: Small Crown. Imperforate. Letters in lower corners only.

1d red brown	£275	9.00	3.00
1d deep red brown	£550	15.00	4.00
1d orange brown	£1,200	£120	12.00
1d lake red	£3,500	£550	£100

Plate 1b	£18,000	£275	40.00
Plate 2	£18,000	£225	25.00
Plate 5	£5,000	£175	20.00
Plate 8	£8,000	90.00	20.00
Plate 9	£4,000	90.00	20.00
Plate 10	£2,000	90.00	20.00
Plate 11	£4,000	75.00	15.00
Wmk inverted	£4,000	£325	£150
Lavender paper	£1,000	£150	40.00
Red Maltese cross cancellation	–	£3,850	£875
Black Maltese cross cancellation	–	40.00	6.00
Blue Maltese cross cancellation	–	£375	75.00
Green Maltese cross cancellation	–	£8,000	£1,000
Violet Maltese cross cancellation	–	£9,000	£1,500
Number in cross (1–12)	–	£110	30.00
Penny Post cancellation only	–	£700	£125
Black town datestamp only	–	£300	95.00
Blue town datestamp only	–	£1,200	£275
Green town datestamp only	–	£2,750	£650
Black 1844 cancellation	–	9.00	3.00
Blue 1844 cancellation	–	£100	25.00
Green 1844 cancellation	–	£1,250	£250
Red 1844 cancellation	–	£12,000	£3,000
Violet 1844 cancellation	–	£2,500	£600
B blank error	–	£40,000	£18,000

1d rose-red

2d blue

■ 1854
Designs as above. Wmk: Small Crown. Perf: 16.

1d red-brown (February 1854)	£195	12.00
2d blue (March 1, 1854)	£2,100	60.00

■ 1855
Designs as above. Wmk: Small Crown. Perf: 14.

1d red-brown (January 1855)	£450	45.00
2d blue (March 4, 1855)	£7,000	£160

■ 1855
Designs as above. Wmk: Large Crown. Perf: 16.

1d red-brown (May 15, 1855)	£700	65.00
2d blue (July 20, 1855)	£9,000	£230

■ 1855
Designs as above. Wmk: Large Crown. Perf: 14.

1d red-brown (August 18, 1855)	£160	8.00
2d blue (July 20, 1855)	£1,600	30.00

2d blue

■ 1841, March 13. Twopenny Blue
Engraved by Charles and Frederick Heath. Printed in recess by Perkins, Bacon. Wmk: Small Crown. Imperforate. Letters in lower corners only. Horizontal white lines added to design.

2d blue	£3,000	50.00	12.00
2d pale blue	£3,200	55.00	12.00
2d deep full blue	£4,000	70.00	15.00
2d violet (lavender paper)	£22,000	£950	£175
Plate 3	£3,000	60.00	12.00
Plate 4	£3,500	50.00	12.00
Wmk inverted	£7,500	£400	£125
Black Maltese cross cancel	–	£150	22.50
Blue Maltese cross cancel	–	£3,000	£400
Number in cross (1–12)	–	£500	£120
Black town datestamp only	–	£1,000	£275
Blue town datestamp only	–	£4,000	£700
Black 1844 cancel	–	50.00	12.00
Blue 1844 cancel	–	£475	£100
Green 1844 cancel	–	£2,750	£750
Red 1844 cancel	–	£17,500	£3,500

1d rose-red

2d blue

■ 1858–1879
Designs as above. Wmk: Large Crown. Perf: 14. Letters in all four corners. Plate number included in design.

1d rose-red (April 1, 1864)

Plate 71	22.00	2.00
Plate 72	27.00	2.50
Plate 73	24.00	2.00
Plate 74	25.00	1.50
Plate 76	25.00	1.50
Plate 77	–	–
Plate 78	45.00	1.50
Plate 79	22.00	1.50
Plate 80	30.00	1.50
Plate 81	35.00	1.50

Plate 82	85.00	2.75	Plate 144	75.00	16.00
Plate 83	£120	6.00	Plate 145	23.00	1.75
Plate 84	40.00	1.60	Plate 146	25.00	4.50
Plate 85	27.00	1.60	Plate 147	30.00	2.00
Plate 86	35.00	2.75	Plate 148	25.00	2.00
Plate 87	22.00	1.50	Plate 149	25.00	4.50
Plate 88	£170	7.00	Plate 150	12.00	1.50
Plate 89	25.00	1.50	Plate 151	40.00	7.50
Plate 90	25.00	1.50	Plate 152	40.00	4.00
Plate 91	35.00	4.50	Plate 153	90.00	7.00
Plate 92	21.00	1.50	Plate 154	30.00	1.50
Plate 93	30.00	1.50	Plate 155	30.00	1.75
Plate 94	28.00	4.00	Plate 156	35.00	1.50
Plate 95	25.00	1.50	Plate 157	30.00	1.50
Plate 96	28.00	1.50	Plate 158	23.00	1.50
Plate 97	25.00	2.50	Plate 159	23.00	1.50
Plate 98	30.00	4.50	Plate 160	23.00	1.50
Plate 99	35.00	4.00	Plate 161	40.00	5.00
Plate 100	40.00	1.50	Plate 162	30.00	5.00
Plate 101	40.00	7.50	Plate 163	30.00	2.00
Plate 102	28.00	1.50	Plate 164	30.00	2.00
Plate 103	30.00	2.75	Plate 165	35.00	1.50
Plate 104	90.00	4.00	Plate 166	35.00	4.50
Plate 105	£110	5.50	Plate 167	35.00	1.50
Plate 106	35.00	1.50	Plate 168	30.00	6.00
Plate 107	40.00	5.00	Plate 169	30.00	6.00
Plate 108	60.00	1.75	Plate 170	21.00	1.50
Plate 109	65.00	2.50	Plate 171	12.00	1.50
Plate 110	40.00	7.50	Plate 172	23.00	1.50
Plate 111	36.00	1.75	Plate 173	48.00	6.50
Plate 112	50.00	1.70	Plate 174	23.00	1.50
Plate 113	30.00	9.00	Plate 175	40.00	2.50
Plate 114	£240	9.00	Plate 176	40.00	1.75
Plate 115	85.00	1.75	Plate 177	32.00	1.50
Plate 116	60.00	7.50	Plate 178	40.00	2.50
Plate 117	28.00	1.50	Plate 179	30.00	1.75
Plate 118	30.00	1.50	Plate 180	40.00	4.00
Plate 119	28.00	1.50	Plate 181	36.00	1.50
Plate 120	12.00	1.50	Plate 182	75.00	4.00
Plate 121	25.00	8.00	Plate 183	35.00	2.00
Plate 122	12.00	1.50	Plate 184	23.00	1.75
Plate 123	25.00	1.50	Plate 185	30.00	2.00
Plate 124	22.00	1.50	Plate 186	35.00	1.75
Plate 125	25.00	1.50	Plate 187	30.00	1.50
Plate 127	35.00	1.75	Plate 188	50.00	7.50
Plate 129	25.00	6.50	Plate 189	50.00	5.50
Plate 130	35.00	1.75	Plate 190	30.00	4.50
Plate 131	45.00	12.00	Plate 191	23.00	5.50
Plate 132	£160	18.00	Plate 192	30.00	1.50
Plate 133	£105	7.50	Plate 193	23.00	1.50
Plate 134	12.00	1.50	Plate 194	30.00	6.50
Plate 135	70.00	22.00	Plate 195	30.00	6.50
Plate 136	65.00	17.00	Plate 196	30.00	4.00
Plate 137	22.00	1.75	Plate 197	35.00	7.00
Plate 138	14.00	1.50	Plate 198	32.00	4.50
Plate 139	40.00	12.50	Plate 199	35.00	4.50
Plate 140	14.00	1.50	Plate 200	40.00	2.00
Plate 141	£100	7.00	Plate 201	23.00	4.00
Plate 142	50.00	22.00	Plate 202	40.00	6.50
Plate 143	40.00	12.00	Plate 203	23.00	13.00

Plate 204	35.00	1.75				

Plate 204	35.00	1.75
Plate 205	35.00	2.25
Plate 206	35.00	7.00
Plate 207	40.00	7.00
Plate 208	35.00	12.50
Plate 209	30.00	8.00
Plate 210	45.00	10.00
Plate 211	50.00	18.00
Plate 212	40.00	10.00
Plate 213	40.00	10.00
Plate 214	45.00	15.00
Plate 215	45.00	15.00
Plate 216	50.00	15.00
Plate 217	50.00	6.00
Plate 218	45.00	7.00
Plate 219	£100	58.00
Plate 220	32.00	6.00
Plate 221	50.00	15.00
Plate 222	60.00	30.00
Plate 223	75.00	50.00
Plate 224	£110	45.00
Plate 225	£2,900	£650

2d blue (July 1858)

Plate 7	£1,200	40.00
Plate 8	£1,200	25.00
Plate 9	£250	8.00
Plate 12	£1,800	£100
Plate 13	£260	15.00
Plate 14	£340	16.00
Plate 15	£320	16.00

½d rose-red (October 1, 1870)

Plate 1	£180	50.00
Plate 3	£120	25.00
Plate 4	£100	18.00
Plate 5	75.00	10.00
Plate 6	80.00	10.00
Plate 8	£225	60.00
Plate 9	£5,000	£600
Plate 10	85.00	10.00
Plate 11	80.00	10.00
Plate 12	80.00	10.00
Plate 13	80.00	10.00
Plate 14	80.00	10.00
Plate 15	£115	24.00
Plate 19	£140	28.00
Plate 20	£200	50.00

1½d rose-red (October 1, 1870)

Plate 1	£450	48.00
Plate 3	£275	32.00

EMBOSSED ISSUES

6d lilac

10d brown

1/- green

½d rose-red

1½d rose-red

■ **1870–1879**
Printed in recess by Perkins, Bacon. Wmk: Half Penny extending over three stamps (½d) or Large Crown (1½d). Perf: 14. Letters in all four corners. Plate number included in design, except plate 1 of the 1½d value.

■ **1847–1854. High values**
Die engraved at the Royal Mint by William Wyon. Printed using the embossed process at Somerset House. Wmk: VR (6d), or unwatermarked (10d, 1/-). Imperforate.

6d lilac (March 1, 1854)	£17,000	£525
10d brown (November 6, 1848)	£8,000	£775
1/- green (September 11, 1847)	£20,000	£550

(* The above are priced cut square; examples cut to shape are worth considerably less.)

Q. How to Build a Good Stamp Collection?
A. (Hint) If it's easy – maybe it is TOO easy...
10+ 'TOP TIPS' for Successful Collecting

As many of you know I made the decision to give up collecting when I started full-time in the trade 43 years ago. But here's what I perceive as a mistake I made in terms of re-sale value and in enjoyment. If you are not bothered about V A L U E then you don't need to read further...

What I collected then was easy to source. It was good quality. They were (and still are) lovely stamps but they would be worth less now than when I collected and that's more than 40 years ago. The basic mistake I made then was thinking that 'easy' made for a good stamp collection. Yes, 'easy' made for a lovely collection but I could buy those same stamps – in the SAME quality – from any number of differ-ent sources. I still can today … so if I can buy them easily today – will their value have appreciated? Has demand for what is/was easily available increased? The answer is a firm **NO**.

TIP As an 'aside'. In particular be wary of 'inertia' selling delivery systems – where you pay on direct debit / standing order sytem / monthly invoice. These systems usually hide the highest mark-ups in our industry and the lowest recovery value when it comes to sale. You are going to find this story particularly incredible – but about 13 years ago I was once called to clear a house-full of stamps. The owner had died leaving many 100's of *unopened New Issue delivery envelopes*. I opened one of the oldest envelopes. Inside was a note from the supplier saying sorry they had not delivered the MINT 1929 PUC £1 ! Ah well, I thought "such is life" – the collection included both mint Wembleys + literally masses more. Imagine my surprise when the next envelope opened included a MINT PUC £1 with a note saying "we found one for you" (and then the realisation that this High Value stamp had lain inside the same envelope for so long that it had a large brown 'rust-spot' on the reverse!

Returning to subject: So, what forms the basis of a **GOOD** stamp collection if I want **'resale VALUE'**?

TIP 1). The answer is, as usual, a combination of factors… BUT, if you think in terms of desirability and then dial in quality… this makes for a collection that others will wish to purchase. Of course collect-ing means that some of the stamps you source will be easily available … but if ALL the stamps you collect are easily available and on average they cost very little each… then you may have 1,000's of different stamps whose value lies in the actual handling cost of the supplier – not in their intrinsic value. So when it comes to selling this may result in little / no interest. Of course it goes without saying **TIP** – *Always collect the Best quality that you can afford.*

Where Do I Source Good Stamps?

2). Sadly, in some senses, the Philatelic World has changed. Gone are the days when in 1980 100,000 different Collectors descended upon the 1980 International Stamp Exhibition at Earls Court. I know because I was there. An International Stamp Show in the 'west' today may be lucky to see 10,000 visitors. A stamp fair today in a local village / town may be lucky to see 30 visitors let alone 20 actual buyers … when you consider that 15 dealers may have travelled to such a venue – is it any surprise that many Collectors may see the same stamps they saw at that same venue a month before?

Please turn to page 261 ☞

SURFACE-PRINTED ISSUES

Most issues from 1862–64 to 1880–83 have the plate number incorporated into their design. Many can be found with wing margins, where the vertical gutters between panes were perforated by way of a single row of holes down the centre.

4d carmine

■ 1855–1857

Surface-printed by De La Rue. Wmk: Small Garter (1855), Medium Garter (1856) or Large Garter (1857). Perf: 14.   No corner letters.

4d carmine (July 31, 1855)	£8,000	£275
4d carmine (February 25, 1856)	£9,000	£325
4d rose (January, 1857)	£1,600	55.00

6d lilac

1/– green

■ 1856

Surface-printed by De La Rue. Wmk: Emblems. Perf: 14. No corner letters

6d lilac (October 21, 1856)	£775	68.00
1/– green (November 1, 1856)	£2,200	£160

3d carmine   4d red

6d lilac   9d bistre

1/– green

■ 1862–1864

Surface-printed by De La Rue. Wmk: Large Garter (4d), Emblems (3d, 6d, 9d, 1/–). Perf: 14. Small corner letters.

3d carmine (May 1, 1862)	£1,800	£225
4d red (January 15, 1862)	£875	55.00
6d lilac (December 1, 1862)	£1,600	50.00
9d bistre (January 15, 1862)	£4,000	£280
1/– green (December 1, 1862)	£2,200	£150

3d carmine · 4d vermilion

6d lilac (with hyphen) · 9d bistre

10d brown · 1/- green

■ 1865–1867

Surface-printed by De La Rue. Wmk: Large Garter (4d) or Emblems (3d, 6d, 9d, 10d, 1/-). Perf: 14. Large corner letters.

3d carmine (March 1, 1865)

Plate 4	£1,000	£125

4d vermilion (July 4, 1865)

Plate 7	£500	65.00
Plate 8	£400	40.00
Plate 9	£400	40.00
Plate 10	£475	85.00
Plate 11	£400	40.00
Plate 12	£400	40.00
Plate 13	£400	40.00
Plate 14	£440	60.00

6d lilac (April 1, 1865)

Plate 5	£650	55.00
Plate 6	£2,200	£100

9d bistre (December 1, 1865)

Plate 4	£4,000	£360

10d brown (November 11, 1867)

Plate 1	–	£55,000

1/- green (February 1, 1865)

Plate 4	£2,000	£125

(* Mint examples of the 9d exist from a perforated imprimatur sheet of plate 5.)

6d lilac (without hyphen) · 2/- blue

■ 1867–1880

Surface-printed by De La Rue. Perf: 14. Wmk: Spray of Rose. Designs as above except 6d and 2/-.

3d red (July 12, 1867)

Plate 4	£1,100	£125
Plate 5	£375	35.00
Plate 6	£400	35.00
Plate 7	£500	35.00
Plate 8	£400	35.00
Plate 9	£400	35.00
Plate 10	£550	75.00

6d lilac (June 21, 1867)

Plate 6, with hyphen	£1,400	55.00
Plate 8, without hyphen	£600	55.00
Plate 9, without hyphen	£500	55.00
Plate 10, without hyphen	–	£32,000

9d bistre (October 3, 1867)

Plate 4	£1,300	£200

10d brown (July 1, 1867)

Plate 1	£1,900	£225
Plate 2	£50,000	£16,000

1/- green (July 13, 1867)

Plate 4	£675	40.00
Plate 5	£500	25.00
Plate 6	£700	25.00
Plate 7	£750	45.00

2/- blue (July 1, 1867)

Plate 1	£2,100	£140

2/- brown (February 27, 1880)

Plate 1	£27,000	£4,000

6d grey

■ 1872–1873

Surface-printed by De La Rue. Perf: 14. Wmk: Spray of Rose.

6d brown (April 12, 1872)

Plate 11	£450	35.00
Plate 12	£2,400	£160

6d grey (April 24, 1873)

Plate 12	£1,100	£130

5/- red

10/- grey-green

2½d mauve

3d red

£1 brown

4d green

6d buff

£5 orange

8d orange

1/- green

■ 1867–1883. High values
Surface-printed by De La Rue.

A) Wmk: Maltese Cross. Perf: 15.

5/– red (July 1, 1867)		
Plate 1	£3,850	£450
Plate 2	£5,000	£550
10/– grey-green (September 26, 1878)		
Plate 1	£55,000	£2,500
£1 brown (September 26, 1878)		
Plate 1	£85,000	£4,000

B) Wmk: Large Anchor. Perf: 14.

5/– red (November 25, 1882)		
Plate 4	£35,000	£1,950
10/– grey-green (February, 1883)		
Plate 1	£120,000	£4,000
£1 brown (December, 1882)		
Plate 1	£140,000	£6,500
£5 orange (March 21, 1882)		
Plate 1	£13,000	£4,500

3d on 3d lilac

6d on 6d lilac

■ 1873–1883
Surface-printed by De La Rue. Perf: 14.

A) Wmk: Small Anchor.

2½d mauve (July 1, 1875)		
Plate 1	£385	55.00
Plate 2	£385	55.00
Plate 3	£600	80.00

B) Wmk: Orb.

2½d mauve (May 16, 1876)		
Plate 3	£750	75.00
Plate 4	£350	35.00
Plate 5	£350	35.00

Plate 6	£350	35.00
Plate 7	£350	35.00
Plate 8	£350	35.00
Plate 9	£350	35.00
Plate 10	£375	40.00
Plate 11	£350	35.00
Plate 12	£350	35.00
Plate 13	£350	35.00
Plate 14	£350	35.00
Plate 15	£350	35.00
Plate 16	£350	35.00
Plate 17	£1,050	£190

2½d blue (February 5, 1880)

Plate 17	£325	40.00
Plate 18	£350	22.50
Plate 19	£325	22.50
Plate 20	£350	22.50

C) Wmk: Spray of Rose.
3d red (July 5, 1873)

Plate 11	£300	30.00
Plate 12	£325	30.00
Plate 14	£375	30.00
Plate 15	£300	30.00
Plate 16	£300	30.00
Plate 17	£325	30.00
Plate 18	£325	30.00
Plate 19	£300	30.00
Plate 20	£300	55.00

6d buff (March 15, 1873)

Plate 13	–	£22,000

6d grey (March 31, 1874)

Plate 13	£300	40.00
Plate 14	£300	40.00
Plate 15	£300	40.00
Plate 16	£300	40.00
Plate 17	£525	90.00

1/– green (September 1, 1873)

Plate 8	£700	80.00
Plate 9	£700	80.00
Plate 10	£700	90.00
Plate 11	£700	80.00
Plate 12	£475	65.00
Plate 13	£475	65.00
Plate 14	–	£28,000

1/– brown (October 14, 1880)

Plate 13	£4,000	£400

D) Wmk: Large Garter.
4d vermilion (March 1, 1876)

Plate 15	£2,000	£300
Plate 16	–	£24,000

4d green (March 12, 1877)

Plate 15	£825	£180
Plate 16	£775	£170
Plate 17	–	£14,000

4d brown (August 15, 1880)

Plate 17	£2,250	£325

8d orange (September 11, 1876)

Plate 1	£900	£175

E) Wmk: Imperial Crown.
2½d blue (March 23, 1881)

Plate 21	£350	18.00
Plate 22	£325	18.00
Plate 23	£325	14.00

3d red (February 1881)

Plate 20	£500	90.00
Plate 21	£380	55.00

3d (in red) **on 3d** lilac (January 1, 1883)

Plate 21	£400	80.00

4d brown (December 9, 1880)

Plate 17	£300	38.00
Plate 18	£300	38.00

6d grey (January 1, 1881)

Plate 17	£350	45.00
Plate 18	£310	45.00

6d (in red) **on 6d** lilac (January 1, 1883)

Plate 18	£425	80.00

1/– brown (May 29, 1881)

Plate 13	£525	90.00
Plate 14	£425	90.00

½d green 1d Venetian red

1½d Venetian red 2d red

5d indigo

■ 1880–1881
Surface-printed by De La Rue. Perf: 14. Wmk: Imperial Crown.

½d green (October 14, 1880)	35.00	6.00
1d Venetian red (January 1, 1880)	18.00	3.00
1½d Venetian red (October 14, 1880)	£140	30.00
2d red (December 8, 1880)	£180	60.00
5d indigo (March 15, 1881)	£600	65.00

1d lilac

■ 1881–1901
Surface-printed by De La Rue. Perf: 14. Wmk: Imperial Crown.

A) Die I. 14 white dots in each corner.
1d lilac (July 12, 1881)   £200   15.00

B) Die II. 16 white dots in each corner.
1d lilac (December 12, 1881)   1.75   0.75

2/6 lilac   5/- red

10/- blue

£1 green

■ 1883–1891. High values
Surface-printed by De La Rue. Perf: 14.

A) Wmk: Large Anchor.
2/6 lilac (July 2, 1883)   £350   70.00
5/- red (April 1, 1884)   £700   £110
10/- blue (April 1, 1884)   £1,800   £275

B) Wmk: Imperial Crown.
£1 brown (April 1, 1884)   £30,000   £2,500
£1 green (January 27, 1891)   £6,000   £700

C) Wmk: Orbs.
£1 brown (February 1, 1888)   £70,000   £4,000

½d blue   1½d lilac and 5d green

3d lilac and 1/- green   4d green

6d green and 2d lilac   9d green and 2½d lilac

■ 1883–84. 'Lilac & Green' series
Surface-printed by De La Rue. Perf: 14. Wmk: Imperial Crown (sideways on 2d, 2½d, 6d, 9d).

½d blue (April 1, 1884)	14.00	3.50
1½d lilac (April 1, 1884)	80.00	23.00
2d lilac (April 1, 1884)	£140	40.00
2½d lilac (April 1, 1884)	57.50	5.00
3d lilac (April 1, 1884)	£135	38.00
4d green (April 1, 1884)	£325	£100
5d green (April 1, 1884)	£325	£100
6d green (April 1, 1884)	£300	£110
9d green (August 1, 1883)	£725	£300
1/- green (April 1, 1884)	£775	£150

1d RED PLATES

Plate	m/m	Used	Plate	m/m	Used	Plate	m/m	Used	Plate	m/m	Used	Plate	m/m	Used
71	£25.00	£0.60	116	£30.00	£1.80	161	£18.75	£1.40	204	£15.00	£0.50			
72	£27.50	£0.80	117	£18.00	£0.50	162	£18.75	£1.40	205	£15.00	£0.60			
73	£27.50	£0.60	118	£20.00	£0.50	163	£18.75	£0.60	206	£15.00	£1.80			
74	£27.50	£0.50	119	£18.00	£0.50	164	£17.50	£0.60	207	£15.00	£1.80			
76	£27.50	£0.50	120	£11.50	£0.50	165	£18.75	£0.50	208	£15.00	£3.20			
78	£27.50	£0.50	121	£16.00	£1.90	166	£11.50	£1.20	209	£15.00	£1.80			
79	£18.75	£0.50	122	£11.50	£0.50	167	£11.50	£0.50	210	£19.50	£2.40			
80	£18.00	£0.50	123	£16.00	£0.50	168	£12.50	£1.40	211	£23.00	£5.75			
81	£20.00	£0.55	124	£11.50	£0.50	169	£15.00	£1.40	212	£19.50	£2.25			
82	£85.00	£0.80	125	£16.00	£0.50	170	£11.50	£0.50	213	£19.50	£2.25			
83	£95.00	£1.50	127	£22.00	£0.55	171	£11.50	£0.50	214	£19.50	£3.60			
84	£27.50	£0.55	129	£16.00	£1.60	172	£11.50	£0.50	215	£19.50	£3.60			
85	£16.00	£0.55	130	£22.00	£0.55	173	£17.50	£1.80	216	£19.50	£3.60			
86	£20.00	£0.80	131	£26.00	£3.20	174	£11.50	£0.50	217	£19.50	£1.50			
87	£13.75	£0.50	132	£95.00	£10.00	175	£15.00	£0.70	218	£19.50	£1.75			
88	£130.00	£2.00	133	£60.00	£3.00	176	£17.50	£0.55	219	£38.50	£25.00			
89	£16.00	£0.50	134	£11.50	£0.50	177	£15.00	£0.50	220	£12.50	£1.50			
90	£16.00	£0.50	135	£38.00	£5.25	178	£19.50	£0.70	221	£17.50	£4.00			
91	£22.00	£1.20	136	£36.00	£4.00	179	£15.00	£0.55	222	£23.00	£14.00			
92	£16.50	£0.50	137	£11.00	£0.55	180	£20.00	£1.00	223	£37.50	£25.00			
93	£20.00	£0.50	138	£11.50	£0.50	181	£11.50	£0.50	224	£40.00	£25.00			
94	£18.00	£1.00	139	£24.00	£3.50	182	£32.50	£1.00	225	£950.00	£280.00			
95	£16.00	£0.50	140	£11.50	£0.50	183	£19.50	£0.60						
96	£18.00	£0.50	141	£44.00	£1.80	184	£11.50	£0.50	SG48/9	½d	Plates			
97	£16.00	£0.70	142	£28.00	£4.80	185	£19.50	£0.60	1	£50.00	£13.75			
98	£20.00	£1.20	143	£18.75	£3.00	186	£15.00	£0.55	3	£35.00	£3.00			
99	£22.00	£1.00	144	£39.50	£4.00	187	£15.00	£0.50	4	£30.00	£2.25			
100	£24.00	£0.75	145	£12.00	£0.55	188	£19.50	£2.00	5	£20.00	£1.75			
101	£24.00	£1.80	146	£16.00	£1.20	189	£19.50	£1.40	6	£20.00	£1.75			
102	£16.00	£0.50	147	£20.00	£0.60	190	£15.00	£1.20	8	£50.00	£11.50			
103	£20.00	£0.70	148	£16.00	£0.60	191	£11.50	£1.40	9	£1200.00	£150.00			
104	£32.50	£1.00	149	£16.00	£1.20	192	£15.00	£0.50	10	£20.00	£1.75			
105	£37.50	£1.50	150	£11.50	£0.50	193	£12.50	£0.50	11	£20.00	£1.75			
106	£22.00	£0.50	151	£20.00	£1.80	194	£15.00	£2.00	12	£20.00	£1.75			
107	£24.00	£1.50	152	£15.00	£1.10	195	£15.00	£2.00	13	£20.00	£1.75			
108	£36.00	£0.55	153	£45.00	£2.00	196	£15.00	£1.00	14	£20.00	£1.75			
109	£35.00	£0.70	154	£15.00	£0.50	197	£20.00	£1.80	15	£20.00	£2.75			
110	£24.00	£1.80	155	£15.00	£0.55	198	£11.50	£1.20	19	£40.00	£6.00			
111	£29.00	£0.55	156	£15.00	£0.50	199	£17.50	£1.20	20	£47.50	£9.50			
112	£28.00	£0.55	157	£15.00	£0.50	200	£15.00	£0.50						
113	£20.00	£2.50	158	£15.00	£0.50	201	£11.50	£1.00	SG51/2	1½d	Plates			
114	£115.00	£2.50	159	£15.00	£0.50	202	£15.00	£1.60	1	£100.00	£10.00			
115	£36.00	£0.55	160	£17.50	£0.50	203	£11.50	£3.20	3	£85.00	£10.00			

All the above are offered on 7 days approval against cash with order subject only to remaining unsold, and are all sound good used (Mint are mounted with gum). **REFUND** is guaranteed provided stamps are returned within 7 days (21 days for overseas clients). To all orders under £50 please add 90p to help with post and packing. (Overseas customers please add £2.50 to all orders regardless of value.)

Reconstructors Wants Lists Welcomed!

GRAHAME W. MANN
Dept. BSMV17, P.O. Box 116, LUDLOW, Shropshire, SY8 3WQ
Tel: 01584 891303 Mon.-Sat. (9.00am to 5.00pm)
E mail: stampmann@btinternet.com

½d orange

1½d purple and green

6d purple on red

9d violet and blue

2d green and red

2½d purple on blue

10d purple and red

1/– green

3d purple on yellow

4d green and brown

4½d green and red

5d purple and blue

■ 1887–92. 'Jubilee' series

Surface-printed by De La Rue. Perf: 14. Wmk: Imperial Crown.

A) Wmk upright.

½d orange (January 1, 1887)	1.20	0.50
½d green (April 17, 1900)	1.40	0.60
1½d purple and green (January 1, 1887)	10.00	2.00
2d green and red (January 1, 1887)	18.00	8.00
2½d purple, blue paper (January 1, 1887)	14.00	0.75
3d purple, yellow paper (January 1, 1887)	18.00	1.50
4d green and brown (January 1, 1887)	22.00	7.00
4½d green and red (September 15, 1892)	7.00	25.00
5d purple and blue (January 1, 1887)	26.00	5.00
6d purple, red paper (January 1, 1887)	20.00	5.00
9d violet and blue (January 1, 1887)	45.00	25.00
10d purple and red (January 1, 1887)	40.00	24.00
1/– green (January 1, 1887)	£150	40.00
1/– green and red (July 11, 1900)	45.00	70.00
Set	**£400**	**£200**

B) Wmk inverted.

½d orange	60.00	60.00
½d green	60.00	60.00
1½d purple and green	£1,400	£400
2d green and red	£1,400	£400
2½d purple, blue paper	£3,500	£1,200
4d green and brown	£1,400	£500
5d purple and blue	£15,000	£1,200
6d purple, red paper	£8,000	£1,500
9d violet and blue	£7,000	£1,800
10d purple and red	£8,000	£2,700
1/– green	£1,600	£800
1/– green and red	£1,700	£900

Insured, cover to cover

H W Wood Limited is the preferred insurance broker for many stamp collectors and dealers. We provide a range of flexible insurance plans that we consider are sure to offer you the coverage you need. Contact us today to discuss your philatelic insurance needs.

Telephone: 01438 742033   Fax: 01438 367785   E-mail: finearts@hwint.com
Visit us online at www.hwiuk.com

H W Wood Limited is authorised and regulated by the Financial Conduct Authority (FCA). FCA register number 309408.
For confirmation of our regulatory status please visit the FCA website www.fca.org.uk

KING EDWARD VII

For this reign, most stamps are priced in three columns: unmounted mint (left), mounted mint (centre) and fine used (right). However, booklet panes are priced for mounted mint only.

De La Rue printings are generally cleaner, with good centring and neat perforations. Harrison and Somerset House printings are coarser, with poor centring and ragged perfs.

A vast range of shades exists, the details of these being beyond the scope of this publication.

½d yellow–green

1d scarlet

1½d purple and green

2d green and red

2½d blue

3d purple on yellow

4d orange

5d purple and blue

6d purple

7d grey

9d purple and blue

10d purple and red

1/– green and red

2/6 lilac

5/– red

10/– blue

£1 green

▪ 1902–10

Surface-printed by De La Rue. Wmk: Imperial Crown (½d to 1/-), Large Anchor (2/6, 5/-, 10/-), Three Imperial Crowns (£1). Perf: 14.

½d blue-green (Jan 1, 1902)	2.00	1.00	0.70
½d yellow-green (Jan 1, 1902)	2.00	1.00	0.70
Wmk inverted	20.00	12.00	12.00
1d scarlet (Jan 1, 1902)	1.75	1.00	0.50
Wmk inverted	7.00	5.00	6.00
1½d purple and green (Jan 1, 1902)	60.00	30.00	10.00
on chalky paper	60.00	30.00	10.00
2d green and red (Mar 25, 1902)	70.00	30.00	10.00
on chalky paper	60.00	28.00	12.00
2½d blue (Jan 1, 1902)	25.00	12.00	3.00
3d purple on yellow (Jan 1, 1902)	70.00	30.00	7.00
on chalky paper	60.00	30.00	10.00
4d green and brown (Jan 1, 1902)	95.00	40.00	18.00
on chalky paper	65.00	30.00	15.00
4d orange (Nov 1, 1909)	32.00	15.00	10.00
5d purple and blue (May 14, 1902)	90.00	40.00	15.00
on chalky paper	85.00	45.00	15.00
Wmk inverted	£6,500	£4,000	£3,000
6d purple (Jan 1, 1902)	60.00	28.00	14.00
on chalky paper	60.00	30.00	14.00
7d grey (May 4, 1910)	10.00	7.00	16.00
9d purple and blue (Jan 1, 1902)	£170	70.00	40.00
on chalky paper	£155	60.00	40.00
10d purple and red (Jul 3, 1902)	£210	60.00	40.00
on chalky paper	£175	55.00	40.00
1/- green and red (Mar 24, 1902)	£165	60.00	20.00
on chalky paper	£165	60.00	24.00
2/6 lilac (Apr 5, 1902)	£450	£200	75.00
on chalky paper	£450	£300	90.00
Wmk inverted	£7,500	£4,000	£2,500
5/- red (Apr 5, 1902)	£700	£280	£120
10/- blue (Apr 5, 1902)	£1,800	£525	£350
£1 green (Jun 16, 1902)	£2,800	£1,200	£600

Booklet panes	Wmk Upright	Inverted
Pane of five ½d with label showing St Andrew's Cross	£500	£500
Pane of six ½d	55.00	90.00
Pane of six 1d	40.00	70.00

2d Tyrian plum

▪ 1910

Surface-printed by De La Rue. Wmk: Imperial Crown. Perf: 14. Prepared for use but not issued. One example is known used.

2d Tyrian plum	£115,000	–

▪ 1911–13

Designs as 1902–10 series.

A) Surface-printed by Harrison. Wmk: Imperial Crown. Perf: 14.

½d yellow-green (May 3, 1911)	3.50	2.00	1.30
Wmk inverted	60.00	40.00	40.00
1d red (May 3, 1911)	10.00	6.00	8.00
Wmk inverted	60.00	40.00	40.00
2½d blue (Jul 10, 1911)	£100	45.00	18.00
Wmk inverted	£1,800	£1,000	£1,000
3d purple (Sep 12, 1911)			
on yellow paper	£140	80.00	£140
4d orange (Jul 13, 1911)	£130	60.00	45.00

Booklet panes	Wmk Upright	Inverted
Pane of five ½d with label showing St Andrew's Cross	£1,100	£1,100
Pane of six ½d	80.00	£110
Pane of six 1d	70.00	90.00

B) Surface-printed by Somerset House. Wmk: Imperial Crown (½d to 1/-), Large Anchor (2/6, 5/-, 10/-), or Three Imperial Crowns (£1). Perf: 14.

1½d purple and green (Jul 13, 1911)	50.00	25.00	12.00
2d green and red (Mar 11, 1912)	46.00	24.00	11.00
5d purple and blue (Aug 7, 1911)	50.00	28.00	11.00
6d purple (Oct 31, 1911)	50.00	26.00	14.00
chalky paper	50.00	28.00	60.00
7d grey (Aug 1, 1912)	20.00	12.00	15.00
9d purple and blue (Jul 24, 1911)	£105	65.00	40.00
10d purple and red (Oct 9, 1911)	£140	75.00	45.00
1/- green and red (Jul 17, 1911)	£115	58.00	25.00
Wmk inverted	£250	£150	–
2/6 purple (Sep 27, 1911)	£450	£190	85.00
5/- red (Feb 29, 1912)	£700	£280	£120
10/- blue (Jan 14, 1912)	£1,800	£600	£400
£1 green (Sep 3, 1911)	£2,800	£1,200	£700

C) Surface-printed by Harrison. Wmk: Imperial Crown. Perf: 15x14.

½d green (Oct 30, 1911)	50.00	30.00	30.00
1d red (Oct 5, 1911)	32.00	16.00	8.50
2½d blue (Oct 14, 1911)	45.00	21.00	7.00
3d purple on yellow (Sep 22, 1911)	55.00	30.00	13.00
4d orange (Nov 22, 1911)	48.00	26.00	10.00

KING GEORGE V

For this reign, the stamps are priced in three columns: unmounted mint (left), mounted unused (centre) and fine used (right).

Stamps are found in a wide range of shades, details of which are beyond the scope of this guide.

½d green   1d red

▦ 1911–1912

Des: Bertram Mackennal and G. W. Eve. Portrait based on photograph by W. and D. Downey. Die engraved by J. A. C. Harrison. Printed in typography by Harrison. Perf: 15x14.

A) Wmk: Imperial Crown. Issued in sheets and booklets.

½d green (Jun 22, 1911)	7.50	3.50	2.00
Wmk inverted	15.00	7.50	3.50
1d red (Jun 22, 1911)	6.50	3.00	1.50
Wmk inverted	12.50	7.00	3.00

(* These stamps also exist with Wmk sideways and printed in error with perf: 14.)

Booklet panes	Wmk Upright	Inverted
Pane of six ½d	80.00	£120
Pane of six 1d	75.00	£110

B) Wmk: Simple Royal Cypher GVR. Issued only in booklets.

½d green (Sep 28, 1912)	80.00	30.00	28.00
Wmk inverted	80.00	30.00	28.00
1d green (Sep 28, 1912)	35.00	16.00	18.00
Wmk inverted	35.00	16.00	18.00

Booklet panes	Wmk Upright	Inverted
Pane of six ½d	£550	£550
Pane of six 1d	£250	£240

▦ 1912

Designs as above, except that the King's hair is lighter on the ½d and the lion is shaded on the 1d. Printed in typography by Harrison. Perf: 15x14.

A) Wmk: Imperial Crown

½d green (Jan 1, 1912)	8.50	4.50	1.00
Wmk inverted	£1,400	£800	£500
1d red (Jan 1, 1912)	5.00	2.00	0.80
Wmk inverted	£450	£350	£250

B) Wmk: Simple Royal Cypher GVR.

½d green (Aug 1912)	8.00	4.00	1.25
Wmk inverted	£500	£300	£200
1d red (Aug 1912)	7.00	3.50	1.00
Wmk inverted	22.00	14.00	12.00

C) Wmk: Multiple Royal Cypher GVR.

½d green (Oct 1912)	12.00	7.00	9.00
Wmk inverted	15.00	12.00	12.50
Wmk sideways	–	–	£3,250
1d red (Sep 1912)	15.00	9.00	4.50
Wmk inverted	20.00	15.00	16.00
Wmk sideways	£220	£150	£160

½d green, 1½d brown

1d red, 2½d blue

2d orange, 3d violet, 4d green   5d brown, 6d purple, 7d green, 8d black

9d black, 9d green, 10d blue, 1/– brown

▦ 1912–1924

Des: Bertram Mackennal and G. W. Eve. Die engraved by J. A. C. Harrison. Printed in typography by Harrison (all values except 6d) and Somerset House (all values except 1d). Perf: 15x14.

A) Wmk: Simple Royal Cypher GVR.

i) Wmk upright

½d green (Jan 16, 1913)	1.00	0.40	0.40
Wmk inverted	4.00	2.25	1.10
1d red (Oct 8, 1912)	1.00	0.40	0.40
Wmk inverted	4.00	2.25	0.90
1½d brown (Oct 15, 1912)	3.50	2.00	0.80
Wmk inverted	8.00	4.00	1.60
2d orange (Aug 20, 1912)	3.50	1.75	0.60
Wmk inverted	20.00	10.00	8.50
2½d blue (Oct 18, 1912)	16.00	8.00	2.25
Wmk inverted	£110	75.00	75.00
3d violet (Oct 9, 1912)	8.00	3.75	1.00
Wmk inverted	£160	95.00	95.00
4d green (Jan 15, 1913)	16.00	7.00	1.50
Wmk inverted	40.00	25.00	25.00
5d brown (Jun 30, 1913)	20.00	8.00	4.00
Wmk inverted	£1,100	£700	£700
6d purple (Aug 1, 1913)			
chalky paper	18.00	8.00	2.00
Wmk inverted	85.00	50.00	50.00
7d green (Aug 1, 1913)	28.00	11.00	7.50
Wmk inverted	80.00	50.00	50.00
8d black (Aug 1, 1913)			
yellow paper	42.00	20.00	11.00
Wmk inverted	£180	£110	£110
9d black (Jun 30, 1913)	20.00	10.00	3.75
Wmk inverted	£200	£125	£125
9d green (Sep 1922)	£200	75.00	24.00
Wmk inverted	£1,200	£800	£750
10d blue (Aug 1, 1913)	32.00	15.00	18.00
Wmk inverted	£3,750	£2,500	£1,800
1/– brown (Aug 1, 1913)	28.00	13.00	1.80
Wmk inverted	£300	£250	£200

Booklet panes	*Wmk Upright*	*Inverted*
Pane of six ½d	35.00	45.00
Pane of six 1d	35.00	45.00
Pane of six 1½d	60.00	75.00
Pane of four 1½d with two advert labels	£750	£750
Pane of six 2d	80.00	£130

B) Wmk: Multiple Royal Cypher GVR.

½d green (Aug 1913)	£160	£100	95.00
Wmk inverted	£500	£350	£350
1d red (Aug 1913)	£350	£225	£180
Wmk inverted	£800	£600	£600

◼ 1924–1926

Designs as above, but printed by typography by Waterlow (all values except 6d), Harrison (all values) or Somerset House (1½d, 6d), Wmk: Multiple Crowns and block GVR.

½d green (Feb 1924)	0.60	0.30	0.20
Wmk inverted	5.00	2.50	1.00
Wmk sideways	11.00	5.50	4.50
1d red (Feb 1924)	0.85	0.35	0.20
Wmk inverted	5.00	2.50	1.25
Wmk sideways	26.00	15.00	16.00
1½d brown (Feb 1924)	0.90	0.40	0.20
Wmk inverted	2.50	1.25	1.00

Wmk sideways	14.00	7.00	4.50
2d orange (Sep 1924)	2.00	0.85	0.70
Wmk inverted	60.00	40.00	40.00
Wmk sideways	£175	60.00	65.00
2½d blue (Oct 1924)	7.50	4.00	1.10
Wmk inverted	125.00	70.00	50.00
3d violet (Oct 1924)	11.00	5.00	1.00
Wmk inverted	125.00	70.00	50.00
4d green (Nov 1924)	18.00	7.00	1.40
Wmk inverted	£200	£110	75.00
5d brown (Nov 1924)	30.00	12.00	2.00
Wmk inverted	£140	95.00	80.00
6d purple (Sep 1924)	3.80	1.50	0.50
chalky paper	15.00	9.00	1.75
ordinary paper, Wmk inverted	£120	70.00	60.00
chalky paper, Wmk inverted	80.00	60.00	40.00
9d green (Dec 1924)	20.00	7.00	2.50
Wmk inverted	£120	75.00	70.00
10d blue (Nov 1924)	65.00	28.00	22.00
Wmk inverted	£3,500	£2,200	£1,600
1/– brown (Oct 1924)	35.00	16.00	1.40
Wmk inverted	£550	£400	£260

Booklet panes	*Wmk Upright*	*Inverted*
Pane of six ½d	35.00	45.00
Pane of six 1d	35.00	45.00
Pane of six 1½d	60.00	75.00
Pane of four 1½d with two advert labels	£125	£125

(* A wide range of advertising labels exists.)

2/6 brown

◼ 1913–1934. High values. 'Seahorses'

Des: Bertram Mackennal. Dies engraved by J.A.C. Harrison. Wmk: Simple Royal Cypher GVR. Perf: 11x12

A) Printed in recess by Waterlow. White gum. 22mm high.

2/6 brown (Jun 30, 1913)	£600	£175	£100
5/– red (Jun 30, 1913)	£1,000	£325	£175
10/– blue (Aug 1, 1913)	£1,900	£700	£300
£1 green (Aug 1, 1913)	£4,000	£2,250	£1,100

B) Printed in recess by De La Rue. Yellowish gum. 22mm high.

2/6 brown (Oct 1915)	£500	£200	£100
5/– red (Sep 1915)	£900	£280	£190
10/– blue (Dec 1915)	£3,500	£2,000	£600

C) Printed in recess by Bradbury, Wilkinson. White gum. 22.5mm–23mm high.

2/6 brown (Dec 1918)	£225	75.00	32.00
5/– red (Jan 1919)	£325	£150	45.00
10/– blue (Jan 1919)	£600	£300	£100

D) Printed in recess by Waterlow. Die re-engraved so that the background to the portrait consists of horizontal and diagonal lines.

2/6 brown (Oct 16, 1934)	£130	60.00	12.00
5/– red (Oct 16, 1934)	£350	£120	45.00
10/– blue (Oct 16, 1934)	£500	£300	50.00

1d red, 1½d brown (1924 issue)

1d red, 1½d brown (1925 issue)

▨ 1924–1925. British Empire Exhibition

Des: H. Nelson. Printed in recess by Waterlow. Wmk: Multiple Crowns and block GVR. Perf: 14.

Set (April 23, 1924)	18.00	8.00	8.00
Set (May 9, 1925)	45.00	30.00	30.00
First day cover (1924)	–	–	£375
First day cover (1925)	–	–	£1,600

½d green   1d red

1½d brown

2½d blue

£1 black

▨ 1929, May 10. Postal Union Congress

Des: J. Farleigh (½d, 2½d), E. Linzell (1d, 1½d), H. Nelson (£1). Printed in typography by Waterlow (½d to 2½d) or in recess by Bradbury, Wilkinson (£1). Wmk: Multiple Crowns and block GVR (½d to 2½d), or Large Crown and script GVR (£1). Perf: 15x14 (½d to 2½d), or 12 (£1).

½d green	1.50	0.50	0.45
Wmk inverted	20.00	11.00	8.00
Wmk sideways	70.00	25.00	25.00
1d red	2.50	1.50	1.00
Wmk inverted	25.00	13.00	14.00
Wmk sideways	90.00	60.00	60.00
1½d brown	2.00	1.25	0.80
Wmk inverted	12.00	6.00	4.50
Wmk sideways	65.00	20.00	20.00
2½d blue	16.00	7.00	5.00
Wmk inverted	£3,500	£2,000	£1,000
Set	20.00	9.00	6.75
First day cover	–	–	£450
£1 black	£1,000	£550	£550
First day cover	–	–	£12,000

Booklet panes	Wmk Upright	Inverted
Pane of six ½d	40.00	£120
Pane of six 1d	45.00	£200
Pane of six 1½d	30.00	90.00
Pane of four 1½d with two advert labels	£250	£280

½d green, 1½d brown

1d red, 2½d blue

2d orange, 3d violet, 4d green

5d brown

9d deep green, 10d blue, 1/- brown

5d brown (Feb 17, 1936)	9.00	5.00	2.50
9d deep green (Dec 2, 1935)	16.00	7.00	2.25
10d blue (Feb 24, 1936)	25.00	11.00	9.00
1/- brown (Feb 24, 1936)	32.00	12.00	0.75

Booklet panes	Wmk Upright	Inverted
Pane of six ½d	60.00	£100
Pane of six 1d	60.00	£150
Pane of six 1½d	20.00	25.00
Pane of four 1½d with two advert labels	75.00	75.00

½d green, 1d red, 1½d brown, 2½d blue

1935, May 7. Silver Jubilee

Des: B. Freedman. Printed in photogravure by Harrison. Wmk: Multiple Crowns and block GVR. Perf: 15x14.

½d green	0.80	0.40	0.30
Wmk inverted	11.00	6.00	6.00
1d red	1.40	0.70	0.70
Wmk inverted	11.00	6.00	6.00
1½d brown	1.25	0.50	0.40
Wmk inverted	2.00	1.00	0.90
2½d blue	3.00	2.00	4.00
2½d Prussian blue	£17,000	£13,000	£15,000
Set (excluding Prussian blue)	6.00	3.25	4.75
First day cover	–	–	80.00
Pictorial cover	–	–	£800

Booklet panes	Wmk Upright	Inverted
Pane of four ½d	30.00	60.00
Pane of four 1d	30.00	60.00
Pane of four 1½d	15.00	20.00

1934–1936

Designs as 1912–24 and 1924–26 issues, but with dark shading behind the portrait. Printed in photogravure by Harrison. Wmk: Multiple Crowns and block GVR. Perf: 15x14.

½d green (Nov 19, 1934)	0.25	0.10	0.15
Wmk inverted	15.00	7.00	3.00
Wmk sideways	9.00	6.00	3.00
1d red-brown (Sep 24, 1934)	0.25	0.20	0.15
Wmk inverted	15.00	7.00	2.50
Wmk sideways	22.00	11.00	14.00
1½d brown (Aug 20, 1934)	0.20	0.15	0.10
Wmk inverted	2.50	1.25	0.60
Wmk sideways	10.00	6.00	2.50
2d orange (Jan 21, 1935)	0.60	0.35	0.40
Wmk sideways	£175	70.00	65.00
2½d blue (Mar 18, 1935)	1.40	0.90	0.75
3d violet (Mar 18, 1935)	1.80	1.00	0.75
4d grey-green (Dec 2, 1935)	2.50	1.40	0.75

KING EDWARD VIII

For this reign stamps are priced in two columns: unmounted mint (left) and fine used (right). The exception is booklet panes, which are priced only for unmounted mint with good perforations.

½d, 1d, 1½d, 2½d

■ 1936. Accession

Des: H. Brown, adapted by Harrison. Portrait by H. Cecil. Printed in photogravure by Harrison. Wmk: Multiple Crown and E8R. Perf: 15x14.

½d green (September, 1, 1936)	0.10	0.10
Wmk inverted	6.00	2.50
1d red (September 14, 1936)	0.20	0.20
Wmk inverted	5.00	2.25
1½d brown (September 1, 1936)	0.20	0.10
Wmk inverted	0.75	0.80
2½d blue (September 1, 1936)	0.20	0.30
Set	0.50	0.50

Booklet panes	Wmk Upright	Inverted
Pane of six ½d	15.00	42.00
Pane of six 1d	15.00	42.00
Pane of two 1½d	10.00	10.00
Pane of four 1½d with two advert labels	95.00	95.00
Pane of six 1½d	8.00	14.00

KING GEORGE VI

For this reign, prices are priced in two columns: unmounted mint (left) and fine used (right). The exception is booklet panes, which are priced only for unmounted mint with good perforations.

1½d

■ 1937, May 13. Coronation
Des: E. Dulac. Printed in photogravure by Harrison. Wmk: Multiple Crown and GVIR. Perf: 15x14.

1½d	0.25	0.15
First day cover	–	3.00
Pictorial cover	–	20.00

½d, 1d, 1½d, 2d, 2½d, 3d

4d, 5d, 6d

7d, 8d, 9d, 10d, 11d, 1/–

■ 1937–51. Definitives
Des: E. Dulac and E. Gill (½d to 6d), E. Dulac (7d to 1/–). Printed in photogravure by Harrison. Wmk: Multiple Crown and GVIR. Perf: 15x14.

A) Original colours

½d green (May 10, 1937)	0.15	0.10
Wmk inverted	7.00	0.50
Wmk sideways	0.25	0.30
1d red (May 10, 1937)	0.15	0.10
Wmk inverted	30.00	2.50
Wmk sideways	15.00	5.00
1½d red-brown (July 30, 1937)	0.15	0.15
Wmk inverted	9.00	1.00
Wmk sideways	1.00	0.50
2d orange (January 31, 1938)	0.50	0.35
Wmk inverted	36.00	2.50
Wmk sideways	36.00	20.00
2½d blue (May 10, 1937)	0.25	1.00
Wmk inverted	32.00	3.00
Wmk sideways	50.00	25.00
3d violet (January 31, 1938)	1.50	0.60
4d green (November 21, 1938)	1.75	0.20
5d brown (November 21, 1938)	2.00	0.30
6d purple (January 30, 1939)	1.00	0.15
7d emerald (February 27, 1939)	3.50	0.50
8d carmine (February 27, 1939)	5.00	0.50
9d deep green (May 1, 1939)	4.00	0.50
10d blue (May 1, 1939)	3.00	0.50
11d brown-purple (December 29, 1947)	1.75	1.00
1/– brown (May 1, 1939)	4.00	0.15
Set	24.00	4.00

Booklet panes	Wmk Upright	Inverted
Pane of two ½d	60.00	60.00
Pane of six ½d	30.00	60.00
Pane of two 1d	60.00	60.00
Pane of six 1d	30.00	£170
Pane of two 1½d	20.00	30.00
Pane of four 1½d with two advert labels (*)	£120	£120
Pane of six 1½d	30.00	60.00
Pane of six 2d	£120	£300
Pane of six 2½d	£120	£250
		Wmk Sideways
Pane of four ½d	–	70.00
Pane of four 1d	–	£110

(* 15 different combinations of advertising labels exist. Prices quoted are for the cheapest; scarcer panes can fetch up to twice as much.)

B) As above, but with paler colours.

½d pale green (September 1, 1941)	0.15	0.10
Wmk inverted	3.00	0.40
1d pale red (August 11, 1941)	0.20	0.10
Wmk sideways	3.00	3.00
1½d pale red-brown (September 28, 1942)	0.50	0.35
2d pale orange (October 6, 1941)	0.50	0.25
Wmk inverted	3.00	0.40
Wmk sideways	10.00	8.00
2½d pale blue (July 21, 1941)	0.15	0.10

Wmk inverted	1.00	0.50
Wmk sideways	7.00	6.00
3d pale violet (November 3, 1941)	1.00	0.25
Set	1.50	1.00

Booklet panes	Wmk Upright	Inverted
Pane of two ½d	9.00	–
Pane of six ½d	20.00	30.00
Pane of two **1d**	25.00	–
Pane of two 1½d	9.00	–
Pane of six **2d**	20.00	30.00
Pane of six 2½d pale blue	10.00	15.00

C) As above, but with colours changed

½d orange (May 3, 1951)	0.10	0.20
Wmk inverted	0.20	0.30
1d blue (May 3, 1951)	0.10	0.10
Wmk inverted	2.25	1.00
Wmk sideways	0.20	0.40
1½d green (May 3, 1951)	0.25	0.20
Wmk inverted	2.75	2.00
Wmk sideways	1.25	1.50
2d red–brown (May 3, 1951)	0.25	0.25
Wmk inverted	4.00	3.50
Wmk sideways	0.75	0.75
2½d red (May 3, 1951)	0.15	0.15
Wmk inverted	1.00	0.50
Wmk sideways	0.60	0.85
4d blue (October 2, 1950)	1.00	0.65
Set	1.50	1.10

Booklet panes	Wmk Upright	Inverted
Pane of two ½d	10.00	–
Pane of four ½d	10.00	10.00
Pane of six ½d	6.00	6.00
Pane of two **1d**	10.00	–
Pane of three **1d** with three labels reading 'MINIMUM INLAND PRINTED PAPER RATE 1½d'	25.00	25.00
Pane of three **1d** with three labels reading 'SHORTHAND IN ONE WEEK'	35.00	35.00
Pane of four **1d**	10.00	20.00
Pane of six **1d**	20.00	25.00
Pane of two 1½d	10.00	–
Pane of four 1½d	10.00	15.00
Pane of six 1½d	20.00	25.00
Pane of six **2d**	20.00	60.00
Pane of six 2½d	6.00	8.00

2/6, 5/–

10/–, £1

■ 1939–1948. High values

Des: E. Dulac (2/6, 5/–), G. R. Bellew (10/–, £1). Printed in recess by Waterlow. Wmk: Single Crown and GVIR. Perf: 14.

2/6 brown (September 4, 1939)	70.00	5.00
2/6 green (March 9, 1942)	9.00	0.50
5/– red (August 21, 1939)	18.00	1.25
10/– dark blue (October 30, 1939)	£220	17.00
10/– ultramarine (November 30, 1942)	30.00	3.50
£1 brown (October 1, 1948)	18.00	12.00
Set	£280	40.00

½d green, 1d red, 1½d brown, 2d orange, 2½d blue, 3d violet

■ 1940, May 6. Centenary of the First Adhesive Postage Stamps

Des: H. L. Palmer. Printed in photogravure by Harrison. Wmk: Multiple Crown and GVIR. Perf: 14½ x 14.

Set	4.00	3.50
First day cover	–	7.50
Pictorial cover	–	35.00

Farming, homes, industry, transport (2½d)
Dove of peace (3d)

■ 1946, June 11. Victory

Des: H. L. Palmer (2½d), Reynolds Stone (3d). Printed in photogravure by Harrison. Wmk: Multiple Crown and GVIR. Perf: 15x14.

Set	0.20	0.25
First day cover	–	9.00
Pictorial cover	–	45.00

2½d

£1

■ 1948, April 26. Royal Silver Wedding

Des: G.T. Knipe (2½d) and Joan Hassall (£1), from photographs by Dorothy Wilding. Printed in photogravure by Harrison. Wmk: Multiple Crown and GVIR. Perf: 15x14 (2½d), 14 x 15 (£1).

Set	27.00	25.00
First day cover	–	50.00
Pictorial cover	–	£425

■ 1948, May 10. Liberation of the Channel Islands

Although this set was also placed on sale at eight post offices in Great Britain, it is listed under Regional Issues.

Globe surrounded by a laurel wreath (2½d)
Globe with Olympic rings (3d)
Olympic rings (6d)
Victory and Olympic rings (1/–)

■ 1948, July 29. Olympic Games

Des: P. Metcalfe (2½d), A. Games (3d), S. Scott (6d) and E. Dulac (1/–). Printed in photogravure by Harrison. Wmk: Multiple Crown and GVIR. Perf: 15x14.

Set	7.00	1.20
First day cover	–	8.00
Pictorial cover	–	35.00

Two hemispheres (2½d)
UPU monument (3d)
Globe and compass (6d)
Globe and posthorn (1/–)

■ 1949, October 10. 75th Anniversary of the Universal Postal Union

Des: Mary Adshead (2½d), P. Metcalfe (3d). H. Fleury (6d), G. R. Bellew (1/–). Printed in photogravure by Harrison. Wmk: Multiple Crown and GVIR. Perf: 15x14.

Set	1.50	1.25
First day cover	–	9.50
Pictorial cover	–	47.00

H.M.S. Victory (2/6)
White Cliffs of Dover (5/–)
St. George and the Dragon (10/–)
Royal Coat of Arms (£1)

■ 1951, May 3. High values

Des: Mary Adshead (2/6, 5/–), P. Metcalfe (10/–, £1). Printed in recess by Waterlow. Wmk: Single Crown and GVIR. Perf: 11x12.

Set	65.00	15.00

Commerce and prosperity (2½d)
Festival symbol (4d)

■ 1951, May 3. Festival of Britain

Des: E. Dulac (2½d), A. Games (4d). Printed in photogravure by Harrison. Wmk: Multiple Crown and GVIR. Perf: 15x14.

Set	0.35	0.40
First day cover	–	3.00
Pictorial cover	–	17.00

QUEEN ELIZABETH II PRE-DECIMALS

In this section, prices are priced in two columns: unmounted mint (left) and fine used (right). The exception is booklet panes, which are priced only for unmounted mint with good perforations.

Except where otherwise stated, all the stamps have the same technical details: Printed in photogravure by Harrison. Perf: 15x14 (definitives), 15x14 (special issues with a horizontal design) or 14x15 (special issues with a vertical design).

½d, 1d, 1½d, 2d

2½d, 3d

4d, 4½d

5d, 6d, 7d

8d, 9d, 10d, 11d

1/-, 1/6

1/3

■ **1952–1967. Wilding definitives**

Des: Miss E. Marx (½d, 1d, 1½d, 2d). M.C. Farrar–Bell (2½d, 3d, 4d, 4½d), G. Knipe (5d, 6d, 7d), Miss M. Adshead (8d, 9d, 10d, 11d), E. Dulac (1/–, 1/3, 1/6): portrait by Dorothy Wilding Studios. On the 2½d value the top line of the diadem was initially broken (Type I), but this was later corrected (Type II).

A) Wmk: Multiple Tudor Crown and E2R.

½d orange (August 31, 1953)	0.10	0.10
Wmk inverted	0.15	0.40
1d blue (August 31, 1953)	0.15	0.10
Wmk inverted	4.50	2.50
1½d green (December 5, 1952)	0.10	0.10
Wmk inverted	0.35	0.30
Wmk sideways	0.35	0.30
2d deep brown (August 31, 1953)	0.20	0.15
Wmk inverted	20.00	12.00
Wmk sideways	0.75	0.50
2½d carmine (type 1) (December 5, 1952)	0.15	0.10
Wmk inverted (type 2)	0.40	0.30
Wmk sideways (type 1)	3.50	4.00
3d violet (January 18, 1954)	1.00	0.20
4d blue (November 2, 1953)	1.00	0.70
5d brown (July 6, 1953)	4.00	2.50
6d purple (January 18, 1954)	3.00	0.75
7d pale green (January 18, 1954)	8.00	2.00
8d magenta (July 6, 1953)	5.00	0.75
9d myrtle–green (February 8, 1954)	14.00	1.50
10d blue (February 8, 1954)	12.00	1.50
11d brown–red (February 8, 1954)	30.00	10.00
1/– bistre (July 6, 1953)	1.00	0.50
1/3 deep green (November 2, 1953)	3.00	1.50
1/6 grey–blue (November 2, 1953)	12.00	1.25
Set	70.00	20.00
Set Wmk inverted	18.00	14.00
Set Wmk sideways	4.50	4.50
First day covers (set of 6)	–	£140
Pictorial cover	–	£600

Booklet panes	Wmk Upright	Inverted
Pane of two **½d**	2.00	–
Pane of four **½d**	4.00	4.00
Pane of six **½d**	2.00	4.00
Pane of two **1d**	2.00	–
Pane of four **1d**	3.00	25.00
Pane of three **1d** with three labels reading: MINIMUM INLAND PRINTED PAPER RATE 1½d	£300	£300
Pane of three **1d** with three labels reading: PLEASE POST EARLY IN THE DAY	40.00	40.00
Pane of three **1d** with three labels reading: PACK YOUR PARCELS SECURELY/ ADDRESS YOUR LETTERS CORRECTLY/ POST EARLY IN THE DAY	40.00	40.00
Pane of six **1d**	8.00	30.00
Pane of two **1½d**	2.00	–
Pane of four **1½d**	4.00	4.00
Pane of six **1½d**	2.00	4.00
Pane of six **2d**	27.00	£160
Pane of six **2½d**	3.50	3.50

B) As before but Wmk: St. Edward's Crown and E2R.

½d orange (August 1955)	0.15	0.10
Wmk inverted	0.20	0.20
1d blue (September 19, 1955)	0.20	0.10
Wmk inverted	0.50	0.50

1½d green (August 1955)	0.15	0.10
Wmk inverted	0.30	0.20
Wmk sideways	0.20	0.25
2d deep brown (September 6, 1955)	0.25	0.30
Wmk inverted	7.00	5.00
Wmk sideways	0.50	0.50
2d brown (October 17, 1956)	0.25	0.10
Wmk inverted	5.00	4.00
Wmk sideways	5.00	3.00
2½d carmine (type 1) (September 28, 1955)	0.25	0.15
Wmk inverted	0.75	1.00
Wmk sideways	0.75	1.00
2½d carmine (type 2) (September 1955)	0.30	0.60
Wmk inverted	0.30	0.30
3d violet (July 17, 1956)	0.25	0.20
Wmk inverted	1.75	1.50
Wmk sideways	12.00	7.50
4d blue (November 14, 1955)	1.50	2.00
5d brown (September 21, 1955)	5.00	3.00
6d purple (December 20, 1955)	3.50	1.00
6d deep purple (May 8, 1958)	3.00	1.00
7d pale green (April 23, 1956)	30.00	7.00
8d magenta (December 21, 1955)	4.00	1.25
9d myrtle-green (December 15, 1955)	12.00	2.00
10d blue (September 22, 1955)	10.00	2.00
11d brown-red (October 28, 1955)	0.50	1.25
1/– bistre (November 3, 1955)	6.50	0.50
1/3 deep green (March 27, 1956)	14.00	1.00
1/6 grey-blue (March 27, 1956)	20.00	0.75
Set	100.00	25.00
Set (Wmk inverted)	14.00	7.00
Set (Wmk sideways)	14.00	9.00

Booklet panes	Wmk Upright	Inverted
Pane of two ½d	3.00	–
Pane of four ½d	4.00	4.00
Pane of six ½d	2.00	3.50
Pane of two 1d	3.50	–
Pane of three 1d with three labels reading:		
PACK YOUR PARCELS SECURELY/		
ADDRESS YOUR LETTERS CORRECTLY/		
POST EARLY IN THE DAY	30.00	35.00
Pane of four 1d	4.00	4.00
Pane of six 1d	2.50	3.00
Pane of two 1½d	3.50	–
Pane of four 1½d	4.00	4.00
Pane of six 1½d	2.00	2.00
Pane of six 2d deep brown	13.00	65.00
Pane of six 2d brown	8.00	22.50
Pane of six 2½d	3.00	3.00
Pane of four 3d	10.00	15.00
Pane of six 3d	6.00	20.00

C) As before but Wmk: Multiple St. Edward's Crown.

½d orange (November 25, 1958)	0.10	0.10
chalky paper (July 15, 1963)	2.00	2.50
Wmk inverted	0.30	0.10
chalky paper and Wmk inverted	1.50	2.00
Wmk sideways	0.25	0.15

1d blue (November 1958)	0.10	0.10
Wmk inverted	0.20	0.20
Wmk sideways	0.60	0.35
1½d green (December 1958)	0.15	0.15
Wmk inverted	1.00	0.40
Wmk sideways	4.50	3.50
2d brown (December 4, 1958)	0.10	0.10
Wmk inverted	75.00	40.00
Wmk sideways	0.50	0.40
2½d carmine (type 1) (October 4, 1961)	0.10	0.40
Wmk inverted	0.20	0.25
2½d carmine (type 2) (November 1958)	0.35	0.20
chalky paper (July 15, 1963)	0.30	0.25
Wmk inverted	3.50	0.90
chalky paper & Wmk inverted	0.30	0.25
Wmk sideways	0.40	0.50
3d violet (November 1958)	0.15	0.10
Wmk inverted	0.25	0.20
Wmk sideways	0.25	0.15
4d blue (October 29, 1958)	0.50	0.25
4d deep blue (April 28, 1965)	0.20	0.12
Wmk inverted	0.35	0.20
Wmk sideways	0.35	0.15
4½d red-brown (February 9, 1959)	0.12	0.12
5d brown (November 10, 1958)	0.20	0.10
6d deep purple (December 23, 1958)	0.25	0.10
7d pale green (November 26, 1958)	0.50	0.20
8d magenta (February 24, 1960)	0.35	0.10
9d myrtle-green (March 24, 1959)	0.35	0.20
10d blue (November 18, 1958)	0.75	0.25
1/– bistre (October 30, 1958)	0.35	0.25
1/3 deep green (June 17, 1959)	0.35	0.15
1/6 grey-blue (December 16, 1958)	3.00	0.15
Set	5.00	1.50
Set (Wmk inverted)	80.00	42.00
Set (Wmk sideways)	5.50	4.00

Booklet panes	Wmk Upright	Inverted
Pane of three ½d and one 2½d (chalky paper)	8.00	8.00
Pane of four ½d	2.50	2.50
Pane of six ½d	1.25	2.00
Pane of four 1d	2.50	2.50
Pane of six 1d	1.50	2.50
Pane of four 1½d	2.50	2.50
Pane of six 1½d	5.00	6.00
Pane of six 2d	40.00	£500
Pane of four 2½d (chalky paper)	1.00	1.00
Pane of six 2½d	3.00	15.00
Pane of four 3d	2.00	2.00
Pane of six 3d	1.50	1.50
Pane of six 4d deep blue	1.50	1.50
		Wmk Sideways
Pane of two ½d se-tenant with two 2½d (type 2)		1.00
Pane of four ½d		2.00
Pane of two 1d se-tenant with two 3d to left		5.00
Pane of two 1d se-tenant with two 3d to right		5.00
Pane of four 1d		3.00
Pane of four 1½d		25.00
Pane of four 3d		2.00
Pane of four 4d		2.00

■ Graphite-lined issue
Designs as above, but with black graphite lines on the back. All values have two vertical lines, except for the 2d which has just one line, on the right as viewed from the back.

A) Wmk: St. Edward's Crown and E2R upright. Released on November 19, 1957.

½d orange	0.20	0.20
1d blue	0.20	0.20
1½d green	1.25	0.50
2d brown	1.00	1.25
2½d carmine (type 2)	4.50	3.50
3d violet	0.75	0.50
Set	6.75	5.50
First day cover	–	75.00

B) Wmk: Multiple St. Edward's Crown.

½d orange (June 15, 1959)	5.00	5.00
Wmk inverted	1.00	1.25
1d blue (December 18, 1958)	1.00	1.00
Wmk inverted	1.00	0.75
1½d green (August 4, 1959)	60.00	50.00
Wmk inverted	20.00	20.00
2d brown (December 4, 1958)	4.75	2.50
2½d carmine (type 2) (June 9, 1959)	6.00	6.00
Wmk inverted	35.00	30.00
3d violet (November 24, 1958)	0.60	0.45
Wmk inverted	0.55	0.40
4d blue (April 29, 1959)	3.25	3.25
4½d red-brown (June 3, 1959)	3.50	2.25
Set	70.00	55.00
Set (Wmk inverted)	60.00	50.00

Booklet panes	Wmk Upright	Inverted
Pane of six ½d	20.00	12.00
Pane of six 1d	7.50	7.00
Pane of six 1½d	£500	£125
Pane of six 2½d	30.00	£300
Pane of six 3d	4.00	4.00

■ Phosphor-graphite issue
Designs as above, but with phosphor bands on the front in addition to the graphite lines on the back. All values have two bands, except for the 2d which has just one band to the left.

A)Wmk: St. Edward's Crown and E2R upright. Released on November 18, 1959.

½d orange	3.00	3.00
1d blue	9.00	9.00
1½d green	2.50	3.00
2d brown	£100	£100

B) Wmk: Multiple St. Edwards Crown.

2d brown	4.00	3.00
2½d carmine (type 2)	10.00	10.00
3d violet	14.00	7.50
4d blue	8.00	5.00
4½d red-brown	25.00	20.00
Set	50.00	40.00
First day cover	–	75.00

■ Phosphor issue
Designs as above, but without graphite lines. All values have two phosphor bands on the front, except where stated. Released on June 22, 1960 except where stated. Wmk: Multiple St. Edward's Crown.

½d orange	0.15	0.15
Wmk inverted	1.00	1.00
Wmk sideways	5.00	7.50
1d blue	0.10	0.10
Wmk inverted	0.35	0.30
Wmk sideways	0.40	0.50
1½d green	0.12	0.20
Wmk inverted	20.00	18.00
Wmk sideways	12.00	10.00
2d brown (one band)	14.00	12.00
2d brown (October 4, 1961)	0.20	0.10
Wmk inverted	0.30	0.25
2½d carmine (type 2)	0.20	0.20
Wmk inverted	£160	£140
2½d carmine (type 2, one band)	1.50	0.50
Wmk inverted	35.00	30.00
2½d carmine (type 1, one band)	40.00	35.00
3d violet	0.50	0.35
Wmk inverted	0.80	0.50
Wmk sideways	1.25	0.55
3d violet (April 29, 1965) (one band at left)	0.30	0.40
Wmk inverted	60.00	60.00
Wmk sideways	4.00	4.00
3d violet (one band at right)	0.30	0.40
Wmk inverted	6.00	6.50
Wmk sideways	4.00	4.00
se-tenant pair	0.60	1.50
se-tenant pair with Wmk inverted	65.00	65.00
se-tenant pair with Wmk sideways	8.00	10.00
3d violet (December 8, 1966) (one band)	0.25	0.25
Wmk inverted	3.00	3.50
Wmk sideways	0.40	0.50
4d blue	2.75	3.25
4d deep blue (April 28, 1965)	0.15	0.25
Wmk inverted	0.25	0.20
Wmk sideways	0.35	0.25
4½d red-brown (September 13, 1961)	0.15	0.25
5d brown (June 9, 1967)	0.20	0.25
6d deep purple (June 27, 1960)	0.20	–
7d pale green (February 15, 1967)	0.20	0.25
8d magenta (June 28, 1967)	0.20	0.25
9d myrtle green (December 29, 1966)	0.50	0.25
10d blue (December 30, 1966)	0.50	0.40
1/– bistre (June 28, 1967)	0.40	0.20
1/3 deep green	1.00	1.00
1/6 grey-blue (December 12, 1966)	2.00	2.00

Set	4.50	5.00
Set (Wmk inverted)	£180	£170
Set (Wmk sideways)	15.00	18.00

Booklet panes	Wmk Upright	Inverted
Pane of six ½d	3.00	4.00
Pane of six 1d	2.00	2.00
Pane of six 1½d	8.00	£120
Pane of six 2½d (type 2, two bands)	80.00	£1,100
Pane of six 2½d (type 2, one band)	22.00	£220
Pane of six 3d (two bands)	5.00	5.00
Pane of six 3d (one band at left or right)	20.00	£130
Pane of six 3d (one centre band)	4.00	15.00
Pane of six 4d	2.00	3.00
		Wmk sideways
Pane of four ½d		35.00
Pane of two 1d, two 3d (two bands)	–	3.00
Pane of two 1d, two 3d (one band, left)	–	11.00
Pane of two 1d, two 3d (one band, right)	–	11.00
Pane of four 1d	–	5.00
Pane of four 1½d	–	50.00
Pane of four 3d (two bands)	–	5.00
Pane of four 4d	–	1.00

Crowns and orb (2½d)
Rose, daffodil, thistle and shamrock (4d)
Coronation robe (1/3)
Crowns and cypher (1/6)

■ **1953, June 3. Coronation**
Des: E.G. Fuller (2½d), M. Goaman (4d), E. Dulac (1/3), M. C.
Farrar–Bell (1/6). Wmk: Tudor Crown and E2R.

Set	11.00	6.00
First day cover		30.00

(* The 1/3 design was reissued with a face value of £1 in the
2000 Her Majesty's Stamps miniature sheet and the 2003 A
Perfect Coronation prestige stamp book.)

Carrickfergus Castle (2/6)
Caernarvon Castle (5/–)
Edinburgh Castle (10/–)
Windsor Castle (£1)

■ **1955–1968. Castle high value definitives**
Des: L. Lamb. Printed in recess. Perf: 11x12.

A) Wmk: St. Edward's Crown and E2R.
i) Printed by Waterlow.

2/6 brown (September 23, 1955)	14.00	2.00
5/– carmine (September 23, 1955)	30.00	3.00
10/– blue (September 1, 1955)	60.00	10.00
£1 black (September 1, 1955)	85.00	20.00
Set	£160	30.00
First day cover	–	£300
Pictorial cover	–	£850

ii) Printed by De La Rue.

2/6 (July 17, 1958)	25.00	3.50
5/– (April 30, 1958)	50.00	8.00
10/– (April 25, 1958)	£150	14.00
£1 (April 28, 1958)	£200	30.00
Set	£425	47.00

(* The top perforation tooth of each side of stamps from the De
La Rue printing is narrower than on the Waterlow printing.)

B) Wmk: Multiple St. Edward's Crown.
i) Printed by De La Rue.

2/6 (July 22, 1959)	12.00	0.50
5/– (June 15, 1959)	50.00	1.00
10/– (July 21, 1959)	40.00	2.75
£1 (June 23, 1959)	80.00	12.00
Set	£150	15.00

ii) Printed by Bradbury Wilkinson.

2/6 (July 1, 1963)	0.50	0.15
5/– (September 3, 1963)	2.00	0.40
10/– (October 16, 1963)	3.50	2.50
£1 (November 14, 1963)	9.50	3.00
Set	13.50	7.00

iii) Printed by Bradbury Wilkinson on chalky paper.

2/6 (May 30, 1968)	0.50	0.75

(* The Queen's diadem is more detailed on the Bradbury
Wilkinson printing than on the De La Rue printing.)

C) No Wmk. Printed by Bradbury Wilkinson.

2/6 (July 1, 1968)	0.30	0.40
5/– (April 10, 1968)	1.50	0.75
10/– (April 10, 1968)	6.00	4.00
£1 (December 4, 1967)	7.00	4.50
Set	10.50	10.50

Scouting badge (2½d)
Flying swallows (4d)
Globe within compass (1/3)

■ **1957, August 1. World Scout Jubilee Jamboree**
Des: Mary Adshead (2½d), P. Keely (4d), W. H. Brown (1/3). Wmk:
St Edward's Crown and E2R.

Set	3.75	3.25
First day cover	–	22.00

(* These stamps were issued in coils as well as counter sheets.)

Wilding design with added inscription (4d)

■ 1957, September 12. Inter–Parliamentary Union Conference
Des: F. Langfield. Wmk: Multiple St. Edward's Crown and E2R.

4d	0.50	0.50
First day cover	–	82.00

Welsh dragon (3d)
Games emblem (6d)
Welsh dragon (1/3)

■ 1958, July 18. British Empire & Commonwealth Games
Des: Reynolds Stone (3d), W.H. Brown (6d), Pat Keely (1/3).
Wmk: Multiple St. Edward's Crown and E2R.

Set	1.25	1.25
First day cover	–	60.00

1660 postboy (3d)
1660 posthorn (1/3)

■ 1960, July 7. Anniversary of General Letter Office
Des: Reynolds Stone (3d), Faith Jaques (1/3). Wmk: Multiple St.
Edward's Crown.

Set	2.00	1.75
First day cover	–	32.00

Europa emblem (6d, 1/6)

■ 1960, September 19. First Anniversary of CEPT
Des: P. Rahikainen and Reynolds Stone. Wmk: Multiple St.
Edward's Crown.

Set	5.50	3.75
First day cover	–	25.00

Thrift plant (2½d)
Squirrel and tree (3d)
Thrift plant (1/6)

■ 1961, August 28. Post Office Savings Bank Centenary
Des: P. Gauld (2½d), M. Goaman (3d, 1/6). Wmk: Multiple St.
Edward's Crown.
A) Printed on a Timson machine.

Set	1.25	1.25
First day cover	–	38.00

B) Printed on a Thrissell machine (2½d, 3d only).

Pair	1.60	1.50

(* The portrait on the 2½d is greyer from the Thrissell machine,
and that on the 3d is much clearer on the Timson printing.)

CEPT emblem (2d)
Doves and emblem (4d)
Doves and emblem (10d)

■ 1961, September 18. CEPT Conference
Des: M. Goaman and T. Kurperschoek. Wmk: Multiple St.
Edward's Crown.

Set	0.25	0.30
First day cover	–	5.00

Roof of Westminster Hall (6d)
Palace of Westminster (1/3)

■ **1961, September 23. Commonwealth Parliamentary Conference**
Des: Faith Jaques. Wmk: Multiple St. Edward's Crown.

Set	1.25	1.25
First day cover	–	20.00

Boxes bearing arrows (2½d)
Arrows over the British Isles (3d)
Joining arrows (1/3)

■ **1962, November 14. National Productivity Year**
Des: D. Gentleman. Wmk: Multiple St. Edward's Crown, inverted on 2½d and 3d values.
A) Non-phosphor issue.

Set	1.25	1.15
First day cover	–	25.00

B) Phosphor issue (one band on 2½d, three bands on 3d, 1/3).

Set	12.00	12.50
First day cover	–	£100

Ears of wheat (2½d)
Three children (1/3)

■ **1963, March 21. Freedom From Hunger**
Des: M. Goaman. Wmk: Multiple St. Edward's Crown, inverted on both values.
A) Non-phosphor issue.

Set	1.25	1.25
First day cover	–	20.00

B) Phosphor issue (one band on 2½d, three bands on 1/3).

Set	14.00	12.25
First day cover	–	32.00

Centenary of the 1863 Paris Postal Conference (6d)

■ **1963, May 7. Paris Postal Conference Centenary**
Des: Reynolds Stone. Wmk: Multiple St. Edward's Crown, inverted.
A) Non-phosphor issue.

6d	0.20	0.25
First day cover	–	10.00

B) Phosphor issue (three bands).

6d	3.75	3.75
First day cover	–	25.00

Bee on flowers (3d)
Selection of wildlife (4½d)

■ **1963, May 16. National Nature Week**
Des: S. Scott (3d), M. Goaman (4½d). Wmk: Multiple St. Edward's Crown.
A) Non-phosphor issue.

Set	0.20	0.20
First day cover	–	14.00

B) Phosphor issue (three bands).

Set	1.75	1.75
First day cover	–	30.00

Helicopter over lifeboat (2½d)
Lifeboat (4d)
Lifeboatmen (1/6)

■ **1963, May 31. International Lifeboat Conference**
Des: D. Gentlemen. Wmk: Multiple St. Edward's Crown.
A) Non-phosphor issue.

Set	1.75	1.50
First day cover	–	20.00

B) Phosphor issue (one band on 2½d, three bands on 4d, 1/6).

Set	20.00	15.00
First day cover	–	36.00

Red Cross (3d, 1/3, 1/6 with different borders)

■ 1963, August 15. Red Cross Centenary Congress
Des: H. Bartram. Wmk: Multiple St. Edward's Crown.
A) Non-phosphor issue.

Set	2.75	3.00
First day cover	–	22.00

B) Phosphor issue (three bands).

Set	28.00	26.00
First day cover	–	55.00

Cable over globe (1/6)

■ 1963, December 3. Opening of Compac Cable
Des: P. Gauld. Wmk: Multiple St. Edward's Crown.
A) Non-phosphor issue.

1/6	1.25	1.25
First day cover	–	15.00

B) Phosphor issue (three bands).

1/6	8.00	8.00
First day cover	–	35.00

A Midsummer Night's Dream: Puck and Bottom (3d)
Twelfth Night: Feste (6d)
Romeo and Juliet (1/3)
King Henry V (1/6)
Hamlet (2/6)

■ 1964, April 23. Shakespeare Festival
Des: D. Gentleman (3d to 1/6); C. and R. Ironside (2/6). Printed
in recess by Bradbury, Wilkinson (2/6). Perf: 11x12 (2/6). Wmk:
Multiple St. Edward's Crown.
A) Non-phosphor issue.

Set	2.25	2.50
First day cover	–	6.50

B) Phosphor issue (three bands on 3d, 6d, 1/3, 1/6).

Set	6.50	7.50
First day cover	–	10.00

Flats, Richmond Park (2½d)
Shipbuilding, Belfast (4d)
Forest Park, Snowdonia (8d)
Nuclear Reactor, Dounreay (1/6)

■ 1964, July 1. International Geographical Congress
Des: D. Bailey. Wmk: Multiple St. Edward's Crown.
A) Non-phosphor issue.

Set	2.00	2.25
First day cover	–	12.00

B) Phosphor issue (one band on 2½d, three bands on 4d, 8d, 1/6).

Set	12.00	11.00
First day cover	–	25.00

Spring gentian (3d)
Dog rose (6d)
Honeysuckle (9d)
Fringed water lily (1/3)

■ 1964, August 5. International Botanical Congress
Des: M. and S. Goaman. Wmk: Multiple St. Edward's Crown.
A) Non-phosphor issue.

Set	2.25	2.50
First day cover	–	14.00

B) Phosphor issue (three bands).

Set	12.00	11.00
First day cover	–	25.00

Forth Road Bridge (3d)
Forth Road Bridge and Foth Bridge (6d)

■ 1964, September 4. Opening of the Forth Road Bridge
Des: A. Restall. Wmk: Multiple St. Edward's Crown.
A) Non-phosphor issue.

Set	0.25	0.30
First day cover	–	3.50

B) Phosphor issue (three bands).

Set	2.75	2.75
First day cover	–	10.00

Sir Winston Churchill (4d, 1/3 with different designs)

■ 1965, July 8. Churchill Commemoration

Des: D. Gentleman and R. Dease. Wmk: Multiple St. Edward's Crown.
A) Non-phosphor issue.

Set	0.25	0.30
First day cover	–	2.50

B) Phosphor issue (three bands).

Set	1.25	1.50
First day cover	–	5.00

C) Printed on a Timson machine

4d	0.20	0.20

(* The Timson printing shows more detail on the Churchill portrait.)

Seal of Simon de Montfort (6d)
Parliament buildings (2/6)

■ 1965, July 19. 700th Anniversary of Simon de Montfort's Parliament

Des: S.R. Black (6d), Professor R. Guyatt (2/6). Wmk: Multiple St. Edward's Crown.
A) Non-phosphor issue.

Set	0.65	0.65
First day cover	–	8.00

B) Phosphor issue (three bands): 6d only

6d	0.50	0.60
First day cover	–	15.00

Salvation Army band (3d)
Three Salvation Army members (1/6)

■ 1965, August 9. Centenary of Salvation Army

Des: M.C. Farrar-Bell (3d), G. Trenaman (1/6). Wmk: Multiple St. Edward's Crown.
A) Non-phosphor issue.

Set	0.60	0.60
First day cover	–	12.00

B) Phosphor issue: 3d (one band), 1/6 (three bands).

Set	1.35	1.50
First day cover	–	22.00

Carbolic spray (4d)
Joseph Lister (1/–)

■ 1965, September 1. Centenary of Joseph Lister's Discovery of Antiseptic Surgery

Des: P. Gauld (4d), F. Ariss (1/–). Wmk: Multiple St. Edward's Crown.
A) Non-phosphor issue.

Set	0.50	0.75
First day cover	–	8.00

B) Phosphor issue (three bands).

Set	1.50	1.75
First day cover	–	10.00

Trinidad carnival dancers (6d)
Canadian folk dancers (1/6)

■ 1965, September 1. Commonwealth Arts Festival

Des: D. Gentleman and Rosalind Dease. Wmk: Multiple St. Edward's Crown.
A) Non-phosphor issue.

Set	0.60	0.70
First day cover	–	9.50

B) Phosphor issue (three bands).

Set	1.70	1.75
First day cover	–	15.00

Spitfires (4d)
Pilot in Hurricane (4d)
Overlapping wings (4d)
Spitfires attacking Heinkel bomber (4d)
Spitfire attacking Stuka bomber (4d)
Tail wing of Dornier bomber (4d)
Anti-aircraft artillery (9d)
St Paul's Cathedral (1/3)

■ 1965, September 13. 25th Anniversary of the Battle of Britain

Des: D. Gentleman and R. Dease (4d, 1/3), A. Restall (9d). Wmk:
Multiple St. Edward's Crown. Six 4d values se-tenant.
A) Non-phosphor issue.

Set	4.00	4.50
First day cover	–	12.00

B) Phosphor issue (three bands).

Set	6.50	6.50
First day cover	–	15.00

Post Office Tower and Georgian buildings (3d)
Post Office Tower and Nash Terrace (1/3)

■ 1965, October 8. Opening of the Post Office Tower

Des: C. Abbott. Wmk: Multiple St. Edward's Crown.
A) Non-phosphor issue.

Set	0.30	0.35
First day cover	–	4.50

B) Phosphor issue (one band on the 3d, three bands on the1/3).

Set	0.40	0.50
First day cover	–	5.00

UN emblem (3d)
ICY emblem (1/6)

■ 1965, October 25. 20th Anniversary of United Nations and International Co-Operation Year

Des: J. Matthews. Wmk: Multiple St. Edward's Crown.
A) Non-phosphor issue.

Set	0.50	0.60
First day cover	–	5.50

B) Phosphor issue (one band on the 3d, three bands on the 1/6).

Set	1.60	1.75
First day cover	–	9.00

Telecommunications (9d)
Radio waves (1/6)

■ 1965, November 15. International Telecommunication Union Centenary

Des: A. Restall. Wmk: Multiple St. Edward's Crown.
A) Non-phosphor issue.

Set	0.75	0.75
First day cover	–	8.50

B) Phosphor issue (three bands).

Set	2.50	3.00
First day cover	–	13.00

Robert Burns portrait by Skirving (4d)
Robert Burns portrait by Nasmyth (1/3)

■ 1966, January 25. Robert Burns

Des: G.F. Huntly. Wmk: Multiple St. Edward's Crown.
A) Non-phosphor issue.

Set	0.30	0.40
First day cover	–	1.50

B) Phosphor issue (three bands).

Set	1.25	1.25
First day cover	–	3.50

Exterior of Westminster Abbey (3d)
Fan vaulting of Westminster Abbey (2/6)

1966, February 28. 900th Anniversary of Westminster Abbey

Des: Sheila Robinson (3d), Bradbury Wilkinson (2/6). Printed in recess by Bradbury Wilkinson (2/6). Wmk: Multiple St. Edward's Crown. Perf: 11 x 12 (2/6)

A) Non-phosphor issue.

Set	0.50	0.50
First day cover	–	3.25

B) Phosphor issue (one band on the 3d).

3d	0.20	0.20
First day cover	–	8.00

Sussex Downs (4d)
Antrim, Northern Ireland (6d)
Harlech Castle (1/3)
The Cairngorms (1/6)

1966, May 2. Landscapes

Des: L. Rosoman. Wmk: Multiple St. Edward's Crown.

A) Non-phosphor issue.

Set	0.50	0.75
First day cover	–	3.50

B) Phosphor issue (three bands).

Set	0.60	0.75
First day cover	–	5.00

Two footballers (4d)
Four footballers (6d)
Goalkeeper catching ball (1/3)

1966, June 1. World Cup

Des: D. Gentleman (4d), W. Kempster (6d), D. Caplan (1/3). Wmk: Multiple St. Edward's Crown.

A) Non-phosphor issue.

Set	0.40	0.40
First day cover	–	10.00

B) Phosphor issue (two bands on the 4d, three bands on the 6d, 1/3).

Set	0.30	0.40
First day cover	–	11.50

Black-headed gull (4d)
Blue tit (4d)
Robin (4d)
Blackbird (4d)

1966, August 8. British Birds

Des: J. Norris Wood. Wmk: Multiple St. Edward's Crown. All four values in se-tenant blocks.

A) Non-phosphor issue.

Set (in se-tenant block of four)	0.50	0.60
First day cover	–	4.00

B) Phosphor issue (three bands).

Set (in se-tenant block of four)	0.50	0.60
First day cover	–	4.50

Two footballers and 'England Winners' (4d)

1966, August 18. England's World Cup Victory

As June 1 issue, with additional inscription 'ENGLAND WINNERS'. Non-phosphor only.

4d	0.20	0.20
First day cover	–	7.50

Jodrell Bank radiotelescope (4d)
Jaguar 'E' type and Mini cars (6d)
SR N6 hovercraft (1/3)
Windscale nuclear reactor (1/6)

■ 1966, September 19. British Technology
Des: D. and A. Gillespie (4d, 6d), A. Restall (1/3, 1/6). Wmk: Multiple St. Edward's Crown.
A) Non-phosphor issue.

Set	0.40	0.55
First day cover	–	1.75

B) Phosphor issue (three bands).

Set	0.45	0.65
First day cover	–	3.00

Scenes from the Bayeux Tapestry (4d, 4d, 4d, 4d, 4d, 4d)
Norman ship (6d)
Norman cavalry attacking English infantry (1/3)

■ 1966, October 14. 900th Anniversary of the Battle of Hastings
Des: D. Gentleman. Wmk: Multiple St. Edward's Crown, sideways on 1/3 value. Six 4d values se-tenant.
A) Non-phosphor issue.

Set	1.00	1.50
First day cover	–	2.50

B) Phosphor issue (three bands on the 4d, 6d, four bands on the 1/3).

Set	1.00	1.50
First day cover	–	3.75

King of the Orient (3d)
Snowman (1/6)

■ 1966, December 1. Christmas
Des: Miss T. Shemza (3d), J. Berry (1/6), both aged six. Wmk: Multiple St. Edward's Crown, upright on both values.
A) Non-phosphor issue.

Set	0.15	0.25
First day cover	–	1.50

B) Phosphor issue (one band on the 3d, two bands on the 1/6).

Set	0.15	0.30
First day cover	–	1.50

(* Phosphor 3d can be found with band at left or right).

Loading freight on a ship (9d)
Loading freight on an aeroplane (1/6)

■ 1967, February 20. European Free Trade Association
Des: C. Abbott. Wmk: Multiple St. Edward's Crown.
A) Non-phosphor issue.

Set	0.15	0.20
First day cover	–	4.00

B) Phosphor issue (three bands).

Set	0.20	0.25
First day cover	–	4.00

Hawthorn and bramble (4d)
Bindweed and viper's bugloss (4d)
Daisy, buttercup and coltsfoot (4d)
Bluebell, anemone and red campion (4d)
Dog violet (9d)
Primrose (1/9)

■ 1967, April 24. British Wild Flowers
Des: W Keble Martin (4d), Mary Grierson (9d, 1/9). Wmk: Multiple St. Edward's Crown. Four 4d values se-tenant.
A) Non-phosphor issue.

Set	0.75	0.80
First day cover	–	2.25

B) Phosphor issue (three bands).

Set	0.40	0.75
First day cover	–	6.50

'Master Lambton' by Sir Thomas Lawrence (4d)
'Mares and Foals in a Landscape' by George Stubbs (9d)
'Children Coming Out of School' by L. S. Lowry (1/6)

■ **1967, July 10. British Paintings**
No Wmk. Two phosphor bands.

Set	0.20	0.30
First day cover	–	1.50

Gipsy Moth IV (1/9)

■ **1967, July 24. Sir Francis Chichester's Single-Handed Voyage Around the World**
Des: M. and S. Goaman. No Wmk. Three phosphor bands.

1/9	0.15	0.15
First day cover	–	0.70

Radar screen (4d)
Penicillin mould (1/–)
Jet engine (1/6)
Television equipment (1/9)

■ **1967, September 19. British Discovery & Invention**
Des: C. Abbott (4d, 1/–), Negus and Sharland (1/6, 1/9). Wmk: Multiple St. Edward's Crown. Three phosphor bands on the 4d.

Set	0.25	0.30
First day cover	–	1.50

'The Adoration of the Shepherds' by the School of Seville (3d)
'Madonna and Child' by Bartolomé Murillo (4d)
'The Adoration of the Shepherds' by Louis Le Nain (1/6)

■ **1967, October 18–November 27. Christmas**
No Wmk. 3d has one central phosphor band. 3d released on November 27, 4d on October 18, 1/6 on November 27.

Set	0.15	0.20
First day cover	–	1.75

Tarr Steps (4d)
Aberfeldy Bridge (9d)
Menai Bridge (1/6)
M4 Viaduct (1/9)

■ **1968, April 29. British Bridges**
Des: J. Matthews (4d, 1/9), A. Restall (9d), L. Rosoman (1/6). No Wmk. Two phosphor bands.

Set	0.25	0.35
First day cover	–	1.25

Trades Union Congress (4d)
Votes for Women: Emmeline Pankhurst statue (9d)
Royal Air Force: Sopwith Camel and modern fighters (1/–)
James Cook's first voyage: signature and H.M.S. Endeavour (1/9)

■ **1968, May 29. Anniversaries**
Des: D. Gentleman (4d), C. Abbott (others). No Wmk.

Set	0.25	0.35
First day cover	–	2.25

'Queen Elizabeth 1' by an unknown artist (4d)
'Pinkie' by Sir Thomas Lawrence (1/-)
'Ruins of St. Mary le Port' by John Piper (1/6)
'The Hay Wain' by John Constable (1/9)

■ 1968, August 12. British Paintings.
No Wmk.

Set	0.25	0.30
First day cover	–	1.50

Boy and girl with rocking horse (4d)
Girl with doll's house (9d)
Boy with train set (1/6)

■ 1968, November 25. Christmas
Des: Rosalind Dease. No Wmk.
A) Printed on a Rembrandt machine.

Set	0.20	0.25
First day cover	–	0.75

B) Printed on a Thrissell machine (4d only).

4d	0.15	0.20

(* The Thrissell printing can be distinguished by the boy's pullover having a more mottled appearance.)

Queen Elizabeth 2 (5d)
Elizabethan galleon (9d)
East Indiaman (9d)
Cutty Sark (9d)
S.S. Great Britain (1/-)
R.M.S. Mauretania (1/-)

■ 1969, January 15. British Ships
Des: D. Gentleman. No Wmk. Three 9d values in se-tenant strip.
Two 1/- values in se-tenant pair.

Set	1.25	1.20
First day cover	–	2.00

Concorde over Great Britain and France (4d)
Silhouettes of Concorde (9d)
Nose and tail of Concorde (1/6)

■ 1969, March 3. First Flight of Concorde
Des: Michael and Sylvia Goaman (4d), D. Gentleman (9d, 1/6).
No Wmk.

Set	0.75	0.70
First day cover	–	3.50

First transatlantic flight: Vickers Vimy, Alcock & Brown (5d)
Europa/CEPT: emblems (9d)
International Labour Organisation: hand holding wrench (1/-)
NATO: flags of member countries (1/6)
First England–Australia Flight: Vickers Vimy, route on globe (1/9)

■ 1969, April 2. Anniversaries
Des: P. Sharland (5d, 1/-, 1/6), Michael and Sylvia Goaman (9d, 1/9). No Wmk.

Set	0.45	0.60
First day cover	–	1.75

Durham Cathedral (5d)
York Minster (5d)
St Giles' Cathedral, Edinburgh (5d)
Canterbury Cathedral (5d)
St Paul's Cathedral (9d)
Liverpool Metropolitan Cathedral (1/6)

■ 1969, May 28. British Cathedrals

Des: P. Gauld. No Wmk. Four 5d values se-tenant.

Set	0.75	0.85
First day cover	–	1.75

The King's Gate, Caernarvon Castle (5d)
The Eagle Tower, Caernarvon Castle (5d)
Queen Eleanor's Gate, Caernarvon Castle (5d)
Celtic Cross, Margam Abbey (9d)
Charles, Prince of Wales (1/–)

■ 1969, July 1. Investiture of the Prince of Wales

Des: D. Gentleman. No Wmk. Three 5d values se-tenant.

Set	0.40	0.70
First day cover	–	1.75

Mahatma Gandhi and flag of India (1/6)

■ 1969, August 13. Gandhi Centenary Year

Des: Biman Mullick.

1/6	0.20	0.20
First day cover	–	0.50

National Giro symbol (5d)
Telephone dials (9d)
Pulse code modulation (1/–)
Automatic sorting (1/6)

■ 1969, October 1. Post Office Technology

Des: D. Gentleman. Printed in litho by De La Rue. No Wmk.
Perf: 13½x14.

Set	0.35	0.45
First day cover	–	1.50

Herald angel (4d)
Three shepherds (5d)
Three kings (1/6)

■ 1969, November 26. Christmas

Des: F. Wegner. No Wmk.

Set	0.25	0.25
First day cover	–	0.75

Fife harling (5d)
Cotswold limestone (9d)
Welsh stucco (1/–)
Ulster thatch (1/6)

■ 1970, February 11. Rural Architecture

Des: D. Gentleman (5d, 9d), Sheila Robinson (1/–, 1/6). No Wmk.

Set	0.40	0.50
First day cover	–	1.50

Declaration of Arbroath: signing ceremony (5d)
Florence Nightingale: attending patients (9d)
International Co-operative Alliance: signing ceremony (1/-)
Sailing of the Mayflower: pilgrims and ship (1/6)
Royal Astronomical Society: Sir William Herschel, Francis Baily,
Sir John Herschel and telescope (1/9)

■ 1970, April 1. Anniversaries
Des: F. Wegner (5d, 9d, 1/6), Marjorie Seynor (1/-, 1/9).
No Wmk.

Set	1.25	0.75
First day cover	–	1.75

Mr Pickwick and Sam (5d)
Mr and Mrs Micawber (5d)
David Copperfield and Betsey Trotwood (5d)
Oliver Twist (5d)
Grasmere (1/6)

■ 1970, June 3. Literary Anniversaries
Des: Rosalind Dease. No Wmk. Four 5d values se-tenant.

Set	1.25	1.25
First day cover	–	1.75

Runners (5d)
Swimmers (1/6)
Cyclists (1/9)

■ 1970, July 15. British Commonwealth Games
Des: A. Restall. Printed in litho by De La Rue. No Wmk. Perf:
13½x14.

Set	0.60	0.70
First day cover	–	1.50

1840 line-engraved Penny Black (5d)
1847 embossed 1/- green (9d)
1855 surface-printed 4d carmine (1/6)

■ 1970, September 18. Philympia 1970 International Stamp Exhibition
Des: D. Gentleman. No Wmk.

Set	0.50	0.40
First day cover	–	1.50

Angel appearing to shepherds (4d)
Mary, Joseph and Jesus (5d)
Wise men bringing gifts (1/6)

■ 1970, November 25. Christmas
Des: Sally Stiff, based on the De Lisle Psalter. No Wmk.

Set	0.25	0.30
First day cover	–	0.75

PRE-DECIMAL MACHIN DEFINITIVES

In this section, prices are given for unmounted mint (left) and fine used (right). Exceptions are made where used prices are not applicable, for example booklet panes and gum varieties.

The Machin head of Queen Elizabeth II is so-called because it is based on a photograph of a sculpture by Arnold Machin. All designs in the series are similar, but small differences can be found in the head itself and in its setting in the design.

There are also varieties in the number and positioning of phosphor bands.

4d sepia

◼ 1967–1969. Machin definitives

Des: A. Machin. Printed in photogravure by Harrisons. No wmk. Head A with two phosphor bands except where stated.

A) Gum Arabic.

3d violet (August 8, 1967) (one band)	0.15	–
4d sepia (June 5, 1967)	0.15	–
head B	£2,000	–
4d red (one centre band)	0.15	–
9d green (August 8, 1967)	0.20	–
1/– pale violet (June 5, 1967)	0.20	–
1/– deep violet	1.75	–
1/6 green, deep blue (August 8, 1967)	0.30	–
1/9 orange, black (June 5, 1967)	0.35	–
First day cover (4d, 1/–, 1/9)	–	1.25
First day cover (3d, 9d, 1/6)	–	1.25

Coil stamps (August 27, 1969)

1d olive (head B, one band)	0.50	–

2d brown (head B, one band)	0.30	0.30
3d violet (head B, one band)	0.30	–
4d red (head B, one band)	0.30	–
Se-tenant coil of two 2d, one 1d, one 3d and one **4d**	1.00	1.10

Booklet panes of six

Six **4d** sepia	8.00	–
Six **4d** red	80.00	–

B) PVA gum.

½d orange (February 5, 1968)	0.10	0.10
1d olive (February 5, 1968)	0.10	0.10
head B	0.10	0.10
head B (one centre band)	0.70	0.50
2d brown (February 5, 1968)	0.10	0.10
setting 2	0.10	0.30
3d violet (one centre band)	0.15	0.10
head B (one centre band)	3.00	0.10
3d violet	0.15	0.10
head B	0.50	0.10
4d sepia (shades)	0.15	0.10
head B	0.35	0.10
4d sepia (one centre band)	0.30	0.20
head B (one centre band)	0.10	0.10
4d red (January 6, 1969) (one centre band)	0.15	0.20
head B (one centre band)	0.10	0.10
head B (one band at left)	0.80	0.80
head B (one band at right)	0.90	0.90
5d blue (July 1, 1968)	0.20	0.30
head B	0.20	0.20
head B (two bands on 'all over' phosphor)	£275	–
6d purple (February 5, 1968)	0.20	0.20
head B	12.00	7.50
7d green (July 1, 1968) (head 2)	0.20	0.30
8d red (July 1, 1968)	0.20	0.25
8d light-blue (January 6, 1969) (head 2)	0.30	0.25
9d green	0.20	0.20
10d brown (July 1, 1968)	0.20	0.30
1/– deep violet	0.20	0.20
1/6 green, deep blue	0.30	0.20
phosphor-coated paper	1.00	0.45
1/9 orange, black	3.50	0.30
Set (one of each value)	3.00	2.00
First day cover (½d, 1d, 2d, 6d)	–	1.00
First day cover (5d, 7d, 8d red, 10d)	–	1.25
First day cover (4d red, 8d light blue)	–	1.00

Booklet panes of four

Four **4d** sepia (head B, two bands)	0.60	–
Four **4d** sepia (head B, one centre band)	0.50	–
Four **4d** red (head B, one centre band)	0.50	–
Two **1d** left of two 3d (head B, two bands)	0.95	–
Two **1d** right of two 3d (head B, two bands)	0.95	–
Two **4d** sepia (head B, one centre band), with two labels reading '£4,315 FOR YOU AT AGE 55' and 'SEE OTHER PAGES'	0.50	–
Two **4d** red (head B, one centre band), with two labels reading '£4,315 FOR YOU AT AGE 55' and 'SEE OTHER PAGES'	0.50	–

Booklet panes of six

Six **1d** olive (head B, two bands)	0.50	–
Six **3d** violet (head A, centre band)	7.50	–
Six **4d** sepia (head A, two bands)	0.50	–
Six **4d** sepia (head A, one centre band)	0.50	–
Six **4d** red (head A, one centre band)	0.75	–
Six **4d** red (head B, one centre band)	1.25	–
Six **5d** blue (head B, two bands)	0.50	–
Four **1d** olive (one centre band) with two **4d** sepia (head B, one centre band)	1.50	–
Four **1d** olive (two bands) with two **4d** red (head B, one left band)	1.50	–

Booklet panes of 15 (all head B)

Six **1d** olive (two bands) with three **4d** red (one band at left), three **4d** red (one band at right) and three **5d** blue, with recipe label	6.00	–
Fifteen **4d** red (one centre band), with 'Stuffed Cucumber' label	1.00	–
Fifteen **4d** red (one centre band), with 'Method' label	1.00	–
Fifteen **5d** blue (two bands), with recipe label	1.00	–

(* These panes come from the £1 Stamps For Cooks booklet and can be found with just four holes in the binding margin, where stapled together, or with a larger number of equally spaced holes, where stitched.)

5/– brown–red

■ **1969, March 5. High values**
Des: A. Machin. Printed in recess by Bradbury Wilkinson. Perf: 12.

2/6 brown	0.25	0.20
5/– brown-red	1.00	0.50
10/– deep blue	3.00	4.00
£1 black	3.00	1.50
Set	5.50	5.00
First day cover	–	5.00

DECIMAL MACHIN DEFINITIVES

In this section, prices are given for unmounted mint (left) and fine used (right). Exceptions are made where used prices are not applicable, for example in the case of booklet panes and gum varieties.

All stamps have fluorescent-coated paper unless otherwise stated.

Gum

Gummed stamps can be found with three different gums. Gum Arabic is either colourless or yellow in appearance and is very shiny. Polyvinyl alcohol gum (PVA) is colourless but has a matt appearance. Polyvinyl alcohol with dextrin gum (PVAD) is also matt, but has a blueish or greenish tinge.

Self-adhesive definitives have become increasingly common since 1993.

Phosphor

Phosphor at first was applied in the form of vertical bands. When you hold a stamp up to the light and look along the surface, the paper itself appears shiny while the bands have a dull appearance.

Most stamps have two phosphor bands, on the two vertical edges; others have just one, which can be central or down the left or right vertical edge.

The width of the bands can vary, as can the size of the printing screen used to apply them, but these differences are beyond the scope of this publication.

Booklet panes, where stamps of the 2nd class rate (requiring a single phosphor band) have been printed se-tenant with other stamps (requiring two phosphor bands), have been found with the phosphor printed as bars rather than bands. Whereas bands extend across the perforations to the next stamp, these bars stop at the edge of the stamp design.

The term 'all over phosphor' is used where the phosphor was printed over the entire surface of the stamp, rather than in the form of bands. In some cases it was printed onto the paper before the stamp design was printed; in other cases it was printed afterwards.

The term 'no phosphor' is often applied to stamps with the phosphor omitted in error; such errors are outside the scope of this publication. However, the 50p and 75p values have been printed without phosphor in the normal course of events.

Paper

At first, from February 1971, these stamps were printed on what is now called 'original coated paper', which gives a dull violet reaction when the front of the stamp is viewed under ultra-violet light.

This was gradually replaced from August 1971 by 'fluorescent coated paper', which gives a bright reaction under ultra-violet light, and then from August 1979 by 'phosphor-coated paper', which adds the after-glow of phosphor and makes the stamp appear uniformly shiny.

Note that stamps with phosphor omitted in error also have a uniformly shiny surface, so those with phosphor-coated paper can only be positively identified by their reaction under

ultra-violet light.

The appearance of stamps with phosphor-coated paper can vary considerably due to variations in their drying time after printing. The abbreviation 'PCPI' is used to denote a dull appearance, and 'PCPII' a highly glazed appearance.

Some stamps with phosphor-coated paper have been found with the fluorescent brightener omitted. These still give a phosphor afterglow, but the paper gives a dull violet reaction similar to that found with original coated paper.

Attempts to standardise the paper produced what is known as 'advanced coated paper' (ACP), in use from March 1983. The visual difference between ACP and PCPI is minimal, but the former gives a brighter reaction under ultra-violet light.

Value and portrait

Minor changes can be noted in the position of the denomination of value in relation to the Queen's portrait, and the position of the portrait in relation to the base of the stamp.

Booklet panes

At first booklets were held together by stitching, so that a number of small holes can be found in the binding margin on the left hand side of panes. Later, the panes were stuck into booklet covers by the binding margins; in many such cases, panes can be found with the binding margin to the left or to the right.

In the case of stitched booklets, the booklet panes are recorded separately. Where the panes are stuck into the covers, most collectors prefer these as complete booklets, so the separate panes are not recorded.

Many of the early decimal booklet panes included non-postal labels se-tenant with the stamps in the pane, adjacent to the binding margin. At first these panes were perforated between the labels and the margin, but later they were not.

In 1987, as an experiment to counter complaints about the poor guillotining of panes, some booklet panes were produced with stamps with either the left or right-hand edge imperforate.

Coils

There are two different types of coils or rolls from which stamps may be found.

Where the source of a stamp is listed as 'coils', this refers to coils of the same value, usually 1st class or 2nd class, joined either horizontally or vertically. These were usually produced for use by businesses.

Where the source is listed as 'se-tenant coils', this refers to coils containing a mixture of values joined as a strip, These were usually produced for sale through vending machines.

Cartons

In an experiment staged in Scotland in 1976–78, 1st class and 2nd class definitives (including country definitives) were sold in cartons from vending machines. Sold at 30p or 60p, they contained either 6½p and 8½p, or 7p and 9p stamps.

LOW VALUES WITHOUT ELLIPTICAL PERFORATIONS, 1971–96

Des. A. Machin. Printed in photogravure by Harrisons. No Wmk. Perf: 15x14, except where stated.

■ ½p turquoise, February 15, 1971
A) gum Arabic, two phos bands
i. original coated paper	0.30	–	se-tenant coils
ii. original coated paper with silicone	30.00	–	se-tenant coils
iii. fluorescent coated paper	0.10	–	sheets
iv. fluorescent coated paper with silicone	0.40	–	se-tenant coils

B) PVA gum, two phos bands
i. original coated paper	0.20	–	sheets, se-tenant coils, booklets
ii. fluorescent coated paper	0.20	–	sheets, booklets
C) PVA gum, one band at left	35.00	15.00	£1 Wedgwood booklet
D) PVAD gum, two phos bands	0.10	0.15	sheets, se-tenant coils, booklets
E) PVAD gum, one centre band	0.20	0.15	se-tenant coils, booklets

F) PVAD gum, phos-coated paper
i. PCPI	0.20	0.20	sheets, se-tenant coils
ii. PCPII	0.25	0.30	sheets
iii. fluorescent brightener omitted (poor gum)	£125	30.00	se-tenant coils
iv. fluorescent brightener omitted (good perfs and gum)	£950	–	se-tenant coils

■ 1p purple, February 15, 1971
A) gum Arabic, two phos bands
i. original coated paper	0.40	–	se-tenant coils
ii. original coated paper with silicone	30.00	–	se-tenant coils
iii. fluorescent coated paper	0.60	–	coils
iv. fluorescent coated paper with silicone	0.60	–	se-tenant coils

B) PVA gum, two phos bands
i. original coated paper	0.10	–	sheets
ii. fluorescent coated paper	1.25	–	sheets, booklets

C) PVAD gum, two phos bands
i. value low	0.40	0.30	10p booklets
ii. value in intermediate position	0.40	0.35	10p se-tenant coils, 50p booklets,
iii. value high	0.20	0.30	sheets, 5p se-tenant coils

D) PVAD gum, one centre phos band
i. portrait above bottom margin	0.10	0.15	se-tenant coils

ii. portrait closer to bottom margin	0.40	0.30	se-tenant coils, 10p, 50p booklets,
E) PVAD gum, all over phos	0.20	0.20	sheets
F) PVAD gum, phos-coated paper			
i. PCPI, portrait above bottom margin	0.10	0.10	sheets
ii. PCPI, portrait closer to bottom margin	0.20	0.15	sheets, se-tenant coils
iii. PCPII	0.30	0.25	sheets
iv. ACP	0.30	0.25	sheets
G) PVAD gum, one phos band at left	1.00	0.60	50p booklet
H) PVAD gum, one phos band at right	1.50	2.00	£5 P&O booklet

■ 1½p black, February 15, 1971

A) PVA gum, two phos bands			
i. original coated paper	0.10	0.10	sheets, booklets
ii. fluorescent coated paper	0.50	0.50	sheets, booklets
B) PVAD gum, two phos bands	0.20	0.30	sheets, booklets

■ 2p green, February 15, 1971

A) gum Arabic, two phos bands			
i. original coated paper	2.00	–	se-tenant coils
ii. original coated paper with silicone	£120	–	se-tenant coils
iii. fluorescent coated paper with silicone	2.00	–	se-tenant coils
B) PVA gum, two phos bands			
i. original coated paper	0.20	–	sheets, booklets
ii. fluorescent coated paper	1.50	–	sheets, booklets
C) PVAD gum, two phos bands			
i. portrait above bottom margin	0.20	0.20	sheets, se-tenant coils, booklets
ii. portrait close to bottom margin	0.40	0.40	booklets
D) PVAD gum, all over phos	0.20	0.15	sheets
E) PVAD gum, phos-coated paper			
i. PCPI	0.10	0.10	sheets
ii. PCPII	0.20	0.15	sheets
F) PVAD gum, phos-coated paper, litho by Questa, perf 13½x14	0.25	0.20	sheets
G) PVAD gum, phos-coated paper, litho by Questa, perf 15x14	0.30	0.30	sheets
H) PVAD, phos-coated paper, ACP, litho by Questa, perf 15x14	0.30	0.40	sheets

■ 2p deep green, February 23, 1988

A) PVAD gum, phos paper	0.20	0.20	sheets, booklets
B) PVAD gum phos paper, litho by Walsall	0.60	0.60	booklets

■ 2½p pink, February 15, 1971

A) gum arabic, one centre phos band	0.20	–	sheets, coils
B) PVA gum, one centre phos band			
i. original coated paper	0.20	0.20	sheets, coils, booklets,
ii. fluorescent coated paper	0.40	0.40	sheets, booklets
C) PVA gum, one phos band at left			
i. original coated paper	5.00	1.50	50p booklets,
ii. fluorescent coated paper	1.00	1.00	50p, £1 Wedgwood booklets
D) PVA gum, one phos band at right	1.50	1.50	£1 Wedgwood booklet
E) PVAD gum, two phos bands	0.30	0.40	sheets
F) PVAD gum, one centre phos band	0.20	0.20	sheets

■ 2½p rose, January 14, 1981

A) PVAD gum, phos-coated paper			
i. PCPI	0.40	0.20	sheets, se-tenant coils
ii. PCPII	0.15	0.20	sheets,
iii. fluorescent brightener omitted	30.00	30.00	se-tenant coils
B) PVAD gum, two phos bands	0.35	0.30	50p booklets

■ 3p blue, February 15, 1971

A) gum Arabic, two phos bands

i. original coated paper	30.00	–	coils
ii. fluorescent coated paper	0.75	–	sheets, coils
B) gum arabic, one centre phos band	0.40	–	sheets
C) PVA gum, two phos bands			
i. original coated paper	0.15	0.15	sheets, coils, booklets
ii. fluorescent coated paper	0.20	0.30	sheets, booklets
iii. phos-coated paper	£1,200	–	only two examples known
D) PVA gum, one centre phos band	0.10	–	sheets, booklets
E) PVAD gum, one centre phos band	0.15	0.20	sheets, coils, booklets

■ 3p pink, October 22, 1980

A) PVAD gum, phos-coated paper			
i. PCPI	0.20	0.20	sheets, se-tenant coils
ii. PCPII	0.30	0.20	
iii. fluorescent brightener omitted	5.00	4.00	se-tenant coils
iv. ACP	0.50	0.20	sheets, £4 Royal Mint booklet
B) PVAD gum, two phos bands	0.15	0.20	50p, £4 SG booklets

■ 3¹/₂p olive green, February 15, 1971

A) PVA gum, two phos bands			
i. original coated paper	0.10	0.20	sheets
ii. fluorescent coated paper	2.00	–	sheets, 35p booklets
B) PVAD gum, two phos bands			
i. original coated paper	£150	50.00	sheets
ii. fluorescent coated paper	0.60	0.25	sheets, coils, 35p, 50p booklets
C) PVAD gum, one centre phos band	0.10	0.10	sheets, coils, 35p, 85p booklets

■ 3¹/₂p light red-brown, March 30, 1983

A) PVA gum, two phos bands			
i. PCPI	0.40	0.30	sheets,
ii. ACP	1.10	0.60	sheets, £4 Royal Mint booklet
B) PVAD gum, one centre phos band	0.70	0.40	50p booklets

■ 4p bistre, February 15, 1971

A) gum arabic, two phos bands	0.50	–	sheets
B) PVA gum, two phos bands			
i. original coated paper	0.30	0.20	sheets
ii. fluorescent coated paper	3.50	–	sheets
C) PVAD gum, two phos bands	0.10	0.20	sheets

■ 4p greenish-blue, January 30, 1980

A) PVA gum, two phos bands, litho by Waddingtons	0.20	0.15	sheets
B) PVAD gum, phos-coated paper, litho by Waddingtons	0.30	0.20	sheets
C) PVAD gum, phos-coated paper, litho by Questa, perf 15x14	0.40	0.40	sheets
D) PVAD gum, two phos bands	1.00	0.85	50p booklets
E) PVAD gum, phos-coated paper			
i. PCPI	0.20	0.20	se-tenant coils
ii. fluorescent brightener omitted (perfect gum)	£370	35.00	se-tenant coils
iii. PCPI, value high	0.35	0.20	se-tenant coils
F) PVAD gum, one centre phos band	0.65	0.65	50p booklets
G) PVAD gum, one phos band at left	1.35	1.15	£5 booklet
H) PVAD gum, one phos band at right	1.50	1.30	£5 booklet

■ 4p bright blue, July 26, 1988

A) PVAD gum, phos paper, litho by Questa	0.45	0.50	sheets
A) PVAD gum, phos paper	0.20	0.25	sheets, coils

■ 4¹/₂p grey-blue, October 24, 1973

A) PVAD gum, two phos bands	0.10	0.10	sheets, coils, 45p, 85p booklets
B) PVAD gum, two phos bands on all-over phos	0.65	–	sheets

■ 5p violet, February 15, 1971

A) PVA gum, two phos bands			
i. original coated paper	0.15	0.20	sheets
ii. fluorescent coated paper	2.50	–	sheets
B) PVAD gum, two phos bands	0.10	0.10	sheets
C) PVAD gum, phos–coated paper			
i. PCPI	0.20	0.20	sheets
ii. PCPI, value high	0.50	0.35	sheets
D) PVAD gum, phos-coated paper, litho by Questa	0.30	0.20	sheets
E) PVA gum, phos-coated paper, litho by Questa	0.40	0.40	sheets

■ 5p red-brown, January 27, 1982

A) PVAD gum, phos-coated paper, litho by Questa, perf 13½x14	0.40	0.30	sheets
B) PVAD gum, phos-coated paper, litho by Questa, perf 15x14	0.50	0.40	sheets
C) PVAD gum, ACP, litho by Questa, perf 15x14	0.45	0.40	sheets
D) PVAD gum, one centre phos band	1.00	1.00	50p booklet

■ 5½p deep purple, October 24, 1973

A) PVAD gum, two phos bands	0.10	0.10	sheets
B) PVAD gum, one centre phos band	0.10	0.10	sheets

■ 6p light green, February 15, 1971

A) gum arabic, two phos bands	2.25	–	sheets
B) PVA gum, two phos bands			
i. original coated paper	0.30	–	sheets, se-tenant coils
ii. fluorescent coated paper	25.00	–	sheets
C) PVAD gum, two phos bands	0.20	0.20	sheets, se-tenant coils, 10p booklet

■ 6p olive, September 10, 1991

A) PVAD gum, phos paper	0.30	0.20	sheets

■ 6½p green-blue, September 7, 1974

A) PVA gum, two phos bands	30.00	–	sheets
B) PVAD gum, two phos bands	0.20	0.20	sheets
C) PVAD gum, one centre phos band			
i. portrait above bottom margin	0.20	0.20	sheets
ii. portrait close to bottom margin	0.20	0.25	sheets, coils, 65p booklets
D) PVAD gum, one phos band at left	0.50	0.30	50p booklets
E) PVAD gum, one phos band at right	0.70	0.30	50p booklets

■ 7p red-brown, January 15, 1975

A) PVAD gum, two phos bands	0.20	0.20	sheets
B) PVAD gum, one centre phos band			
i. portrait above bottom margin	0.20	0.20	sheets, coils
ii. portrait close to bottom margin	0.40	0.30	sheets, coils, se-tenants coils, booklets
C) PVAD gum, one phos band at left	0.40	0.45	50p booklets
D) PVAD gum, one phos band at right	0.40	0.50	50p booklets

■ 7p brick-red, October 29, 1985

A) PVAD gum, phos-coated paper	1.00	0.90	sheets

■ 7½p brown, February 15, 1971

A) PVA gum, two phos bands			
i. original coated paper	0.50	0.40	sheets
ii. fluorescent coated paper	3.00	–	sheets
B) PVAD gum, two phos bands	0.20	0.20	sheets

■ 8p red, October 24, 1973

A) PVAD gum, two phos bands	0.20	0.20	sheets
B) PVAD gum, one centre phos band, printed by Harrisons			

i. portrait high, value low	0.35	0.25	sheets
ii. portrait low, value high	0.50	0.30	sheets, coils, booklets
C) PVAD gum, one centre phos band, printed by Enschedé	0.35	0.25	sheets
D) PVAD gum, one phos band at left	0.40	0.30	50p booklets
E) PVAD gum, one phos band at right	0.40	0.30	50p booklets

■ 8½p lime green, September 24, 1975
A) PVAD gum, two phos bands

i. value high	0.20	0.25	sheets, coils, 85p booklets
ii. value low	0.45	0.35	50p booklets
B) PVAD gum, phos–coated paper	0.40	0.20	sheets

■ 9p orange and black, February 15, 1971
A) PVA gum, two phos bands

i. original coated paper	0.30	0.30	sheets
ii. fluorescent coated paper	2.50	–	sheets
B) PVAD gum, two phos bands	1.00	0.90	sheets

■ 9p violet, February 25, 1976
A) PVAD gum, two phos bands	0.30	0.30	sheets, coils, 50p, 90p, £1.60 booklets

■ 9½p purple, February 25, 1976
A) PVAD gum, two phos bands	0.20	0.20	sheets

■ 10p yellow and orange, August 11, 1971
A) PVA gum, two phos bands	0.40	–	sheets
B) PVAD gum, two phos bands	0.40	0.40	sheets

■ 10p orange, February 25, 1976
A) PVAD gum, two phos bands

i. base of value above edge of bust	0.30	0.20	sheets, £1.80 booklets
ii. base of value at edge of bust	0.30	0.25	50p booklets
iii. re–drawn (narrower) value	8.00	8.00	£4 Heritage booklet
B) PVAD gum, all–over phos	0.30	0.30	sheets, £1 booklets
C) PVAD gum, phosphor coated paper, PCPI	0.30	0.30	sheets
D) PVAD gum, ACP	0.40	0.25	sheets
E) PVAD gum, one centre phos band	0.35	0.20	sheets, £1, £2.20, £3 booklets
F) PVAD gum, one phos band at left	0.60	0.50	50p, £3 booklets
G) PVAD gum, one phos band at right	0.70	0.50	50p booklets
H) PVAD gum, two phos bands, PCPI	0.50	–	sheets
gutter pair	1.25	–	sheets
I) PVAD gum, two phos bands, fluorescent–coated paper	0.45	0.35	sheets
gutter pair	1.00	1.50	sheets
J) PVAD gum, one centre phos band, PCPI	0.70	–	sheets

■ 10½p yellow, February 25, 1976
A) PVAD gum, two phos bands	0.40	0.40	sheets

■ 10½p blue, April 26, 1978
A) PVAD gum, two phos bands	0.35	0.40	sheets

■ 11p orange–pink, February 25, 1976
A) PVAD gum, two phos bands	0.30	0.30	sheets
B) PVAD gum, phos–coated paper, PCPI	0.50	0.50	sheets

■ 11½p sepia, August 15, 1979
A) PVAD gum, phos–coated paper PCP1	0.30	0.30	sheets

■ 11½p mushroom, January 14, 1981
A) PVAD gum, one centre phos band	0.30	0.20	sheets, coils, £1.15, £2.55 booklets

B) PVAD gum, one phos band at left	0.50	0.30	50p, £1.30 booklets
C) PVAD gum, one phos band at right	0.50	0.30	50p, £1.30 booklets

■ 12p yellow–green, January 30, 1980

A) PVAD gum, phos–coated paper			
i. PCPI	0.50	0.45	sheets, coils, £1.20 booklet
ii. PCPII	0.80	0.50	sheets
B) PVAD gum, two phos bands	0.35	0.35	50p, £2.20, £3 booklets

■ 12p emerald–green, October 29, 1985

A) PVAD gum, one centre phos band	0.35	0.35	sheets, 50p, £1.20, £5 booklets
B) PVAD gum, one centre phos band, blue star on gummed side	0.50	–	sheets
C) PVAD gum, one centre phos band in ACP–type phos	0.50	0.35	sheets
D) PVAD gum, one phos band at left	0.50	0.50	£1.50, £5 booklets
E) PVAD gum, one phos band at right	0.50	0.50	£1.50, £5 booklets

■ 12½p light green, January 27, 1982

A) PVAD gum, one centre phos band	0.35	0.30	sheets, coils, 50p, £1.25, £4 SG booklets
B) PVAD gum, one centre phos band, PCPI	5.00	–	sheets
C) PVAD gum, one phos band at left	0.50	0.50	50p, £1.43, £1.46, £4 booklets
D) PVAD gum, one phos band at right	0.50	0.50	50p, £1.43, £1.46, £4 booklets
E) PVAD gum, one centre band, blue star on gummed side	0.55	0.50	£2.50 booklet
F) PVAD gum, one centre band, simple blue star on gummed side	0.50	0.40	£2.20 booklet

■ 13p olive, August 15, 1979

A) PVAD gum, phos–coated paper, PCPI	0.40	0.40	sheets

■ 13p light brown, August 28, 1984

A) PVAD gum, one centre phos band	0.30	0.35	sheets, 50p, £1.30, £5 booklets
B) PVAD gum, one centre phos band, blue star on gummed side	0.70	–	£1.20 booklet
C) PVAD gum, one centre phos band in ACP–type phos	0.50	0.35	sheets
D) PVAD gum, one phos band at left	0.45	0.50	50p, £1.54, £4 Heritage, £5 booklets
E) PVAD gum, one phos band at right	0.45	0.50	£1, £1.54, £4 Heritage, £5 booklets
F) PVAD gum, one centre phos band, litho by Questa	0.45	0.45	booklets
G) PVAD gum, one phos band at left, litho by Questa	0.45	0.45	booklets
H) PVAD gum, one phos band at right, litho by Questa	0.45	0.45	booklets

■ 13½p red–brown, January 30, 1980

A) PVAD gum, phosphor coated paper, PCPI	0.40	0.45	sheets

■ 14p grey–blue, January 14, 1981

A) PVAD gum, phos–coated paper			
i. PCPI	0.40	0.30	sheets, coils, £1.40 booklets
ii. PCPII	0.50	0.50	sheets, coils £1.40 booklets
iii. fluorescent brightener omitted	2.00	–	£1.40 booklets
B) PVAD gum, two phos bands	0.40	0.40	50p, £1.30, £2.55 booklets

■ 14p deep blue, August 23, 1988

A) PVAD gum, one centre phos band	0.35	0.35	sheets, booklets
B) PVAD gum, one phos band at right	1.50	1.00	booklets
C) PVAD gum, one centre phos band, litho by Questa	1.00	1.10	booklets
D) PVAD gum, one phos band at right, litho by Walsall	1.50	1.50	booklets

■ 15p blue, August 15, 1979

A) PVAD gum, phos–coated paper			
i. PCPI	0.40	0.45	sheets
ii. PCPII	0.50	0.55	sheets
B) PVAD gum, one phos band at left	2.20	2.00	50p booklets
C) PVAD gum, one centre phos band	0.40	0.30	sheets, coils
D) PVAD gum, one phos band at right	1.50	1.50	£5 booklets

■ 15p bright blue, September 26, 1989
A) PVAD gum, one centre phos band	0.45	0.50	sheets, coils
B) PVAD gum, one phos band at left	1.80	1.50	50p booklet
B) PVAD gum, one phos band at right	1.50	1.50	£5 London Life booklet

■ 15½p pale purple, January 14, 1981
A) PVAD gum, phos-coated paper
i. PCPI	0.40	0.45	sheets, coils, £1.55 booklets
ii. PCPI	0.40	0.45	sheets
iii. fluorescent brightener omitted	15.00	–	sheets
iv. advanced coated paper	3.00	2.50	sheets, £1.55 booklets
B) PVAD gum, two phos bands	0.40	0.45	£1.43, £4 SG booklets
C) PVAD gum, two phos bands, blue star on gummed side	0.60	0.45	£2.50 booklets

■ 16p light mushroom, March 30, 1983
A) PVAD gum, phos-coated paper, PCPI	0.40	0.45	sheets, £1.60, £4 Royal Mint booklets
B) PVAD gum, PCPI and D on gummed side	0.60	0.45	£1.45 booklet
C) PVAD gum, ACP	0.60	0.45	sheets
D) PVAD gum, two phos bands	1.00	0.70	£1.46 booklet

■ 16½p light brown, January 27 1982
A) PVAD gum, phos-coated paper
i. PCPI	0.50	0.65	sheets
ii. PCPII	3.00	2.50	sheets

■ 17p sage green, January 30, 1980
A) PVAD gum, phos-coated paper
i. PCPI	0.50	0.45	sheets
ii. PCPII	3.00	2.50	sheets
iii. fluorescent brightener omitted	1.50	–	sheets

■ 17p steel blue, March 30, 1983
A) PVAD gum, PCPI	0.50	0.45	sheets, £1.70, £4 Heritage booklets
B) PVAD gum, PCPI, D on gummed side	1.00	–	£1.55 booklet
C) PVAD gum, ACP	0.50	0.45	sheets, £1.70, £5 booklets
D) PVAD gum, two phos bands	0.45	0.45	50p, £1.50, £1.54, £4 Heritage, £5 booklets
E) PVAD gum, two phos bands, stars on gummed side	0.70	0.45	50p booklet

■ 17p deep blue, September 4, 1990
A) PVAD gum, one centre phos band	0.50	0.60	sheets
B) PVAD gum, one phos band at left	0.60	0.60	booklets
C) PVAD gum, one phos band at right	1.50	1.50	booklets
D) PVAD gum, one centre phos band, litho by Questa	0.55	0.60	booklets

■ 17½p light brown, January 30, 1979
A) PVAD gum, phos-coated paper
i. PCPI	0.50	0.50	sheets
ii. PCPII	2.00	1.75	sheets

■ 18p violet, January 14, 1981
A) PVAD gum, phos-coated paper
i. PCPI	0.50	0.50	sheets
ii. PCPII	0.70	0.60	sheets

■ 18p grey–green, August 28, 1984
A) PVAD gum, ACP	0.50	0.40	sheets
B) PVAD gum, two phos bands	1.00	0.50	50p, £1 booklets
C) PVAD gum, phos-coated paper	0.70	0.60	£1.80 booklet
D) PVAD gum, phos paper, litho by Questa	0.50	0.50	booklets
E) PVAD gum, two phos bands, litho by Questa	3.75	4.00	booklets

■ 18p bright green, September 10, 1991

A) PVAD gum, one centre phos band	0.40	0.45	sheets
B) PVAD gum, one centre phos band, litho by Questa	0.50	0.50	booklets
C) PVAD gum, one phos band at left, litho by Questa	1.20	1.35	booklets
D) PVAD gum, one phos band at right, litho by Questa	0.80	0.90	booklets

■ 19p orange–red, August 23, 1988

A) PVAD gum, phos paper	0.50	0.50	sheets, booklets
B) PVAD gum, phos paper, litho by Questa	1.20	1.40	booklets
C) PVAD gum, two phos bands, litho by Walsall	1.50	1.50	booklets

■ 19½p olive grey, January 27, 1982

A) PVAD gum, phosphor coated paper, PCPI	1.00	1.00	sheets

■ 20p dull purple, February 25, 1976

A) PVA gum, two phos bands, litho by Waddingtons	0.80	0.90	sheets
B) PVAD gum, phos-coated paper, litho by Waddingtons	1.15	1.00	sheets
C) as above but dull purple and sepia	1.00	1.00	sheets
D) PVAD gum, phos-coated paper, litho by Questa, perf 15x14	0.80	0.50	sheets
E) PVAD gum, two phos bands	0.50	0.50	sheets
F) PVAD gum, phos-coated paper			
i. PCPI	0.40	0.50	sheets
ii. PCPII	0.55	0.60	sheets

■ 20p turquoise, August 23, 1988

A) PVAD gum, phos paper	0.55	0.50	sheets

■ 20p brownish–black, September 26, 1989

A) PVAD gum, phos paper	0.70	0.70	sheets, booklets
B) PVAD gum, two phos bands	0.70	0.70	sheets

■ 20½p bright blue, March 30, 1983

A) PVAD gum, phos-coated paper, PCPI	0.75	0.50	sheets

■ 22p deep blue, October 22, 1980

A) PVAD gum, phos-coated paper			
i. PCPI	0.55	0.50	sheets
ii. PCPII	0.55	0.50	sheets
B) PVAD gum, experimental coated paper	2.50	2.00	sheets

■ 22p yellow–green, August 28, 1984

A) PVAD gum, ACP	0.55	0.50	sheets
B) PVAD gum, two phos bands, litho by Questa	5.00	4.50	booklets

■ 22p orange–red, September 4, 1990

A) PVAD gum, fluorescent-coated paper	0.80	0.70	sheets
B) PVAD gum, phos paper	0.55	0.55	sheets
C) PVAD gum, phos paper, litho by Questa	0.60	0.50	booklets

■ 23p rose, March 30, 1983

A) PVAD gum, phos-coated paper, PCPI	0.70	0.70	sheets

■ 23p bright green, August 23, 1988

A) PVAD gum, phos paper	0.65	0.70	sheets

■ 24p light purple, August 28, 1984

A) PVAD gum, ACP	1.00	0.70	sheets

■ 24p red, September 26, 1989

A) PVAD gum, phos paper	1.00	0.70	sheets

■ 24p chestnut, September 10, 1991

A) PVAD gum, phos paper	0.75	0.75	sheets
B) PVAD gum, phos paper, litho by Questa	0.75	0.40	booklets
C) PVAD gum, two phos bands, litho by Questa	1.45	1.20	booklets
D) PVAD gum, phos paper, litho by Walsall	0.75	0.70	booklets

■ 25p purple, January 14, 1981

A) PVAD gum, phos-coated paper

i. PCPI	1.25	0.70	sheets
ii. PCPII	0.65	0.60	sheets

■ 25p rose red, February 6, 1996

A) PVAD gum, two phos bands	7.00	7.00	coils

■ 26p red, January 27, 1982

A) PVAD gum, phos-coated paper, PCPI	0.65	0.60	sheets
B) PVAD gum, ACP	0.65	0.50	sheets
C) PVAD gum, two phos bands	4.00	4.00	£5 P&O booklet
D) PVAD gum, phos paper, narrow value	3.50	3.00	£1.04 booklet

■ 26p drab, September 4, 1990

A) PVAD gum, phos paper	0.80	0.90	sheets

■ 27p chestnut, August 23, 1988

A) PVAD gum, phos paper	0.80	0.90	sheets, booklets

■ 27p violet, September 4, 1990

A) PVAD gum, phos paper	0.80	0.90	sheets

■ 28p blue, March 30, 1983

A) PVAD gum, phos-coated paper, PCPI	0.80	0.90	sheets
B) PVAD gum, ACP	0.80	0.90	sheets

■ 28p ochre, August 23, 1988

A) PVAD gum, phos paper	0.85	0.90	sheets

■ 28p blue-grey, September 10, 1991

A) PVAD gum , phos paper	1.00	1.00	sheets

■ 29p sepia, January 27, 1982

A) PVAD gum, phos-coated paper

i. PCPI	1.00	1.00	sheets
ii. PCPII	4.00	4.00	sheets

■ 29p mauve, September 26, 1989

A) PVAD gum, phos paper	1.25	1.30	sheets
B) PVAD gum, two phos bands, litho by Walsall	1.70	1.70	booklets
C) PVAD gum, phos paper, litho by Walsall	3.00	3.00	booklets

■ 30p olive, September 26, 1989

A) PVAD gum, phos paper	0.80	0.90	sheets

■ 31p purple, March 30, 1983

A) PVAD gum, phos-coated paper, PCPI	1.20	1.10	sheets
B) PVAD gum, ACP	1.20	1.00	sheets
C) PVAD gum, two phos bands	6.00	6.00	£5 British Rail Booklet

■ 31p ultramarine, September 4, 1990

A) PVAD gum, phos paper	1.10	0.90	sheets
B) PVA gum, phosphor paper, litho by Walsall	1.00	1.00	booklets

32p green–blue, August 23, 1988
A) PVAD gum, phos paper	1.00	0.90	sheets

33p emerald, September 4, 1990
A) PVAD gum, phos paper	0.90	0.30	sheets
B) PVA gum, phos paper, litho by Questa	2.00	2.00	booklets
C) PVAD gum, two phos bands, litho by Questa	1.00	1.00	booklets
D) PVA gum, phos paper, litho by Walsall	1.00	1.00	booklets

34p sepia, August 28, 1984
A) PVAD gum, phos–coated paper	0.90	1.00	sheets
B) PVAD gum, two phos bands	3.75	4.00	£5 Times booklet
C) PVAD gum, ACP	1.40	1.25	sheets
D) PVAD gum, two phos bands, litho by Questa	3.75	4.00	booklets

34p blue–grey, September 26, 1989
A) PVAD gum, phos paper	1.25	1.30	sheets

34p mauve, September 10, 1991
A) PVAD gum, phos paper	1.00	1.30	sheets

35p sepia, August 23, 1988
A) PVAD gum, phos paper	1.00	1.00	sheets

35p yellow, September 10, 1991
A) PVAD gum, phos paper	1.25	1.10	sheets

37p rosine, September 26, 1989
A) PVAD gum, phos paper	1.50	1.00	sheets

39p mauve, September 10, 1991
A) PVAD gum, phos paper	1.10	0.50	sheets
B) PVAD gum, two phos bands, litho by Questa	1.00	1.00	booklets
C) PVA gum, phos paper, litho by Walsall	1.10	1.00	booklets

50p dull brown, February 2, 1977
A) PVAD gum, two phos bands	1.30	0.50	sheets
B) PVAD gum, no phos	1.25	0.70	sheets

50p ochre, March 13, 1990
A) PVAD gum, phos paper	2.75	2.00	sheets
B) PVAD gum, two phos bands	1.30	0.50	sheets

75p deep grey, January 30, 1980
A) PVAD gum, no phos, litho by Questa, perf 13½x14	2.00	2.00	sheets
B) PVA gum, no phos, litho by Questa, perf 15x14	3.00	1.50	sheets
C) PVAD gum, no phos, litho by Questa, perf 15x14	3.00	2.00	sheets
D) PVA gum, no phos, litho by Questa: perf 15x14 on paper supplied by Coated Paper Ltd	3.75	–	sheets

75p grey and black, February 23, 1988
A) PVA gum, litho by Questa	5.00	4.00	sheets

75p grey and black, July 26, 1988
A) PVAD gum, no phosphor	2.00	0.60	sheets

First day cover (February 15, 1971)	
½p, 1p, 1½p, 2p, 2½p, 3p, 3½p, 4p, 5p, 6p, 7½p, 9p	2.50
First day cover (August 11, 1971)	
10p	1.25
First day cover (October 24, 1973)	
4½p, 5½p, 8p	1.25
First day cover (September 4, 1974)	
6½p	1.25
First day cover (January 15, 1975)	
7p	1.00
First day cover (September 24, 1975)	
8½p	1.00
First day cover (February 25, 1976)	
9p, 9½p, 10p, 10½p, 11p, 20p	2.25
First day cover (February 2, 1977)	
50p	1.50
First day cover (April 26, 1978)	
10½p	1.00
First day cover (August 15, 1979)	
11½p, 13p, 15p	1.00
First day cover (January 30, 1980)	
4p, 12p, 13½p, 17p, 17½p, 75p	1.00
First day cover (October 22, 1980)	
3p, 22p	1.00
First day cover (January 14, 1981)	
2½p, 11½p, 14p, 15½p, 18p, 25p	1.00
First day cover (January 27, 1982)	
5p, 12½p, 16½p, 19½p, 26p, 29p	1.75
First day cover (March 30, 1983)	
3½p, 16p, 17p, 20½p, 23p, 28p, 31p	1.75
First day cover (August 28, 1984)	
13p, 18p, 22p, 24p, 34p	0.75
First day cover (October 29, 1985)	
7p, 12p	1.00
First day cover (August 23, 1988)	
14p, 19p, 20p, 23p, 27p, 28p, 32p, 35p	2.25
First day cover (September 26, 1989)	
15p, 20p, 24p, 29p, 30p, 34p, 37p	2.25
First day cover (September 4, 1990)	
10p, 17p, 22p, 26p, 27p, 31p, 33p	2.50
First day cover (September 10, 1991)	
6p, 18p 24p, 28p, 34p, 35p, 39p	2.50
First day cover (February 6, 1996)	
25p	10.00

BOOKLET PANES WITHOUT ELLIPTICAL PERFORATIONS, 1971–93

■ Panes of four with PVA gum

Two **2p** with two **½p**	
vertically se-tenant	3.00
horizontally se-tenant, original coated paper	3.00
horizontally se-tenant, fluorescent coated paper	0.75
Two **1p** with two **1½p**	
vertically se-tenant	3.00
horizontally se-tenant, original coated paper	3.00
horizontally se-tenant, fluorescent coated paper	1.25

■ Panes of six with PVA gum

Five **½p** with label 'B ALAN LTD for GB STAMPS'	
perforated label	2.50
imperforate label	4.00
Five **½p** with label 'LICK battery failure'	
perforated label	2.50
imperforate label	6.00
Five **½p** with label 'MAKE YOUR LUCKY FIND PAY'	
imperforate label only	3.00
Four **2½p** (one centre band) with labels 'UNIFLO STAMPS' and 'STICK FIRMLY'	
perforated label	3.50
imperforate label	6.00
Five **2½p** (one centre band) with label 'STICK FIRMLY'	
perforated label	2.50
imperforate label	6.00
Five **2½p** (one centre band) with label 'TEAR OFF to ESSO'	
perforated label	2.50
imperforate label	8.00
Five **2½p** (one centre band) with label 'STAMP COLLECTIONS'	
imperforate label only	2.75
Four **2½p** (one centre band) with labels 'DO YOU COLLECT GB STAMPS' and 'BUYING OR SELLING'	
imperforate label only	2.75
Five **2½p** (one centre band) with label 'B ALAN'	
imperforate label only	2.50
Five **3p** (two bands) with label '£4,315 FOR YOU'	
perforated label	1.75
imperforate label, original coated paper	2.50
imperforate label, fluorescent coated paper	2.00
Four **3p** (two bands) with two **2½p** (one band at left)	
original coated paper	9.50
fluorescent coated paper	5.00
Six **3p** (two bands)	
original coated paper	4.00
fluorescent coated paper	2.50
Five **3p** (one centre band) with blank label	
imperforate label only	3.00
Five **3½p** (two bands) with blank label	
imperforate label only	5.00

■ Panes of four with PVAD gum

Two **2p** horizontally se-tenant with two **½p**	1.25
Two **1p** horizontally se-tenant with two **1½p**	1.50

■ Panes of six with PVAD gum

Five **3p** (one centre band) with blank label	
imperforate label only	3.00
Five **3½p** (two bands) with blank label	
imperforate label only	3.00

Five **3½p** (one centre band) with blank label
imperforate label only   1.75
Five **4½p** (two bands) with blank label
imperforate label only   1.75

SE–TENANT COIL STRIPS WITHOUT ELLIPTICAL PERFORATIONS, 1971–95

■ **Strips with gum Arabic**
One **2p**, two **½p**, two **1p**

original coated paper	3.00
original coated paper, silicone coated	£200
fluorescent coated paper, silicone coated	3.50

■ **Strips with PVA gum**
One **6p**, one **2p**, one **1p**, two **½p** (two bands)

original coated paper	3.00

■ **Strips with PVAD gum**
One **2p**, two **½p**, two **1p** (two bands)

fluorescent coated paper	0.80

One **6p**, one **2p**, one **1p**, two **½p** (two bands)

fluorescent coated paper	0.80

Two **½p** one **7p**, two **1p** (one centre band)

fluorescent coated paper	0.50

One **8p**, two **1p**, two labels (one centre band)

fluorescent coated paper	0.50

One **2½p** rose, three **3p** pink

phosphor–coated paper	0.60
fluorescent brightener omitted	40.00

One **½p**, three **4p** blue

phosphor–coated paper	0.80
fluorescent brightener omitted	£100
perfect gum	£1,500

One **1p** and three **4p** blue

phosphor–coated paper	0.80

One **2p**, three **4p**

phosphor–coated paper	1.20

Three **4p**, one **3p**

phosphor–coated paper	1.25

Three **4p**, one **5p**

phosphor–coated paper	1.00

Two **5p**, two **4p**

phosphor–coated paper	0.80

Three **5p**, one **4p**

phosphor–coated paper	1.00

NON–VALUE INDICATORS WITHOUT ELLIPTICAL PERFORATIONS, 1989–93

From retail stamp books (at least one edge may be imperforate) or prestige stamp books (marked *).

■ **2nd bright blue (August 22, 1989)**
Printed in gravure by Harrison

with one centre phosphor band	1.00	1.55
with one phosphor band at right*	2.00	1.85

Printed in litho by Walsall

with one centre phosphor band	1.00	1.00

Printed in litho by Questa

with one centre phosphor band	1.25	0.50
with one phosphor band at left*	1.00	1.05
with one phosphor band at right*	2.25	1.00

■ **2nd deep blue (August 7, 1990)**
Printed in gravure by Harrison

with one centre phosphor band	1.00	0.55

Printed in litho by Walsall

with one centre phosphor band	1.00	1.00

Printed in litho by Questa

with one centre phosphor band	1.25	0.90
with one phosphor band at left*	1.25	1.30

■ **1st brownish black (August 22, 1989)**
Printed in gravure by Harrison

on phosphor paper	2.00	2.00
with two phosphor bands*	2.00	2.00

Printed in litho by Walsall

with two phosphor bands	2.00	1.35

Printed in litho by Questa

on phosphor paper	2.10	1.10

■ **1st orange red (August 7, 1990)**
Printed in gravure by Harrison

on phosphor paper	1.10	0.65

Printed in litho by Walsall

on phosphor paper. Perf: 14	1.10	0.65
on phosphor paper. Perf: 13	2.00	6.00

Printed in litho by Questa

on phosphor paper	1.20	0.85
with two phosphor bands*	1.50	1.00

First day cover (August 22, 1989)

2nd bright blue, 1st brownish black	–	1.50

First day cover (August 7, 1990)

2nd deep blue, 1st orange red	–	2.50

HIGH VALUES WITHOUT ELLIPTICAL PERFORATIONS, 1970–77

■ 1970, June 17. Large format
Des: Arnold Machin. Printed in recess by Bradbury, Wilkinson.
No wmk. Perf: 12.

10p cerise, phos paper	0.40	0.35
20p olive–green	0.55	0.35
50p ultramarine	1.00	0.40
phosphor paper (Feb 1, 1973)	2.00	1.00
£1 black (Dec 6, 1972)	2.50	0.45
First day cover (10p, 20p, 50p)	–	2.00
First day cover (£1)	–	2.50

(* Initially the £1 was identical to that issued in 1969, although printed in sheets of 100 instead of 40. However, in 1972 it was re-released with the denomination in a different typeface.)

■ 1977, February 2. Large format
Des: Arnold Machin. Printed in photogravure by Harrison. Perf: 14x15.

£1 olive, deep green	2.00	0.30
£1.30 steel blue, buff (Aug 3, 1983)	3.00	2.50
£1.33 lilac, deep blue (Aug 28, 1984)	3.25	3.00
£1.41 deep blue, pale blue, green (Sep 17, 1985)	3.50	2.50
£1.50 rose–lilac, blue–black (Sep 2, 1986)	3.25	2.50
£1.60 buff, blue–green (Sep 15, 1987)	3.25	2.75
£2 emerald, deep purple	3.25	0.50
£5 pink, blue	8.00	2.50
Set	24.00	24.00
Gutter pairs	£100	–
Traffic light gutter pairs	£110	–
First day cover (£1, £2, £5)	–	5.00
First day cover (£1.30)	–	3.00
First day cover (£1.33)	–	3.00
First day cover (£1.41)	–	3.00
First day cover (£1.50)	–	3.00
First day cover (£1.60)	–	3.25

SPECIAL ISSUES WITHOUT ELLIPTICAL PERFORATIONS, 1990–99

■ 1990, January 10. 150th Anniversary of the Penny Black
Des: Jeffery Matthews. Issued in sheets and booklets; the stamps from booklets can have one or more edges imperforate.
A) Printed in photogravure by Harrison. Issued in sheets and booklets and, where marked *, in the London Life prestige stamp book

15p bright blue (one centre phos band)	0.50	0.75
(one phos band at left)*	2.75	2.00
(one phos band at right)*	2.25	3.00
20p brownish–black and cream (phos paper)	0.55	0.65
(two phos bands)*	2.00	2.00
29p mauve (phosphor paper)	1.00	1.10
(two phos bands)*	6.00	5.00
34p blue–grey	1.00	1.25
37p rosine	1.00	1.25
First day cover	–	8.00

B) Printed in litho by Walsall. Issued in booklets

15p bright blue (one centre phos band)	1.20	0.90
20p brownish–black and cream (phos paper)	1.50	0.90

C) Printed in litho by Questa. Issued in booklets

15p bright blue (one centre phos band)	1.25	1.30
20p brownish–black (phos paper)	1.50	0.90

D) Printed in gravure by Walsall. Issued in the Special by Design prestige stamp book of 2000

1st brownish black and cream	1.20	1.00

E) Printed in litho by Cartor. Issued only in the Treasures of the Archive prestige stamp book of 2009

1st brownish black and cream	1.30	1.10
20p brownish black and cream	1.10	1.00

■ 1999, February 6. Large format
Issued only in the Profile On Print prestige stamp book.
A) Printed in litho and embossed by Walsall. Self-adhesive

1st pale grey	1.00	1.00

B) Printed in recess by Enschedé. Engraved by C. Slania. Two phosphor bands

1st grey–black	1.00	1.00

C) Printed in typography by Harrison. Two phosphor bands

1st black	1.00	1.00

LOW VALUES WITH ELLIPTICAL PERFORATIONS, 1993–2010

With an elliptical perforation towards the lower end of each vertical side.

■ 1993–2005. Printed in gravure by Enschedé

Issued in sheets except where stated. Two phosphor bands, except where stated.

1p crimson (June 8, 1993)	0.15	0.10
2p deep green (April 11, 1995)	0.20	0.10
4p new blue (December 14, 1993)	0.20	0.10
5p claret (June 8, 1993)	0.20	0.20
6p lime green (April 27, 1993)	0.20	0.20
10p orange (June 8, 1993)	0.25	0.25
20p sea green (December 14, 1993)	0.40	0.40
25p salmon pink (October 10, 1995)	0.65	0.70
29p light grey (October 26, 1993)	0.75	0.70
30p grey-green (July 27, 1993)	0.75	0.70
31p deep purple (June 25, 1996)	1.25	0.70
35p deep yellow (August 17, 1993)	0.85	0.70
35p lime-green (April 5, 2005) (phos band)	0.80	0.75
35p lime-green (February 23, 2006)		
from Brunel prestige stamp book	1.00	1.00
36p ultramarine (October 26, 1993)	0.80	0.80
37p amethyst (June 25, 1996)	0.80	0.80
38p rosine (October 26, 1993)	1.00	0.80
39p magenta (June 25, 1996)	0.80	0.95
40p turquoise (February 23, 2006)		
from Brunel prestige stamp book	0.95	0.95
41p stone (October 26, 1993)	0.95	0.95
42p olive-grey (May 25, 2004)		
from Glory of the Garden prestige book	0.95	0.95
43p chocolate-brown (June 25, 1996)	1.15	1.10
47p turquoise green (May 25, 2004)		
from Glory of the Garden prestige book	1.30	1.30
50p ochre (December 14, 1993)	1.15	1.20
50p ochre (September 21, 2006)		

from Victoria Cross prestige stamp book	1.15	1.20
63p emerald (June 25, 1996)	1.40	1.30
£1 bluish-violet (August 22, 1995)	2.00	2.00
Stamp **card** (£1 stamp)	7.50	15.00

■ 1994–1996. Printed in litho by Questa

Issued in booklets and prestige stamp books. Two phosphor bands, except where stated.

1p crimson (July 8, 1995)		
from £1 booklets	0.75	0.55
6p lime-green (July 26, 1994)		
from Northern Ireland prestige stamp book	6.50	5.00
10p deep orange (April 25, 1995)		
from National Trust prestige stamp book	2.00	2.00
19p olive green (July 26, 1994) (phos band at left)		
from Northern Ireland prestige stamp book		
and National Trust prestige stamp book	1.00	0.80
(April 25, 1995) (phos band at right)		
from National Trust prestige stamp book	1.20	0.80
20p bright green (July 8, 1996) (centre phos band)		
from £1 and £2 booklets	1.50	1.30
25p salmon-pink (July 26, 1994)		
from £1 and £2 booklets, and Northern Ireland		
and National Trust prestige stamp books	0.70	0.60
26p red-brown (July 8, 1996)		
from £1 and £2 booklets	0.90	0.80
30p grey-green (April 25, 1995)		
from National Trust prestige stamp book	2.00	2.00
35p deep yellow (April 25, 1995)		
from National Trust prestige stamp book	2.00	1.50
41p drab (April 25, 1995)		
from National Trust prestige stamp book	1.15	1.50

■ 1998–1999. Printed in gravure by Questa

Issued in booklets and prestige stamp books. Two phosphor bands, except where stated.

1p crimson (December 1, 1998)		
from £1 booklets and World Changers		
prestige stamp book	0.75	1.00
2p myrtle-green (April 26, 1999)		
from £1 booklets	0.60	0.50
19p olive green (Apr 26, 1999) (centre phos band)		
from £1 and £2 booklets		
and World Changers PSB	0.80	0.80
20p bright green (Dec 1, 1998) (centre phos band)		
from £1 and £2 stamp booklets	10.00	1.20
26p red-brown (December 1, 1998)		
from £1 and £2 booklets and		
World Changers prestige stamp book	0.70	0.70

■ 1993–1996. Printed in litho by Walsall

Issued in booklets. Two phosphor bands.

25p salmon-pink (November 1, 1993)		
from £1 booklets	1.20	1.00
35p deep yellow (November 1, 1993)		
from £1.40 booklets	1.50	1.00
37p amethyst (July 8, 1996)		
from £1.48 booklets	2.50	1.50
41p stone (November 1, 1993)		
from £1.64 booklets	3.50	1.50

60p slate-blue (March 19, 1996)		
from £2.40 booklets	3.00	3.50
63p emerald (July 8, 1996)		
from £2.52 booklets	2.25	3.00

■ **1997–2005. Printed in gravure by Walsall**
Issued in booklets and prestige stamp books. Two phosphor bands, except where stated.

10p deep orange (October 13, 1998)		
from Breaking Barriers prestige stamp book	1.50	1.35
19p olive-green (Feb 15, 2000) (phos band at right)		
from Special By Design prestige stamp book	1.00	1.10
30p grey-green (May 5, 1998)		
from £1.20 booklet	0.95	0.70
37p amethyst (August 26, 1997)		
from £1.48 booklets	0.85	0.80
38p ultramarine (April 26, 1999)		
from £1.52 booklet	1.00	0.90
38p ultramarine (February 15, 2000) (perf: 14)		
from Special By Design prestige stamp book	3.00	1.50
39p grey (February 24, 2005)		
from Bronte prestige stamp book	1.50	1.50
40p grey-blue (April 27, 2000)		
from £1.60 booklets	1.40	1.00
42p olive grey (February 24, 2005)		
from Bronte prestige stamp book	2.00	1.50
43p chocolate brown (October 13, 1998)		
from Breaking Barriers prestige stamp book	1.50	1.50
50p ochre (October 18, 2005)		
from Battle of Trafalgar prestige stamp book	1.50	1.50
63p emerald (August 26, 1997)		
from £2.52 booklets	2.50	1.50
64p sea-green (April 26, 1999)		
from £2.56 booklets	1.50	1.50
65p greenish blue (April 27, 2000)		
from £2.60 booklets	1.50	1.50
68p grey-brown (October 18, 2005)		
from Battle of Trafalgar prestige stamp book	1.50	1.50

■ **1993–2010. Printed in gravure by Harrisons and later by De La Rue**
Issued in sheets. Two phosphor bands, except where stated.

1p crimson (April 1, 1997)	0.30	0.10
2p deep green (May 27, 1997)	0.30	0.10
4p new blue (May 27, 1997)	0.40	0.10
5p claret (May 27, 1997)	0.40	0.20
6p lime green (April 1, 1997)	0.30	0.10
7p light grey (April 20, 1999)	2.25	0.90
7p bright magenta (April 1, 2004)	0.50	0.15
8p deep yellow (April 25, 2000)	0.35	0.30
9p deep orange (April 5, 2005)	0.35	0.25
10p orange (May 8, 1997)	0.40	0.35
12p turquoise (August 1, 2006)	0.40	0.30
14p salmon pink (August 1, 2006)	0.75	0.35
15p shocking pink (April 1, 2008)	0.50	0.35
16p bright pink (March 27, 2007)	0.50	0.35
17p olive green (March 31, 2009)	0.50	0.30
19p olive (Oct 26, 1993) (one phos band)	0.45	0.40
20p bright green		
(June 25, 1996) (centre phos band)	0.45	0.35

(September 23, 1997) (phos band at right)	1.00	1.10
(April 20, 1999) (two phos bands)	0.45	0.50
22p stone (March 31, 2009)	0.65	0.35
25p salmon-pink		
(October 26, 1993) (phos coated paper)	0.60	0.60
(December 20, 1994)	0.60	0.60
26p reddish brown (June 25, 1996)	0.60	0.60
26p gold (April 29, 1997)	0.60	0.55
30p grey-green (May 12, 1997)	0.65	0.65
31p deep mauve (August 26, 1997)	0.65	2.00
33p slate-blue (April 25, 2000)	0.65	0.65
34p lime green (May 6, 2003)	3.00	2.00
35p yellow (Nov 1, 1993) (phos coated paper)	5.00	3.50
35p sepia (April 1, 2004)	1.00	0.75
35p lime-green (April 26, 2005)	0.85	0.75
37p amethyst (July 8, 1996)	1.00	1.05
37p bright mauve (August 7, 1997)	0.80	0.45
37p deep grey (July 4, 2002)	1.00	0.80
37p olive green (March 28, 2006)	0.85	0.45
38p ultramarine (April 20, 1999)	1.50	0.70
39p magenta (May 12, 1997)	0.80	2.15
39p grey (April 1, 2004)	1.00	1.00
40p greyish blue (April 20, 1999)	0.75	0.80
40p turquoise (April 1, 2004)	1.00	1.00
41p drab (Nov 1, 1993) (phos coated paper)	5.50	4.50
41p rosine (April 20, 1999)	0.85	0.90
42p olive-grey (July 4, 2002)	0.85	0.85
43p chocolate-brown (July 8, 1996)	1.10	1.10
43p brown (March 21, 1997)	4.50	3.50
43p emerald (April 1, 2004)	1.20	0.95
44p stone (April 20, 1999)	3.00	0.75
44p ultramarine (March 28, 2006)	2.00	2.00
45p mauve (April 20, 1999)	1.00	0.85
46p light brown (April 5, 2005)	1.95	0.80
47p turquoise green (July 4, 2002)	1.00	0.85
48p purple (March 27, 2007)	1.00	1.00
49p rust (March 28, 2006)	1.00	0.80
50p ochre (April 1, 1997)	1.00	0.95
50p grey (March 27, 2007)	1.00	0.95
54p rust (March 27, 2007)	1.50	1.50
56p lime green (April 1, 2008)	1.20	1.20
60p emerald green (March 30, 2010)	1.15	1.00
62p red (March 31, 2009)	1.20	0.85
63p emerald (December 12, 1996)	1.20	1.10
64p sea green (April 20, 1999)	2.35	2.35
65p greenish blue (April 25, 2000)	1.20	1.10
67p rhododendron (March 30, 2010)	1.25	1.25
68p grey-brown (July 4, 2002)	1.95	1.50
72p red (March 28, 2006)	1.40	1.20
78p emerald green (March 27, 2007)	1.50	1.20
81p sea green (April 1, 2008)	1.50	1.25
88p shocking pink (March 30, 2010)	1.50	1.50
90p ultramarine (March 31, 2009)	1.75	1.10
97p mauve (March 30, 2010)	2.00	1.60
£1 bluish-violet (April 1, 1997)	1.75	2.75
£1 ruby (June 5, 2007)	1.95	1.25
£1.48 dark turquoise (March 30, 2010)	2.50	2.00
Stamp cards (24 values current in September 2008, including non-value-indicators)	25.00	40.00

(* The 2p, 5p, 37p deep grey, 46p, 48p and £1 ruby also appear in prestige stamp books, and the £1 ruby and £1 bluish–violet in the 40th Anniversary of the Machin miniature sheet of 2007.)

■ 2009. Printed in litho by De La Rue
Issued in prestige stamp books.
5p deep claret (February 12, 2009)
from Darwin prestige stamp book 1.75 1.75
10p orange (February 12, 2009)
from Darwin prestige stamp book 1.50 1.50
48p purple (February 12, 2009)
from Darwin prestige stamp book 1.80 1.80

■ 2009–2010. Printed in litho by Cartor
Issued in prestige stamp books.
1p crimson (September 17, 2009)
from Royal Navy Uniforms prestige book 1.15 1.00
5p deep claret (February 25, 2010) wrong font*
from Classic Album Covers prestige book 2.50 1.75
5p deep claret (May 13, 2010)
from Britain Alone prestige book 1.75 1.75
10p orange–brown (February 25, 2010)
from Classic Album Covers
and Britain Alone prestige books 1.00 2.00
16p bright pink (January 13, 2009)
from Design Classics prestige book 2.00 2.00
17p olive green (August 18, 2009)
from Treasures of the Archive and
Royal Navy Uniforms prestige books 1.25 1.25
20p bright green (February 25, 2010)
from Classic Album Covers prestige book 2.00 1.50
22p stone (August 18, 2009)
from Treasures of the Archive, Classic Album
Covers and Royal Society prestige books 1.95 1.75
50p grey (January 13, 2009)
from Design Classics prestige book 3.00 2.00
54p rust (February 25, 2010) wrong font*
from Classic Album Covers and
Royal Society prestige books 2.00 2.50
60p emerald–green (May 13, 2010)
from Britain Alone prestige book 2.50 2.50
62p red (August 18, 2009)
from Treasures of the Archive and
Classic Album Covers prestige books 1.50 2.25
90p ultramarine (September 17, 2009)
from Royal Navy Uniforms prestige book 3.50 3.50
(* Two prestige stamp books in 2010 included definitives
using the wrong font for the '5' of 5p and '54' of 54p.)

First day cover (October 26, 1993)
19p, 25p, 29p, 36p, 38p, 41p – 2.50
First day cover (August 9, 1994)
60p – 1.50
First day cover (August 22, 1995)
£1 – 1.75
First day cover (June 25, 1996)
20p, 26p, 31p, 37p, 39p, 43p, 63p – 4.25
First day cover (April 21, 1997)
26p, together with 1st gold – 2.00
First day cover (April 20, 1999)
7p, 38p, 44p, 64p – 3.50

First day cover (April 25, 2000)
8p, 33p, 40p, 41p, 45p, 65p – 3.50
First day cover (July 4, 2002)
37p, 42p, 47p, 68p – 4.00
First day cover (May 6, 2003)
34p – 2.50
First day cover (April 1, 2004)
7p, 35p, 39p, 40p, 43p – 5.00
First day cover (April 5, 2005)
9p, 35p, 46p – 3.50
First day cover (March 28, 2006)
37p, 44p, 49p, 72p – 4.00
First day cover (August 1, 2006)
12p, 14p, with Pricing in Proportion stamps – 5.00
First day cover (March 27, 2007)
16p, 48p, 50p, 54p, 78p – 5.50
First day cover (June 5, 2007)
£1 – 4.00
First day cover (April 1, 2008)
15p, 56p, 81p – 3.50
First day cover (March 31, 2009)
17p, 22p, 62p, 90p – 4.00
First day cover (March 30, 2010)
60p, 67p, 88p, 97p, £1.46, with Europe, Worldwide NVIs 7.00

NON–VALUE INDICATORS WITH ELLIPTICAL PERFORATIONS, 1993–2000

Issued in booklets or coils. 2nd class stamps have one centre phosphor band; the others have two phosphor bands, except where stated.

■ 1993–1999. Printed in gravure by Harrison
2nd bright blue (September 7, 1993) 0.80 0.50
1st orange–red*
(April 6, 1993) (phos coated paper) 1.00 0.55
(April 4, 1995) (two phosphor bands) 1.10 0.65
1st gold (April 21, 1997)* 1.20 0.75
E deep blue (October 5, 1999) 1.50 0.85
Stamp card (1st gold) 2.50 7.00

■ 1993. Printed in litho by Walsall

2nd bright blue (April 6, 1993)	1.00	0.60
1st orange-red (April 6, 1993)	1.20	0.60

■ 1997–1999. Printed in gravure by Walsall

2nd bright blue (April 29, 1997)	1.00	0.80
1st gold (April 21, 1997)	1.20	1.20
1st orange-red (August 26, 1997)	0.75	0.60
E deep blue (January 19, 1999)	2.00	1.50

■ 1993. Printed in litho by Questa

2nd bright blue (April 6, 1993)	1.00	0.65
1st orange-red (April 6, 1993)	1.25	0.80

■ 1998–2000. Printed in gravure by Questa

2nd bright blue (Dec 1, 1998) (perf: 14)	1.50	1.50
2nd bright blue (Apr 27, 2000) (perf: 15x14)	1.00	0.65
1st orange-red (Dec 1, 1998) (perf: 14)	1.20	1.20
1st orange-red (Apr 27, 2000) (perf: 15x14)	1.10	0.80

First day cover (April 6, 1993)		
2nd bright blue, 1st orange-red	–	6.00
First day cover (April 21, 1997)		
1st gold, together with 26p	–	2.50
First day cover (January 19, 1999)		
E deep blue	–	2.00

(* The 2nd class bright blue printed in gravure by Enschedé and Walsall, the 1st class orange-red printed in gravure by Questa, the 1st class gold printed in gravure by De La Rue, Enschedé, Questa and Walsall, and the E deep blue printed in gravure by Enschedé and Questa also appear in prestige books.)

NON-VALUE INDICATORS WITH ELLIPTICAL PERFORATIONS IN GREETINGS CARD SHEETLETS, 1994–97

Small sheets including one 1st class orange-red stamp sold in conjunction with greetings cards, through Boots and other retail outlets.

■ 1994–1995. Printed in litho by Questa

1st sheetlet with Boots logo (Aug 17, 1994)	1.50	2.00
1st sheetlet with no logo (Sep 11, 1995)	1.50	1.20

■ 1997. Printed in litho by Enschedé

1st sheetlet with no logo (Apr 29, 1997)	1.50	1.15

PRICING IN PROPORTION ISSUES WITH ELLIPTICAL PERFORATIONS, 2006–07

■ 2006–07. Printed in gravure by De La Rue or Enschedé

Issued in sheets, business sheets and coils.

2nd blue (August 1, 2006)	1.00	0.40
2nd Large blue (August 1, 2006)	1.30	0.60
1st gold (August 1, 2006)	1.20	0.50
1st Large gold (August 1, 2006)	1.60	0.80
First day cover (together with 12p, 14p)	–	5.00

(* All four values also appear printed in gravure by De La Rue, and the 1st class printed in gravure by Enschedé, in prestige stamp books.)

HIGH VALUES WITH ELLIPTICAL PERFORATIONS, 1999–2003

■ 1999. Printed in intaglio by Enschedé

£1.50 red (March 9, 1999)	3.00	1.00
£2 blue (March 9, 1999)	4.00	1.00
£3 violet (March 9, 1999)	5.00	1.00
£5 brown (March 9, 1999)	8.00	3.00
First day cover	–	20.00

■ 2000. Printed in intaglio by De La Rue

£1.50 red (April 11, 2000)	3.00	0.80
£2 blue (April 11, 2000)	4.00	1.00
£3 violet (April 11, 2000)	5.00	1.00
£5 brown (April 11, 2000)	8.00	3.00
First day cover	–	30.00

■ 2003. Printed in gravure by De La Rue

£1.50 brown-red (July 1, 2003)	3.00	3.00
£2 blue-green (July 1, 2003)	4.00	3.00
£3 mauve (July 1, 2003)	6.00	3.00
£5 grey-blue (July 1, 2003)	9.00	5.00
First day cover	–	20.00

SPECIAL ISSUES WITH ELLIPTICAL PERFORATIONS, 2000–11

■ 2000, January 6. Millennium definitive
Des: R. Scholey.
A) Printed in gravure by De La Rue. Perf: 15x14. Issued in sheets.

1st olive–brown	1.20	0.70

B) Printed in gravure by Walsall. Perf: 15x14. Issued in retail books.

1st olive–brown	1.20	0.70

C) Printed in gravure by Walsall. Perf: 14. Issued in the Special By Design and Treasury Of Trees prestige stamp books.

1st olive–brown	1.25	0.90

D) Printed in gravure by Questa. Perf: 14. Issued in retail stamp booklets.

1st olive–brown	0.80	0.70

E) Printed in gravure by Questa. Perf: 15x14. Issued in the Queen Elizabeth The Queen Mother prestige stamp book.

1st olive–brown	1.30	1.00
First day cover	–	2.50
Stamp card	9.00	30.00

■ 2000, May 22. Stamp Show 2000 Exhibition Souvenir
Des: Jeffery Matthews. Printed by De La Rue. Phosphor paper. Miniature sheet comprising 4p blue, 5p claret, 6p lime green, 10p orange, 31p purple, 39p magenta, 64p sea-green, £1 bluish violet, plus labels featuring the Royal Mail crest and the Jeffery Matthews colour palette.

Miniature sheet	15.00	10.00
First day cover	–	20.00

■ 2010, May 8. London 2010 Festival of Stamps Exhibition Souvenir
Printed by De La Rue. Two phosphor bands. Miniature sheet comprising 1p, 2p, 5p, 9p, 10p, 20p, 60p, 67p, 88p, 97p, £1.46, plus a label featuring the London 2010: Festival of Stamps logo.

Miniature sheet	7.00	7.00
First day cover	–	7.50

■ 2011, September 14. Centenary of the Birth of Arnold Machin
Printed by Cartor. Miniature sheet comprising ten 1st class gold, with security overlay.

Miniature sheet	10.00	9.00
First day cover	–	8.50

SELF-ADHESIVES, 1993-2010

All with elliptical perforations except where otherwise stated.

■ 1993, October 19
Des: Jeffery Matthews. Printed in litho by Walsall. Horizontal format. Issued only in booklets of 20.

1st orange-red	1.00	1.20
Stamp card	7.00	8.00
First day cover	–	2.50

■ 1997, March 18
Des: Jeffery Matthews. Printed in gravure by Enschedé. Horizontal format with 'st' or 'nd' in large size. Issued only in rolls of 100.

2nd bright blue	1.35	1.20
1st orange-red	1.40	1.20
First day cover	–	3.50

■ 1998, April 6
Printed in gravure by Walsall in booklets and business sheets of 100, by Questa in business sheets of 100 (1st class only) and by Enschedé in rolls of 200 and business sheets of 100. Die-cut perf: 15x14 except where stated.

2nd bright blue	1.00	1.00
2nd bright blue (Perf: 14½x14)	£175	£175

1st orange-red	1.50	1.50
1st orange-red (Perf: 14½x14)	£175	£175

(* Perf: 14½x14 stamps were printed only by Walsall, and sold only individually through Royal Mail's Tallents House)

■ 2002, June 5
Printed in gravure by De La Rue, Questa and Walsall in retail booklets, and by Enschedé and Walsall in business sheets of 100.

1st gold	1.60	1.00

■ 2002, July 4. Overseas rates
Printed in gravure by Walsall. Issued only in retail booklets.

E deep blue	1.60	1.60
42p olive-grey	2.50	2.50
68p grey-brown	2.85	2.60

■ 2003-2010. Overseas rates with airmail chevrons
Des: Sedley Place. Printed in gravure by Walsall. Issued only in booklets, although individual stamps were sold through Royal Mail's philatelic service.

Europe up to 40g (March 27, 2003)	1.20	1.20
Europe up to 20g (March 30, 2010)	1.50	1.00
Worldwide up to 40g (March 27, 2003)	3.00	1.50
Worldwide up to 20g (March 30, 2010)	1.25	1.25
Worldwide Postcard (April 1, 2004)	1.25	1.25
First day cover (March 27, 2003)	–	4.25
First day cover (April 1, 2004)	–	3.25
First day cover (March 30 2010, with other values)	–	7.50
Stamp cards (E40g, W40g)	2.50	10.00

■ 2006. Pricing in Proportion
Des: Jeffery Matthews. Printed in gravure by Walsall and Enschedé. Issued in booklets, coils and business sheets.

2nd blue (September 12, 2006)	0.90	0.90
2nd Large blue (August 15, 2006)	1.25	1.35
1st gold (September 12, 2006)	1.00	1.00
1st Large gold (August 15, 2006)	1.50	1.50
First day cover (2nd Large, 1st Large)	–	3.00
First day cover (2nd, 1st)	–	3.00

DEFINITIVES WITH ADDITIONAL SECURITY FEATURES, 2009 to date

Stamps feature U-shaped security slits, and/or an iridescent overlay text inscribed 'Royal Mail' but including variant letters which indicate the source of the stamp (if not from counter sheets), and the year of production (from 2010 onwards).

Source codes are 'FOYAL' or 'MF1L' (booklets of four), 'MSIL' (booklets of six), 'MTIL' (booklets of 12), 'MCIL' (booklets which include special issues), 'ROYBL' or 'MBIL' (business sheets), 'MR1L' (rolls) and 'MPIL' (prestige stamp books). In some cases the entire word does not appear.

Year codes are 'MA10' (2010), 'MA11' or 'M11L' (2011), 'MA12' or 'M12L' (2012), 'MA13' or 'M13L' (2013), 'MA14' or 'M14L' (2014), 'M15L' (2015) and 'M16L' (2016).

■ **2009 to date. Non-value indicators**
Printed in gravure by De La Rue (sheets) or Walsall (booklets and business sheets), or litho by Cartor (prestige stamp books). Self-adhesive, with slits and overlay text, except where stated.
2nd blue (February 17, 2009)

no source code, no date code	2.00	2.00
no source code, date code 10	2.00	1.50
no source code, date code 11	2.00	1.50
no source code, date code 12	1.50	1.50
no source code, date code 13	1.50	1.50
no source code, date code 14	1.50	1.30
no source code, date code 15	1.50	1.30
no source code, date code 16	1.50	1.50
source code MTIL, no date code	1.75	1.75
source code MTIL, date code 10	2.75	2.75
source code MTIL, date code 11	2.00	2.00
source code MTIL, date code 12	1.50	1.50
source code MTIL, date code 13	1.50	1.50
source code MTIL, date code 14	1.25	1.25
source code MTIL, date code 15	1.50	1.50
source code MTIL, date code 16	1.50	1.50
source code MBIL, no date code	2.50	2.50
source code MBIL, date code 10	3.50	2.50
source code MBIL, date code 11	3.00	2.50
source code MBIL, date code 12	1.50	1.50
source code MBIL, date code 13	1.50	1.50
source code MBIL, date code 14	1.50	1.50
source code MBIL, date code 15	1.50	1.50
source code MBIL, date code 16	1.50	1.50
source code MRIL, no date code	3.50	3.50
source code MRIL, date code 10	–	30.00
source code MRIL, date code 10, gum, no slits	2.50	2.00
source code MRIL, date code MA12	3.00	3.00
source code MRIL, date code M12L	3.00	3.00
source code MRIL, date code 15	2.00	2.00
source code MPIL, date code 10	5.00	5.00
source code MPIL, date code 15, gum no slits	1.50	1.50

2nd Large blue (February 17, 2009)

no source code, no date code	2.50	2.50
no source code, date code 10	4.50	4.50
no source code, date code 11	2.00	2.00
no source code, date code 12	2.00	2.00
no source code, date code 13	1.75	1.75
no source code, date code 14	1.75	1.75
no source code, date code 15	1.75	1.75
no source code, date code 16	1.75	1.75
source code FOYAL, no date code	2.50	2.50
source code MFIL, date code 10	6.00	6.00
source code MFIL, date code 11	2.00	2.00
source code MFIL, date code 12	2.75	2.75
source code MFIL, date code 13	2.40	2.40
source code MFIL, date code 14	2.00	2.00
source code MFIL, date code 15	2.25	2.25
source code ROYBL, no date code	2.50	2.50
source code MBIL, date code 10	14.50	14.50
source code MBIL, date code 11	2.25	2.25
source code MBIL, date code 12	2.00	2.00
source code MBIL, date code 13	2.00	2.00
source code MBIL, date code 14	1.95	1.95
source code MBIL, date code 15	2.00	2.00
source code MBIL, date code 15	2.00	2.00

1st gold (February 17, 2009)

no source code, no date code	2.50	2.50
no source code, date code 10	2.00	2.00
no source code, date code 11	2.00	2.00
no source code, date code 12	1.25	1.25
source code MSIL, no date code	3.25	3.25
source code MSIL, date code 10	2.00	2.00
source code MSIL, date code 11	2.00	2.00
source code MTIL, no date code	1.75	1.75
source code MTIL, date code 10	3.00	3.00
source code MTIL, date code 11	2.00	2.00
source code MTIL, date code 12	3.00	3.00
source code MCIL, no date code	1.50	1.50
source code MCIL, date code 10	2.00	2.00
source code MCIL, date code 11	2.00	2.00
source code MPIL, date code 10	1.75	1.75
source code MPIL, date code 11, gum, no slits	4.00	4.00
source code MBIL, no date code	2.50	2.50
source code MBIL, date code 10	4.00	3.50
source code MBIL, date code 11	3.00	3.00
source code MRIL, no date code	2.50	2.50
source code MRIL, date code 10	3.50	3.00

source code MRIL, date code 10, gum, no slits	2.50	3.00
source code MRIL, date code 12	3.00	3.00

(*The 1st gold also exists with slits but no overlay text, from rolls.)

1st Large gold (February 17, 2009)

no source code, no date code	2.50	2.50
no source code, date code 10	3.50	3.50
no source code, date code 11	2.50	2.50
source code FOYAL, no date code	2.50	2.50
source code MFIL, date code 10	4.75	4.75
source code MFIL, date code 11	2.50	2.50
source code ROYBL, no date code	2.50	2.50
source code MBIL, date code 10	3.25	3.25
source code MBIL, date code 11	3.50	3.50

1st red (January 3, 2013)

no source code, date code 12	1.25	1.25
no source code, date code 13	1.50	1.25
no source code, date code 14	1.50	1.25
no source code, date code 15	1.50	1.50
no source code, date code 16	1.50	1.50
source code MBIL, date code 12	2.00	2.00
source code MBIL, date code 13	2.50	2.00
source code MBIL, date code 14	2.00	2.00
source code MBIL, date code 15	2.00	2.00
source code MBIL, date code 16	2.00	2.00
source code MSIL, date code 12	1.75	1.75
source code MSIL, date code 13	1.75	1.75
source code MSIL, date code 14	1.50	1.50
source code MSIL, date code 15	1.50	1.50
source code MTIL, date code 12	1.75	1.75
source code MTIL, date code 13	1.75	1.75
source code MTIL, date code 14	1.50	1.50
source code MTIL, date code 15	1.50	1.50
source code MTIL, date code 16	1.50	1.50
source code MCIL, date code 12	1.50	1.50
source code MCIL, date code 13	1.50	1.50
source code MCIL, date code 14	1.25	1.00
source code MCIL, date code 15	1.50	1.25
source code MRIL, date code 12	2.00	2.00
source code MRIL, date code 13	2.00	2.00
source code MPIL, date code 13, gum, no slits	1.75	1.00
source code MPIL, date code 15, gum, no slits	1.50	1.50
source code MPIL, date code 16, gum, no slits	1.50	1.50

1st Large red (January 3, 2013)

no source code, date code 12	2.25	2.25
no source code, date code 13	2.25	2.25
no source code, date code 14	2.25	2.25
no source code, date code 15	2.00	2.00
no source code, date code 16	2.00	2.00
source code MBIL, date code 12	2.25	2.25

source code MBIL, date code 13	2.25	2.25
source code MBIL, date code 14	2.25	2.25
source code MBIL, date code 15	2.25	2.25
source code MBIL, date code 16	2.25	2.25
source code MFIL, date code 12	2.00	2.00
source code MFIL, date code 13	2.00	2.00
source code MFIL, date code 14	2.00	2.00
source code MFIL, date code 15	2.00	2.00
source code MFIL, date code 16	2.00	2.00

■ 2009 to date. Denominated definitives

Printed in gravure by De La Rue or Walsall (sheets), or litho by Cartor (prestige stamp books). Self-adhesive, with security slits and iridescent overlay text, except where stated. From late 2015, overlay text also appears on the backing paper.

1p dark maroon (March 8, 2011)

no overlay text	0.15	0.15
no source code, date code 12	0.20	0.20
no source code, date code 15	0.20	0.20
no source code, date code 16	0.50	0.50
source code MPIL, date code 13, gum, no slits	1.50	1.50
source code MPIL, date code 14 gum, no slits	1.00	1.00

2p dark green (March 8, 2011)

no overlay text	0.35	0.35
no source code, date code 12	0.20	0.20
no source code, date code 14	0.20	0.20
no source code, date code 15	0.20	0.20
no source code, date code 16	0.20	0.20
source code MPIL, date code 13, gum, no slits	1.25	1.25
source code MPIL, date code 14 gum, no slits	1.00	1.00

5p ash pink (March 8, 2011)

no overlay text	0.25	0.50
no source code, date code 12	0.25	0.25
no source code, date code 14	0.25	0.25
no source code, date code 15	0.25	0.25
source code MPIL, date code 12, gum, no slits	1.50	1.50
source code MPIL, date code 13, gum, no slits	1.50	1.50
source code MPIL, date code 15 gum, no slits	0.40	0.40
source code MPIL, date code 16	0.40	0.40

10p light tan (March 8, 2011)

no overlay text	0.50	0.50
no source code, date code 12	0.30	0.30
no source code, date code 13	0.40	0.40
no source code, date code 14	0.40	0.40
no source code, date code 15	0.40	0.40
no source code, date code 16	0.30	0.30
source code MPIL, date code 12, gum, no slits	1.50	1.50
source code MPIL, date code 13, gum, no slits	1.50	1.50
source code MPIL, date code 14, gum, no slits	1.00	1.00
source code MPIL, date code 15, gum, no slits	0.35	0.35
source code MPIL, date code 16	0.35	0.35

20p light green (March 8, 2011)

no overlay text	0.75	0.50
no source code, date code 12	0.50	0.50
no source code, date code 13	0.75	0.50
no source code, date code 14	0.60	0.40
no source code, date code 15	0.60	0.40
no source code, date code 16	0.75	0.75
source code MPIL, date code 12, gum, no slits	2.00	2.00
source code MPIL, date code 14, gum, no slits	1.25	1.00

50p grey (February 17, 2009)

no source code, no date code	1.25	1.25
source code MPIL, date code 10	2.00	2.00
source code MPIL, date code 11	3.00	3.00

50p slate–grey (January 3, 2013)

no source code, date code 12	1.50	1.50
source code MPIL, date code 13, gum, no slits	2.00	2.00
source code MPIL, date code 15, gum, no slits	1.75	1.75

68p sea green (March 29, 2011)

no source code, date code 11	3.25	3.25
no source code, date code 12	4.00	4.00
source code MPIL, date code 11, gum, no slits	3.25	3.25

76p bright pink (March 29, 2011)

no source code, date code 11	3.25	3.25
no source code, date code 12	3.50	3.50
source code MPIL, date code 11, gum, no slits	5.00	5.00

78p orchard mauve (March 27, 2013)

no source code, date code 13 (Walsall)	1.75	1.75
no source code, date code 13 (De La Rue)	3.00	3.00

81p holly green (March 26, 2014)

no source code, date code 14	1.50	1.50

81p sea green (February 19, 2015)

source code MPIL, date code 14, gum, no slits	1.50	1.50

87p orange (April 25, 2012)

no source code, date code 12	2.25	2.25
source code MPIL, date code 12, gum, no slits	4.00	4.00

88p amber yellow (March 27, 2013)

no source code, date code 13 (Walsall)	1.95	1.95
no source code, date code 13 (De La Rue)	2.25	2.25

97p purple (March 26, 2014)

no source code, date code 14	1.80	1.80
source code MPIL, date code 14, gum, no slits	2.50	2.50

£1 ruby (February 17, 2009)

no source code, no date code	2.00	2.00
no source code, date code 11	4.00	4.00
no source code, date code 12	2.50	2.50

£1 wood brown (January 3, 2013)

no source code, date code 12	2.00	2.00
no source code, date code 14	2.50	2.50
no source code, date code 15	2.50	2.50
no source code, date code 16	2.00	2.00
source code MPIL, date code 14, gum, no slits	2.50	2.50
source code MPIL, date code 15, gum, no slits	2.50	2.50

£1.05 gooseberry green (March 22, 2016)

no source code, date code 16	2.00	2.00
source code MPIL, date code 16	2.50	2.50

£1.10 lime green (March 29, 2011)

no source code, date code 11	2.25	2.25

£1.28 emerald green (April 25, 2012)

no source code, date code 12	3.25	3.25
no source code, date code 13	2.50	2.50

no source code, date code 14	2.25	2.25

£1.33 amber yellow (March 24, 2015)

no source code, date code 15	2.00	2.00
no source code, date code 16	2.00	2.00

£1.47 dove grey (March 26, 2014)

no source code, date code 14	2.75	2.75

£1.50 brown–red (February 17, 2009)

no source code, no date code	2.75	2.75

£1.52 orchid mauve (March 24, 2015)

no source code, date code 15	2.25	2.25

£1.65 sage green (March 29, 2011)

no source code, date code 11	3.50	3.50

£1.88 orchard mauve (March 27, 2013)

no source code, date code 13 (Walsall)	3.00	3.00
no source code, date code 13 (De La Rue)	4.00	4.00

£1.90 rhododendron (April 25, 2012)

no source code, date code 12	3.50	3.50

£2 blue–green (February 17, 2009)

no source code, no date code	3.40	3.40
no source code, date code 13	5.50	5.50

£2.15 turquoise (March 26, 2014)

no source code, date code 14	3.50	3.50

£2.25 plum purple (March 24, 2015)

no source code, date code 15	3.25	3.25

£2.45 spruce green (March 24, 2015)

no source code, date code 15	3.50	3.50

£3 mauve (February 17, 2009)

no source code, no date code	4.75	4.75

£3.15 aqua green (March 24, 2015)

no source code, date code 15	4.00	4.00

£3.30 rose pink (March 24, 2015)

no source code, date code 15	4.25	4.25

£5 azure (February 17, 2009)

no source code, no date code	7.50	7.50

(* The 5p and 50p with source code MPIL and date code 13 exist in gummed form with the elliptical perforation towards the top, from the Merchant Navy prestige stamp book. The 2p, 5p and 10p also exist in gummed form, without overlay text, from prestige stamp books.)

First day cover (February 17, 2009)		
2nd, 2nd Large, 1st, 1st Large, 50p, £1	–	5.00
First day cover (February 17, 2009)		
£1.50, £2, £3, £5	–	20.00
First day cover (March 29, 2011)		
1p, 2p, 5p, 10p, 20p	–	2.00
First day cover (March 29, 2011)		
68p, 76p, £1.10, £1.65	–	7.00
First day cover (April 25, 2012)		
87p, £1.28, £1.90, with 1st Large Diamond Jubilee	–	9.50
First day cover (January 3, 2013)		
1p, 2p, 5p, 10p, 20p, 50p, £1, 1st red, 1st Large red	–	10.00
First day cover (March 27, 2013)		
78p, 88p, £1.88, with 1st Signed For, 1st Large Signed For		11.00
First day cover (March 26, 2014)		
81p, 97p, £1.47, £2.15	–	9.00
First day cover (March 24, 2015)		
£1.33, £1.52, £2.25, £2.45, £3.15, £3.30	–	24.00
First day cover (March 22, 2016)		
£1.05	–	2.50

SPECIFIC SERVICE ISSUES WITH ADDITIONAL SECURITY FEATURES

■ **2009, November 7. Recorded Delivery/Signed For**
Printed in gravure by De La Rue. Self-adhesive, with slits and iridescent overlay text.

1st orange-red and yellow

no source code, no date code	3.00	3.00
no source code, date code 10	8.00	8.00

1st Large orange-red and yellow

no source code, no date code	4.00	4.00
no source code, date code 10	9.00	9.00
First day cover	–	6.00

■ **2010, October 26. Special Delivery**
Printed in gravure by De La Rue. Self-adhesive, with slits and iridescent overlay text.

1st up to 100g silver and blue

no source code, date code 10	7.50	7.50
no source code, date code 14	7.50	7.50
no source code, date code 15	4.50	4.50

1st up to 500g blue and silver

no source code, date code 10	10.00	10.00
no source code, date code 14	10.00	10.00
no source code, date code 16	10.00	10.00
First day cover	–	15.00

■ **2013, March 27. Royal Mail/Signed For**
Printed in gravure by De La Rue. Self-adhesive, with slits and iridescent overlay text. As issue of November 7, 2009, but with revised inscription.

1st orange-red and yellow

no source code, date code 13	3.00	3.00
no source code, date code 15	3.50	3.50

1st Large orange-red and yellow

no source code, date code 13	4.00	4.00
no source code, date code 15	4.00	4.00
no source code, date code 16	4.00	4.00
First day cover (with 78p, 88p, £1.88)	–	11.00

SPECIAL ISSUES WITH ADDITIONAL SECURITY FEATURES

■ **2012, February 6. Diamond Jubilee definitives**
Printed in gravure by De La Rue (counter sheets, business sheets) or Walsall (booklets, business sheets). Self-adhesive, with slits and overlay text reading 'DIAMOND JUBILEE'.

1st diamond blue

no source code (counter sheets)	1.20	1.20
source code MSND (booklets of 6)	1.20	1.20
source code MTND (booklets of 12)	1.20	1.20
source code MCND (special issue booklets)	1.20	1.20
source code MBND (business sheets)	1.20	1.20
source code MPND (PSBs), gum, no slits	1.25	1.25
source code MMND (mini sheet), gum, no slits	–	1.25

1st Large diamond blue (April 25, 2012)

no source code (counter sheets)	1.75	1.75
source code JUBILFE (booklets of 4)	1.75	1.75
source code JUBILBE (business sheets)	1.50	1.50
First day cover (1st)	–	2.00

First day cover (1st Large with 87p, £1.28, £1.90)11.00
(* The 1st Large was released early by a number of post offices.)

■ **2015, September 9. Long To Reign Over Us definitives**
Printed in gravure by De La Rue (counter sheets) or ISP (booklets). Self-adhesive, with slits and overlay text reading 'LONG TO REIGN OVER US'.

1st amethyst purple

no source code, date code 15	1.50	1.50
no source code, date code 16	1.50	1.50
source code REIGS, date code 15	1.50	1.50
source code REIGS, date code 16	1.50	1.50
source code REIGC, date code 15	1.50	1.50
source code REIGC, date code 16	1.50	1.50
source code REIGP, date code 16, gum. no slits	1.50	1.50
First day cover	–	2.00

GB.8 KEIR HARDIE Scarce political cover for the Centenary of the death of Keir Hardie. This must be one of the scarcest political covers, due to the fact that only 50 covers were produced; issued to commemorate the centenary of the death of Keir Hardie, the founder of the British Labour Party. The cover depicts the famous man with Royal Mail stamp tied to cover by official Royal Mail Edinburgh Postmark dated 26/09/15, one hundred years to the day of Keir Hardie's death ....Price £11.

CIND 21, "CINDERELLA STAMPS" An amazing esoteric collection of worldwide Cinderella stamps: includes unissued, bogus, forgeries, phantoms, reprints, essays, propaganda issues, proofs and printers progressive proofs. Also noted better local issues, postal strike stamps. From a multitude of countries plus spectacular GB KEVII one pound green imperforate unmounted mint (faux), also India Queen Victorian four annas red and blue inverted head (faux). Spanish Civil War communist legion issue, private delivery company stamps, GB unadopted designs (essays) plus other items. If only a few of these stamps were genuine the catalogue value would be in excess of £20,000. But these are sold "as is" not guaranteed as genuine. The spectacular collection of Cinderella Stamps mint and "used" ....Price £14.30

SW171 STAR WARS A fantastic specialised collection of Star Wars postage stamps and Star Wars first day covers. Contains a mass of different Star Wars stamps including Great Britain (Royal Mail) issues also scarcer Star Wars stamps from other countries; includes stamps for the original film, "Return of the Jedi", "The Phantom Menace", "The Empire Strikes Back". Characters depicted include: Obi Wan Kenobi, Princess Leia, Darth Vader, Anakin Skywalker, Hans Solo, The Jedi Knights plus many others, too many to list. Comprising mostly of complete sets in mint sheetlets plus miniature sheets and First Day Covers. The impressive Star Wars stamp collection .... Price: £29.75

NZ.108 NEW ZEALAND: A superb collection of New Zealand Stamps dating back to King George V follows on to King Geo VI issues, onto early Elizabethan stamps to more recent issues; containing several hundred stamps in mostly fine used condition. Unchecked for catalogue value, this is a great specialized lot to build upon. Several hundred different NZ stamps ....Price £16.50

A.94 ZOOLOGICAL: A glorious collection of worldwide animal stamps. This is virtually a Noah's Ark of all species of animal life; includes everything from insects and butterflies to fish and sea life, birds, domestic animals and wildlife. A colourful collection including many sets with several hundred different animal stamps ....Price £17.25

WWI.74 GHURKA: A valuable and scarce Ghurka cover issued to commemorate the heroic Ghurkas at Gallipoli. In 1915 the Ghurkas gained immortal fame at Gallipoli with the capture of "Ghurka Bluff". The Ghurkas were the only troops in the whole campaign to gain the ultimate objective in capturing the Crest line that overlooked the straits. The cover bears the official Royal Mail Ghurka stamp issue with "Cape Helles" Gallipoli pmk. Dated 14/05/2015 in combination with the Royal Mail "We will remember them" illustrated pmk. Dated 25/04/15. The cover is highly recommended as only 60 covers exist worldwide ....Price £23.

AF. 418 AFGHANISTAN: A specialized collection of stamps from this war-torn country. Comprising of both mint and used Afghan stamps in blocks and singles with miniature sheets. Strength is in used commemoratives, noted earlier mono-coloured crudely printed early Afghan stamps. A lovely lot unchecked for catalogue value and containing hundreds of Afghanistan stamps Price £18.

R. 472 RYUKYU ISLANDS: Rarely offered for sale, this is a superb collection of the stamps of The Ryukyu Islands. Containing only superb unmounted mint stamps. Over 100 different Ryukyu Island Stamps ....Price £18.75

MI 349 MALDIVE ISLANDS: An impressive stamp collection of only unmounted mint blocks of Maldive Island stamps. The collection is rich in thematic commemoratives. Several hundred mint Maldive Islands Stamps ....Price £16

CH 739 CHURCHILL A fantastic thematic collection of Winston Churchill stamps; comprising of hundreds of mint and used Churchill stamps, including blocks, noted scarcer unmounted mint blocks of exile gov't. Churchill stamps dating back to 1952 unlisted in Stanley Gibbons Catalogue (seldom seen). All aspects of the great man's life are portrayed in this collection. Hundreds of Winston Churchill stamps...............................Price £18

SJ120 MEDICAL Stamps with specialised lot of Anti-TB and Red Cross stamps. Also Anti-Malaria stamps Red Cross stamps back to the 1940s or earlier up to more recent. With nursing, doctors and all forms of medicine. A most interesting subject rarely offered for sale ideal for anyone with some medical knowledge to form a valuable collection .... Price £7

NE832 BRITISH ISLES A phenomenal & valuable collection of British Local Island's stamps. Only unmounted mint, including Lundy Island, Davaar Island, Cairn Ia; Isle of Easdale, Bernera Island, Staffa, Stroma, Isle of Pabay, Bardsey, Herm, Calf of Man, Hildasay – Shetland Islands, Jethou, Alderney, St Marys, Calvey Island, Sanda Island, Gugh, St Martins. With blocks, multiples, singles & miniature sheets. This important & valuable collection with only unmounted mint stamps and many high £ values.
The nominal face value is well over £150 ....Price £33

Z33E UNORTHODOX STAMPS One of the most unusual collections we have ever seen assembled, with everything except normal stamps. Including triangular stamps, self adhesive 'free form', map shaped stamps, gold foil round (circular) stamps, diamond shapes, '3 dimensional' and others. Hundreds of different mint and used unorthodox stamps ....Price £13

PM22 – HAROLD WILSON Scarce GB Political Cover, commemorating the 50th Anniversary of the Election of Harold Wilson as Prime Minister. The cover is illustrated with the iconic "Labour will get things done" poster and bears Royal Mail, Wilson stamps with official first day post mark and famous Harold Wilson quote: "The main essentials of a successful prime minister are sleep and a sense of history." Only fifty of this cover are known to exist, reposted on 16/10/14 with official Royal Mail "Big Ben" postmark exactly fifty years to the day of his first election victory. ....Price £14

EI342 IRELAND A superior collection of only unmounted mint Irish stamps; Includes older stamps with definitive, commemoratives and postage dues. Also includes unusual stamps for the Fenian movement, these are imperforate and unmounted mint depicting an Irish harp and priced in "cents" understood to have been issued circa 1860s. The Fenian stamps are offered "as is" and without guarantee, but these form only a small part of the larger collection of 100 plus stamps, which are all guaranteed genuine. Entire Collection ....Price £18.50

AST 3 SPACE POSTAL HISTORY An extremely rare British Space Cover issued to commemorate Major Tim Peake, the first Briton to walk in Space. Only 80 of this Outer Space cover are known to exist. The cover depicts Tim Peake with Royal Mail stamp officially postmarked on the day of the space walk, dated 15/01/2016 used in combination with a Royal Mail space stamp tied to the cover with a blue "First British Space Walk 15" January 2016" Squared Cachet. This sought after item of Space Postal History.................................Price £26

BPO 49 BRITISH POST OFFICES ABROAD An impressive collection of over 100 unmounted mint British stamps overprinted for British Post Offices abroad including surcharges in foreign currencies for use in Bahrain, Kuwait, Morocco and Qatar; with scarcer multiple blocks including overprints on Wilding definitives (St. Edwards Crown E2R wmk.) Circa 1950's. The Specialist collection.........Price £19

ZF20 RUDOLF HESS Nazi cover commemorating the 75th Anniversary of the crash landing by Rudolf Hess, the infamous Nazi. The cover depicts Hess in Nazi uniform and the Messerschmitt Bf 110 aircraft which crash landed in Scotland in 1941. The cover bears a Scotland Royal Mail stamp with the official Royal Mail postmark Edinburgh 10/05/16. Exactly 75 years to the day of his crash landing. The cover was a severely restricted and limited issue of only 60 covers worldwide...Price £19

RSA SOUTH AFRICA A large and valuable collection of South African stamps containing only unmounted mint stamps in superb condition; Includes singles, blocks, plate blocks, complete sets and miniature sheets. Hundreds of stamps plus miniature sheets all unmounted mint........................Price £27

SYR 9 WAR IN SYRIA: A rare cover for the war in Syria. The illustrated cover depicts Russian Foreign Minister Sergei Lavrov and U.S.A Secretary of State John Kerry; Issued to Commemorate the Syrian Cease fire announced by the U.S.A and Russia on 27/2/16. The cover bears a U.K Machin stamp with official Royal Mail illustrated postmark date 27/2/16 in combination with Syrian and United Nations stamps tied to the cover with red cachet inscribed "UN Security Coucil resolution no. 2254. 18/12/15" A fragile cessation of hostilities came into force in Syria. 97 fighting groups as well as the Syrian Govt. and Russian Air Force signed up to a ceasefire. Only 40 of this rare cover exist ....Price £35

MA 275 MALTA: A quality collection of Maltese unmounted mint stamps. Over 100 stamps dating back to King Geo VI to more modern..Price £11.50

GB 4T FLYING SCOTSMAN: Railway Postal History Cover. The illustrated cover depicts the "Flying Scotsman Train" and bears official Royal Mail train stamp tied to the cover with illustrated Royal Mail special Flying Scotsman postmark Manchester to Carlisle 23/1/16 - First Mainline run. The edition was limited to only 100 covers..................Price £8.75

NW8 GRREAT BRITAIN: Hero of World War II Sir Nicholas Winton Commemorative cover. The great humanitarian saved 669 Czech children who would have been transported to Nazi Germany by train. The cover shows Winton as a young man with one of the children he saved and bears the official Royal Mail Commemorative issue for Nicholas Winton with unusual red Royal Mail official First Day Nicholas Winton Postmark. Only 50 of this cover were cancelled by the Royal Mail ....Price £19.50

V34 VATICAN CITY: A small starter collection of unmounted mint Vatican stamps ....Price £4.25

MZ 112 MOZAMBIQUE COMPANY: An impressive old collection of the stamps of the Mozambique Company dating back to the 1930's and earlier; With mint and used stamps in singles and blocks including postage dues and early air mail issues. The stamps are classically engraved and superbly printed approx. 80 stamps ....Price 9.75

SCI 8H ALBERT EINSTEIN: A special cover commemorating the 100th Anniversary of Einstein's theory of relativity. The illustrated cover depicts Einstein and bears a Royal Mail commemorative officially postmarked by the Royal Mail with Mount Pleasant 11/05/16 pmk. In combination with Jersey Einstein commemorative issue tied to the cover with large circular red Theory of Relativity cachet dated 11/05/16. The cover came from a severely restricted issue of only 60 covers ....Price £18

N-M027 MONACO: A fine collection of Monaco stamps dating back to the early issues of the 1920's through to the 1950's and on to more recent issues. Superior engraved stamps. The Collection of over 100 different only contains unmounted mint stamps...Price £13

FS 40 FENCING & SHOOTING: A lovely sports stamps collection, specialising in stamps with fencing and shooting themes in blocks and singles. Approx. 130 stamps of these unusual and interesting specialist sport themes....Price £8.75

E56 EIRE: A political and historical cover commemorating the Easter Rising of 1916. The cover depicts the defence of the Post Office in O'Connell Street. Inscribed in both English and Gaelic the cover bears an offical N. Ireland stamp with Belfast postmark dated 24/4/16 in combination with Eire overprinted stamp commemorating the 1916 Easter Rising tied to the cover with blue cachet inscribed G.P.O Dublin - Sunday 24/4/16. Only 80 of this historic cover exist ....Price £16.50

N-SH 305 SUPER HEROES: A spectacular collection of super heroes on stamps including several issues for: Superman and Batman also includes Spiderman, X Men and The Incredible Hulk, plus other super heroes. Mostly unmounted mint stamps imcluding several miniature sheets ....Price £19.75

EXP3 ANTARCTIC EXPEDITION: A limited edition first day cover only 50 issued, to commemorate the Imperial Trans-Antarctic Expedition by Ernest Shackleton. This superb illustrated cover bears special Royal Mail Antarctica Map F.D. Postmark. issue with special Royal Mail Endurance Ship Commem. issue with special Royal Mail Antarctica Map F.D. Postmark..Price £15

RW 986 RAILWAYS AND LOCOMOTIVES: A fantastic thematic collection of locomotive and railway stamps. The specialised collection contails several hundred train stamps with many scarcer unmounted mint blocks included plus F.D.C also several scarcer local issues, specimen stamps, proofs and progressive proofs, lots of higher $ stamps and £1 values; also many Railway and locomotive miniature sheets. A glorious collection for any philatelic railway enthusiast ....Price £28

DJ. 98 DJIBOUTI A small but specialised collection of Djibouti stamps, mostly used but mint noted. Contains many better catalogued, high denomination stamps ....Price £9.60

GB 38 GREAT BRITAIN WAR OF THE ROSES – Historic Commemorative Cover for the 530th Anniversary of the Battle of Bosworth Field. Less than fifty covers are known to exist, mostly now in collector's hands and elusive to locate; depicting a superb illustration of the last battle of the War of the Roses, one of the most decisive battles in English History. The cover bears the GB green "pound note stamp" tied with Royal Mail official King Richard III illustrated postmark, dated: 22/08/15, the anniv. Date (530 years later ....Price £13

RN4 GREAT BRITAIN – HMS Victory Cover, issued for the 250th anniv. of the launching of Nelson's Flagship, HMS Victory. "The pride of the British Navy". The oldest commissioned warship in the world. Bearing a Royal Mail ensign stamp and cancelled with a Royal Mail illustration ship pmk. dated 7/5/15 – only 100 covers were issued..Price £8.75

Malay. 2 SINGAPORE – A fantastic collection of Singapore stamps. Mainly in fine used condition and containing definitives and commemoratives of Singapore. Hundreds of different stamps .... Price £16.25

E2R GP1. GREAT BRITAIN – Rare Machin gutter pair cover. One of the most sought after Machin definitive covers. The Royal Mail illustrated cover bears the scarce blue 2nd class definitive Machin gutter pair with gold coronation anniv. Royal Mail crown design in Gutter Pair. The cover is postmarked with the official London E2R Coronation anniv. Pmk. Dated 1/1/13. This is of postal history importance as the Machin Coronation Gutter Pair is scarce as mint and rare used on cover .... Price £27.

Parl 92 GREAT BRITAIN – Scarce Parliamentary Cover – This scarce cover issued for the 750th Anniv. of Simon De Montfort's Parliament. Superbly illustrated and bearing the Royal Mail De Montfort commemorative stamp pmkd. with Royal Mail 2/6/15 official Royal Mail illustrated postmark. Only 60 of this cover are known to exist..................... Price £9.25

Alb. 7 ALBANIA – A lovely collection of Albanian stamps, including scarcer older stamps issued for King Zog, unmounted mint. Unusual items noted include 1952 stamps issued by the Albanian Govt. in exile. Also better overprinted stamps. Containing over 100 stamps with blocks and singles mint and used .... Price £15.

HRH 72. Princes Diana – A rare Great Britain cover issued for the interment of Diana Princess of Wales. The illustrated cover has been postmarked twice by the Royal Mail. Once on the actual interment day 6/9/97 and then again on the later date of the Diana memorial British stamp issue on 3/2/98. These covers now mostly in collectors hands are rare and seldom offered for sale .... Price £17

GB10. First Flight Cover – Elusive aviation cover flown on the Boeing 747 Jumbo jet on its maiden flight from New York to London on 22/1/1970. The superb Boeing illustrated cover bears a GPO aircraft stamp and GPO postmark in combination with "Boeing 747" flight cachet in red .... Price £8.

CAM 25. DAVID CAMERON. – A much sought after 2015 General Election cover. The cover bears the QEII "Pound note stamp" with illustrated Pmk. Dated 7/5/15 for the shock election results giving the Conservatives an outright majority. The cover depicts the Prime Minister David Cameron. Less than 65 covers exist world wide making this one of the scarcest political **covers** .... Price £18.50

IN 923. INDONESIA – Super collection of this popular S.E. Asian country dating back to 1945 to more modern with only unmounted mint in blocks & singles. The collection contains hundreds of mint Indonesia stamps....................... Price £18.

GB11. WINSTON CHURCHILL – A superb cover commemorating the 75th Anniversary of Sir Winston Churchill becoming prime minister. The cover depicts the great man and his quote: "All my past life has been but a preparation for this hour and this trial". The cover bears the Winston Churchill Royal Mail commemorative stamp issue and illustrated Royal Mail Churchill postmark (from a limited issue of only 100 covers) ... Price £14.

POW 9. COLDITZ – Official Red Cross commemorative Colditz prison cover. The cover was flown from Colditz to the Channel Islands, the cover depicts the infamous prison with German postage stamp and Colditz postmark........................ Price £10.

MS 493. WORLD WIDE MINIATURE SHEETS COLLECTION – A big collection of well over one hundred mini miniature sheets, countries noted include: Russia, Eq. Guinea, St. Thomas and Prince Islands, Guyana, Cambodia, Gt. Britain, Trucial States, Tanzania, Panama, U.S.A., Korea, Mexico, Belize, Israel, Afghanistan, Philippines, Pakistan & Cuba. A massive lot, with mint and used miniature sheets .... Price £17.25

SNP 12 SCOTLAND – The Special Commemorative cover for the Scottish National Parties Landslide Victory in Scotland; winning virtually 95% of seats. The cover depicts Nicola Sturgeon (SNP Party Leader) and bears Royal Mail Heraldic Lion stamp and official Edinburgh Postmark dated 7/5/15. The cover is sought after in Scotland and elsewhere as only 50 were produced at the time. .... Price £13.75

IOM 8. ISLE OF MAN – Queen Victoria Illustrated commemorative cover for the 175th Anniv. of the world's first stamp. The impressive cover bears a block of six penny black stamps and one two penny blue stamp tied to the cover with 6th May IOM Anniv. pmks. Only 100 of this cover were postmarked by the IOM Post Office...................... Price £9.25

E481. ETHIOPIA – A valuable collection of Ethiopian stamps dating back to circa 1898 Abyssinian issues with many older stamps of the 1930's to 1950's including scarcer early Air Mail overprints and ranges through to more recent issues. Approx. 100 different Ethiopian stamps .... Price £19.50

MAR 7. PRINCESS MARGARET MOURNING COVER – This scarce Royal Cover is hardly ever offered for sale. Illustrated with a classic portrait of Princess Margaret 1930-2002 and postmarked exceptionally with Royal Mail Bognor internal enquiry office postmark dated 9/2/2002. The cover is of special postal history interest due to the use of the rare postmark... Price £21

PRC 10. CHINA – A glorious collection of stamps of China. Mostly People's Republic of China, with interesting group of Hong Kong stamps; also China Stamp Booklets, Mint Complete sheet noted some odd Macau, Several China Miniature Sheets and China First Day Covers. Noted better overprinted stamps, East China 1949 Mao Tse Tung & General Zhu. A highly recommended lot with hundreds of China stamps not counting complete China stamp booklets, miniature sheets and FDC's .... Price £37

LUS 3. RMS LUSITANIA – Special commemorative cover for the centenary of the sinking of the Lusitania. Only 100 covers in existence. Superbly illustrated for the tragic event that brought America into World War I. The cover bears a Royal Mail Navy Ensign Stamp with the 7th May 2015 Lusitania illustrated Royal Mail Liverpool pmk.................................. Price £8.75

JK 106. HARRY POTTER – A fantastic collection of different Harry Potter stamps from various countries. Includes a scarce Isle of Man Prisoner of Azkaban cover with I.O.M. Harry Potter stamp in combination with official Royal Mail Harry Potter stamp, postmarked with illustrated first day issue, Hogwarts postmark. The collection also includes unmounted mint Royal Mail Harry Potter stamps and miniature sheets from various countries, includes catalogued and scarcer unlisted issues the whole collection .... Price £19.75

SA4 NELSON MANDELA – A historic and scarce mourning cover for Nelson Mandela. 'His was a spirit born free, today his spirit is soaring through the heavens. He is now forever free' – Muhammad Ali 5/12/13. The cover bears a South Africa Mandela stamp with cachet 'In Memorial 1918-2013' also Royal Mail gold definitive postmarked Mount Pleasant 5/12/13. Only 50 covers known to exist.................................. Price £14.

GB85 GREAT BRITAIN - An important error on the 1966 Battle of Hastings 6d. value. The wrong colour gold leaf was used in error on the Queens Head. Error – yellow gold instead of normal bronze gold. We can offer the unmounted mint error plus normal stamp for comparison .... Price £7.50

BRP 73. BRITISH PACIFIC ISLANDS – A glorious collection of stamps and covers from the British Pacific Islands. Including unmounted mint in blocks and singles with used stamps and fdc's, dating back to King George VI but mostly more recent issues. Countries noted include: Solomon Islands, Pitcairn, Norfolk Islands, Niue, Samoa, Tonga, Tuvalu, Penrhyn, Kiribati, Christmas Island, Fiji, Nauru, Cook Islands, Papua and New Guinea. Plus others. Over 100 stamps and also several First Day Covers including scarce first day cover signed by the stamp designer. The whole collection .... Price £18.50

GB5 GB WINSTON CHURCHILL D-DAY COVER - A spectacular cover and valuable addition to any WWII Collection. The cover is inscribed 70th Anniv. Of D-Day 6th June 1944. Illustrated with Churchill Storming Street 1940's Photograph, and Churchill's Quote: "And what a plan! This vast operation is undoubtedly the most complicated and difficult that has ever occurred." The cover bears a combination of Royal Mail, Churchill and D-Day stamps. With official Royal Mail, British Forces 3173 Postal Services postmark, D-Day 6th June 2014. The cover also bears the rare Royal Mail GB GPO stamps, with horizontal cachet inscribed "D-Day The Longest Day" in black. The cover issue was restricted to 100 covers only .... Price £13.75

M27A CORONATION STREET. – A specialised and most unusual thematic collection of Coronation street stamps with COMPLETE UNM. MINT SETS. From various British local islands, including scarcer High Values and several £1.00 values. Personalities depicted on stamps include: Jack & Annie Walker, Stan & Hilda Ogden, Ken & Irma Barlow, Jack & Vera Duckworth, Martha Longhurst, Ena Sharples, Mike & Alma Baldwin, Kevin Webster, Raquel Wolstenholme, Ray Langton, Liz McDonald, Alf Roberts, Bet Gilroy, Curly Watts, Leonard Swindly, Elsie Tanner, Reg Holdworth + others... Price £12.00

LIB 92. LIBYA – War in Libya, Liberation Cover. An unusual cover inscribed Official Liberation Day with Iconic Illustration. The cover has Machin Royal Mail stamps and official Royal Mail British Jubilee postmark dated, 23 Oct 2011 (Libya Liberation Day). The cover also bears a Libya Col. Gaddafi

stamp tied to cover with cachet inscribed Oct 2011 Libya. An unusual and important cover......................... Price £14.50

R88A NAZI GERMAN - Occupation of World War II various Croatia Bohemia and Moravia. Occupation of Poland General government (Theresienstadt also Lodz Ghfetto these may not be genuine) plus various other Germany war period Hitler issues. Mainly genuine unmounted mint/used........ Price £10.

HRH7 RARE ROYAL COVER - Extremely rare Royal Cover for HRH Prince George. This superbly illustrated, Royal Baby, Official first day cover, bears a gutter pair originally printed for Princess Diana's 21st birthday, which was overprinted for the birth of her son Prince William dated 19/07/1982, the cover was re-posted with Royal Mail stamps of three generations: Queen Elizabeth II, Prince Charles & Prince William. Officially postmarked by the Royal Mail for Prince George's christening on 23/10/13 at St James' Palace London. The cover has been signed by the stamp designer – only 40 of this rare cover are understood to exist and are destined to be vital to any future Prince William and Prince George stamp collections .... Price £19.75.

LOT K2 GREAT BRITAIN UNMOUNTED MINT COMMEMORATIVES & DEFINITIVES & DEFINITIVES UNSORTED ACCUMULATION. Items noted include Traffic Light Gutter Pair Missing Phosphor Error voil strips. Well over 500 stamps only unmounted mint ....Price £15

MM28 MARILYN MONROE - A gorgeous collection of Marilyn Monroe stamps. Few other actresses embodies the term 'Hollywood Movie Star' as much as the legendary and iconic screen goddess, Marilyn Monroe. This collection contains many different unmounted mint and used Marilyn Monroe stamps. Including several elusive stamps..Price £11

JB 773 JAMES BOND – An outstanding collection of James Bond Stamps. Includes official James Bond combination cover bearing Ian Fleming's iconic James Bond book issue, with first day of issue 8/1/2008 Royal Mail postmark. The cover was reposted on 1/5/2012 (four years later) with Royal Mail "British Hero James Bond 50th Anniv Postmark" The James Bond Collection continues with many Unmounted Mint James Bond Commemorative Stamps and Miniature Sheets: Including, scarcer unlisted issues from various countries..Price £26

GB.51 - GREAT BRITAIN - Scarce Festival of Britain Commem. Cover. Bearing the Abram Games stamp designer official Royal Mail Commem. Stamp cancelled with iconic Festival of Britain 25/3/14 Postmark. The Cover also bears the complete King George VI 1951 Festival stamps with black cachet "G.P.O. 1951 Festival of Britain Official Stamp Issue" The edition was limited to only 100 of these important covers .... Price £11.25

WE 378 EUROPE Mostly Western Europe, an attractive collection of mint and used stamps with: Switzerland, Yugoslavia, San-Marino also noted Eire, Italy, Spain and Greece – strength in older Yugoslavia. Contains several hundred different European stamps................................Price: £8.75

GB 4K GREAT BRITAIN Postal History Cover for British Parliaments enactment of the stamp act. Commemorating the 250th Anniv of the Stamp Act. In 1766 the controversial stamp act was a major cause of the American Revolution. Benjamin Franklin appealed to the British House of Commons and the act was repealed. The historic cover of which only fifty exist bears the Royal Mail illustrated ship postmark dated 1/1/15. The cover also depicts the 1765 British One Penny Stamp which pre-dated the famous 1d Black Stamp of 1840 by sixty four years ....Price:£19.50

SW171 STAR WARS A fantastic specialised collection of Star Wars postage stamps and Star Wars first day covers. Contains a mass of different Star Wars stamps including Great Britain (Royal Mail) issues also scarcer Star Wars stamps from other countries; includes stamps for the original film, "Return of the Jedi", "The Phantom Menace", "The Empire Strikes Back". Characters depicted include: Obi Wan Kenobi, Princess Leia, Darth Vader, Anakin Skywalker, Hans Solo, The Jedi Knights plus many others, too many to list. Comprising mostly of complete sets in mint sheetlets plus miniature sheets and First Day Covers. The impressive Star Wars stamp collection...Price £29.75

AG.23 BATTLE OF AGINCOURT. The scarce cover issued to commemorate the 600th Anniversary of the Battle of Agincourt. The cover is superbly illustrated with the arms of King Henry V and bears the official British Royal Mail Postmark, depicting King Henry V, dated 25/10/15, six hundred years to the day of the historic battle. Only 50 of this scarce cover exist....Price £15

QUEEN ELIZABETH II
DECIMAL SPECIAL ISSUES

In this section, prices are quoted in two columns: unmounted mint (left) and fine used (right). Most issues, as well as gutter pairs and stamp cards, are priced for complete sets only except where stated.

Except where otherwise stated, all stamps were printed in photogravure by Harrison. Gutter pairs and traffic-light gutter pairs appear from November 1972, blue-tinted polyvinyl alcohol dextrin (PVAD) gum from November 1973 and phosphor-coated paper from September 1979.

'A Mountain Road' by T. P. Flanagan (3p)
'Deer's Meadow' by Tom Carr (7½p)
'Slieve na Brock' by Colin Middleton (9p)

■ 1971, June 16. Ulster Paintings
Des: S. Rose.

Set	0.50	0.60
First day cover	–	1.50

John Keats (3p)
Thomas Gray (5p)
Sir Walter Scott (7½p)

■ 1971, July 28. Literary Anniversaries
Des: Rosalind Dease.

Set	0.50	0.60
First day cover	–	1.50

British Legion: servicemen and nurse (3p)
City of York: Roman centurion (7½p)
Rugby Football Union: rugby players (9p)

■ 1971, August 25. Anniversaries
Des: F. Wegner.

Set	0.55	0.65
First day cover	–	1.50

University College, Aberystwyth (3p)
University of Southampton (5p)
University of Leicester (7½p)
University of Essex (9p)

■ 1971, September 22. Modern University Buildings
Des: N. Jenkins.

Set	0.85	1.00
First day cover	–	1.50

'Dream of the Wise Men' (2½p)
'Adoration of the Magi' (3p)
'Ride of the Magi' (7½p)

■ 1971, October 13. Christmas
Des: Clarke, Clement and Hughes, based on stained glass windows at Canterbury Cathedral.

Set	0.40	0.60
First day cover	–	1.50

Sir James Clarke Ross (3p)
Sir Martin Frobisher (5p)
Sir Henry Hudson (7½p)
Robert Scott (9p)

■ 1972, February 16. Polar Explorers
Des: Marjorie Seynor.

Set	0.90	1.00
First day cover	–	1.50

Tutankhamun discovery: statuette (3p)
H.M. Coastguard: 19th–century coastguard (7½p)
Ralph Vaughan Williams: portrait and score (9p)

■ **1972, April 26. Anniversaries**
Des: Rosalind Dease (3p), F. Wegner (7½p), C. Abbott (9p)

Set	0.50	0.60
First day cover	–	1.50

St. Andrew's, Greensted–juxta–Ongar, Essex (3p)
All Saints, Earls Barton, Northamptonshire (4p)
St. Andrew's, Lethringsett, Norfolk (5p)
St. Andrew's, Helpringham, Lincolnshire (7½p)
St. Mary the Virgin, Huish Episcopi, Somerset (9p)

■ **1972, June 21. Village Churches**
Des: R. Maddox.

Set	1.25	1.40
First day cover	–	2.75

BBC: microphones (3p)
BBC: horn loudspeaker (5p)
BBC: colour television (7½p)
Marconi: oscillator and spark transmitter (9p)

■ **1972, September 13. Broadcasting Anniversaries**
Des: D. Gentleman.

Set	0.75	0.95
First day cover	–	1.45

Angel with trumpet (2½p)
Angel with lute (3p)
Angel with harp (7½p)

■ **1972, October 18. Christmas**
Des: Sally Stiff.

Set	0.30	0.40
First day cover	–	1.25

Queen Elizabeth II and Prince Phillip (3p, 20p)

■ **1972, November 20. Royal Silver Wedding**
Des: J. Matthews from photograph by Norman Parkinson.
All-over phosphor (3p), no phosphor (20p).
i) Printed on a Rembrandt machine

Set	0.90	0.80
First day cover	–	1.25

ii) Printed on a Jumelle machine.

3p	0.20	0.20
Gutter pair	0.40	–
Traffic light gutter pair	11.00	–

(* The portraits tend to be lighter on the Jumelle printing)

Jigsaw pieces representing Europe (3p, 5p, 5p)

■ **1973, January 3. Britain's Entry into European Communities**
Des: P. Murdoch.

Set	0.75	0.85
First day cover	–	1.50

Oak tree (9p)

■ **1973, February 28. British Trees**
Des: D. Gentleman.

9p	0.20	0.25
First day cover	–	1.25

David Livingstone (3p)
Henry Stanley (3p)
Sir Francis Drake (5p)
Sir Walter Raleigh (7½p)
Charles Sturt (9p)

■ **1973, April 18. British Explorers**
Des: Marjorie Seynor. All-over phosphor.

Set	1.10	1.00
First day cover	–	1.40

About to bat (3p)
Watching the ball (7½p)
Leaving the wicket (9p)

■ **1973, May 16. Centenary of County Cricket**
Des: E Ripley, based on drawings by Harry Furniss of W.G. Grace.

Set	1.00	1.00
First day cover	–	1.50
Stamp card (of 3p design)	45.00	–

Self-portrait by Joshua Reynolds (3p)
Self-portrait by Henry Raeburn (5p)
'Nelly O'Brien' by Reynolds (7½p)
'The Skating Minister' by Raeburn (9p)

■ **1973, July 4. British Painters**
Des: S. Rose.

Set	0.70	0.80
First day cover	–	1.25

Court masque costumes (3p)
St Paul's Church, Covent Garden (3p)
Prince's Lodging, Newmarket (5p)
Court masque stage scene (5p)

■ **1973, August 15. 400th Anniversary of Birth of Inigo Jones**
Des: Rosalind Dease. Printed in litho and typo by Bradbury, Wilkinson.

Set	0.65	1.10
First day cover	–	1.75
Stamp card (of 3p St Paul's)	£140	£300

Palace of Westminster from Whitehall (8p)
Palace of Westminster from Millbank (10p)

■ **1973, September 12. Commonwealth Parliamentary Conference**
Des: R. Downer. Printed in recess and litho by Bradbury, Wilkinson.

Set	0.40	0.50
First day cover	–	1.25
Stamp card (of 8p design)	25.00	£175

Princess Anne and Captain Mark Phillips (3½p), (20p)

■ **1973, November 14. Royal Wedding**
Des: C. Clements and E. Hughes, based on photograph by Lord Lichfield.

Set	0.50	0.55
Gutter pair	1.75	–
Traffic light gutter pair	70.00	–
First day cover	–	1.25
Stamp card (of 3½p design)	5.00	20.00

(* The 3½p exists from sheets guillotined in the wrong place giving incorrect inscriptions within the gutter; price £30.)

Good King Wenceslas, the carol story (3p, 3p, 3p, 3p, 3p)
Good King Wenceslas, the page and the peasant (3½p)

■ **1973, November 28. Christmas**
Des: D. Gentleman. 3p values have one phosphor band. These stamps exist with either gum Arabic (3p), PVA gum (3½p) or dextrin gum (both values); prices are the same.

Set	1.50	1.70
First day cover	–	2.00

Horse chestnut (10p)

■ **1974, February 27. British Trees**
Des: D. Gentleman.

10p	0.25	0.25
Gutter pair	1.00	–
Traffic light gutter pair	45.00	–
First day cover	–	1.25
Stamp card	80.00	75.00

First motor fire engine, 1904 (3½p)
Prizewinning fire engine, 1863 (5½p)
First steam fire engine, 1830 (8p)
Fire engine, 1766 (10p)

■ **1974, April 24. Fire Engines**
Des: D. Gentleman. Dextrin gum except where stated.

Set	0.75	0.80
3½p with PVA gum	0.90	–
Gutter pairs	2.75	–
Traffic light gutter pairs	35.00	–
First day cover	–	2.00
Stamp card (of 3½p design)	65.00	70.00

P&O Packet Steamer 'Peninsular', 1888 (3½p)
First official airmail, 1911 (5½p)
Airmail van and postbox, 1930 (8p)
Imperial Airways flying boat, 1937 (10p)

■ **1974, June 12. Centenary of the UPU**
Des: Rosalind Dease.

Set	0.55	0.75
Gutter pairs	1.75	–
Traffic light gutter pairs	40.00	–
First day cover	–	1.50

Robert the Bruce (4½p)
Owain Glyndwr (5½p)
King Henry V (8p)
The Black Prince (10p)

■ **1974, July 10. Medieval Warriors**
Des: F. Wegner.

Set	0.70	0.90
Gutter pairs	3.00	–
Traffic light gutter pairs	40.00	–
First day cover	–	1.75
Stamp cards	16.00	70.00

Lord Warden of the Cinque Ports (4½p)
Prime Minister (5½p)
Secretary for War and Air (8p)
War correspondent in South Africa (10p)

■ 1974, October 9. Birth Centenary of Sir Winston Churchill
Des: C. Clements and E. Hughes.

Set	1.00	0.85
8p with PVA gum	0.50	–
Gutter pairs	1.75	–
Traffic light gutter pairs	24.00	–
First day cover	–	1.50
Stamp card (of 5½p design)	3.00	17.00

'Adoration of the Magi', York Minster (3½p)
'The Nativity', St. Helen's Church, Norwich (4½p)
'Virgin and Child', Ottery St. Mary Church (8p)
'Virgin and Child', Worcester Cathedral (10p)

■ 1974, November 27. Christmas
Des: Peter Hatch Partnership, based on church roof bosses.

3½p with phos band to right	0.20	0.25
Set	0.50	0.60
Gutter pairs	2.25	–
Traffic light gutter pairs	27.00	–
First day cover	–	1.25

Disabled person in wheelchair (4½p + 1½p)

■ 1975, January 22. Health and Handicap Charities
Des: P. Sharland. Surcharge donated to charity.

4½p + 1½p	0.15	0.15
Gutter pair	0.30	–
Traffic light gutter pair	1.00	–
First day cover	–	0.50

'Peace: Burial at Sea' (4½p)
'Snowstorm' (5½p)
'The Arsenal, Venice' (8p)
'St. Laurent' (10p)

■ 1975, February 19. Bicentenary of the Birth of J. M. W. Turner
Des: S. Rose.

Set	0.50	0.60
Gutter pairs	1.25	–
Traffic light gutter pairs	6.00	–
First day cover	–	1.50
Stamp card (of 5½p design)	20.00	12.00

Charlotte Square, Edinburgh (7p)
The Rows, Chester (7p)
Royal Observatory, Greenwich (8p)
St. George's Chapel, Windsor (10p)
National Theatre, London (12p)

■ 1975, April 23. European Architectural Heritage Year
Des: P. Gauld.

Set	0.80	1.00
Gutter pairs	3.00	–
Traffic light gutter pairs	12.00	–
First day cover	–	1.50
Stamp cards (of 7p and 8p designs)	6.00	25.00

Sailing dinghies (7p)
Racing keel boats (8p)
Cruising yachts (10p)
Multihulls (12p)

■ 1975, June 11. Sailing

Des: A. Restall. Printed in photogravure and recess by Harrison.

Set	0.60	0.75
Gutter pairs	1.50	–
Traffic light gutter pairs	16.00	–
First day cover	–	1.20
Stamp card (of 8p design)	3.50	15.00

(* The 7p exists from sheets guillotined in the wrong place, giving gutter pairs with the wrong inscriptions, priced at £45.)

Stephenson's Locomotion, 1825 (7p)
Waverley class, 1876 (8p)
Caerphilly Castle, 1923 (10p)
Inter–City High Speed Train, 1975 (12p)

■ 1975, August 13. 150th Anniversary of Public Railways

Des: B. Cracker.

Set	0.80	0.80
Gutter Pairs	2.25	–
Traffic light gutter pairs	7.00	–
First day cover	–	1.75
Stamp cards (set)	30.00	35.00

Palace of Westminster (12p)

■ 1975, September 3. Inter–Parliamentary Union Conference

Des: R. Downer

12p	0.25	0.25
Gutter pair	0.60	–
Traffic light gutter pair	2.00	–
First day cover	–	1.25

Emma and Mr. Woodhouse, from Emma (8½p)
Catherine Morland, from Northanger Abbey (10p)
Mr. Darcy, from Pride and Prejudice (11p)
Mary and Henry Crawford, from Mansfield Park (13p)

■ 1975, October 22. Birth Bicentenary of Jane Austen

Des: Barbara Brown.

Set	0.80	0.70
Gutter pairs	1.40	–
Traffic light gutter pairs	5.50	–
First day cover	–	1.25
Stamp cards (set)	10.00	30.00

Angel with harp and lute (6½p)
Angel with mandolin (8½p)
Angel with horn (11p)
Angel with trumpet (13p)

■ 1975, November 25. Christmas

Des: R. Downer. Dextrin gum except where stated. The 8½p has the phosphor in the green printing ink

6½p with PVA gum	0.50	–
Set	0.75	0.75
Gutter pairs	1.40	–
Traffic light gutter pairs	5.50	–
First day cover	–	1.40

Housewife with telephone (8½p)
Policeman with telephone (10p)
District nurse with telephone (11p)
Industrialist with telephone (13p)

■ 1976, March 10. Centenary of First Telephone Call by Alexander Graham Bell

Des: P. Sharland.

Set	0.75	0.80
Gutter pairs	1.50	–
Traffic light gutter pairs	5.50	–
First day cover	–	1.40

Mining coal: Thomas Hepburn (8½p)
Machinery: Robert Owen (10p)
Sweeping a chimney: Lord Shaftesbury (11p)
Prison bars: Elizabeth Fry (13p)

■ 1976, April 28. Social Reformers
Des: D. Gentleman.

Set	0.70	0.80
Gutter pairs	1.50	–
Traffic light gutter pairs	5.50	–
First day cover	–	1.40
Stamp card (of 8½p design)	3.00	7.50

Benjamin Franklin (11p)

■ 1976, June 2. Bicentennial of American Independence
Des: P. Sharland.

11p	0.25	0.25
Gutter pair	0.50	–
Traffic light gutter pair	1.25	–
First day cover	–	1.40
Stamp card	2.50	7.50

Elizabeth of Glamis (8½p)
Grandpa Dickson (10p)
Rosa mundi (11p)
Sweet briar (13p)

■ 1976, June 30. Centenary of the Royal National Rose Society
Des: Kristin Rosenberg.

Set	0.70	0.80
Gutter pairs	1.50	–
Traffic light gutter pairs	6.00	–
First day cover	–	1.25
Stamp cards	15.00	25.00

Royal National Eisteddfod of Wales: archdruid (8½p)
Morris dancing (10p)
Highland Gathering: piper (11p)
Royal National Eisteddfod of Wales: harpist (13p)

■ 1976, August 4. British Cultural Traditions
Des: Marjorie Seynor.

Set	0.80	0.80
Gutter pairs	1.50	–
Traffic light gutter pairs	6.00	–
First day cover	–	1.25
Stamp cards	8.00	15.00

Woodcut from 'The Canterbury Tales' (8½p)
Extract from 'The Tretyse of Love' (10p)
Woodcut from 'The Game and Playe of Chesse' (11p)
Early printing press (13p)

■ 1976, September 29. 500th Anniversary of British Printing
Des: R. Gay.

Set	0.80	0.75
Gutter pairs	1.50	–
Traffic light gutter pairs	5.50	–
First day cover	–	1.25
Stamp cards	6.00	15.00

Virgin and child, embroidery c.1272 (6½p)
Angel with crown, embroidery c.1340 (8½p)
Angel appearing to shepherds, embroidery c.1320 (11p)
The three kings, embroidery c.1330 (13p)

■ **1976, November 24. Christmas.**
Des: Enid Marx, based on medieval English embroideries.

Set	0.80	0.70
6½p with one phos band	0.15	0.10
Gutter pairs	1.50	–
Traffic light gutter pairs	7.00	–
First day cover	–	1.25
Stamp cards	2.50	17.00

Lawn tennis (8½p)
Table tennis (10p)
Squash (11p)
Badminton (13p)

■ **1977, January 12. Racket Sports**
Des: A. Restall.

Set	0.75	0.80
Gutter pairs	1.75	–
Traffic light gutter pairs	4.50	–
First day cover	–	1.25
Stamp cards	4.00	17.00

Steroids: conformational analysis (8½p)
Vitamin C: synthesis (10p)
Starch: chromatography (11p)
Salt: crystallography (13p)

■ **1977, March 2. Centenary of the Royal Institute of Chemistry**
Des: J. Karo.

Set	0.75	0.75
Gutter pairs	1.75	–
Traffic light gutter pairs	4.50	–
First day cover	–	1.25
Stamp cards	4.00	10.00

'ER' and Queen Elizabeth II (8½p, 9p, 10p, 11p, 13p)

■ **1977, May 11. Silver Jubilee**
Des: Professor R. Guyatt. 9p issued on June 15.

Set	0.80	0.75
Gutter pairs	1.80	–
Traffic light gutter pairs	3.00	–
First day cover (8½p, 10p, 11p, 13p)	–	1.00
First day cover (9p)	–	0.50
Stamp cards	6.00	11.00

Symbol of meeting (13p)

■ **1977, June 8. Commonwealth Heads of Government Meeting, London**
Des: P. Murdoch. Printed in photogravure and recess by Harrison.

13p	0.25	0.25
Gutter pair	0.50	–
Traffic light gutter pair	1.25	–
First day cover	–	1.00
Stamp card	1.75	2.50

Hedgehog *Erinaceus europaeus*

Hedgehog (9p)
Hare (9p)
Red squirrel (9p)
Otter (9p)
Badger (9p)

1977, October 5. British Wildlife

Des: P Oxenham.

Set (se-tenant strip of five)	0.90	1.20
Gutter strip	1.25	
Traffic light gutter strip	3.50	–
First day cover	–	1.75
Stamp cards	4.00	6.50

(* Gutter strips normally comprise a strip of four designs separated from the fifth design by the gutter.)

THE TWELVE DAYS OF CHRISTMAS

Three hens, two turtle doves, a partridge in a pear tree (7p)
Six geese, five gold rings, four colly birds (7p)
Eight maids, seven swans (7p)
Ten pipers, nine drummers (7p)
Twelve lords, eleven ladies (7p)
Partridge in a pear tree (9p)

1977, November 23. Christmas

Des: D. Gentleman, based on the song 'The Twelve Days of Christmas'. The 7p values, issued se-tenant, have one phosphor band.

Set	0.75	0.85
Gutter pairs	1.50	–
Traffic light gutter pairs	3.50	–
First day cover	–	1.50
Stamp cards	3.00	5.00

(* Gutter pairs of the 7p values comprise two horizontal se-tenant strips of five separated by a horizontal gutter.)

OIL

North Sea oil (9p)
Coal pithead (10½p)
Natural gas flame (11p)
Electricity (13p)

1978, January 25. Energy Resources

Des: P. Murdoch.

Set	0.65	0.75
Gutter pairs	1.50	–
Traffic light gutter pairs	3.00	–
First day cover	–	1.25
Stamp cards	2.50	3.50

Tower of London-The White Tower

Tower of London (9p)
Palace of Holyroodhouse (10½p)
Caernarvon Castle (11p)
Hampton Court Palace (13p)

1978, March 1. Historic Buildings

Des: R. Maddox; miniature sheet by J. Matthews.

Set	0.75	0.80
Gutter pairs	1.60	–
Traffic light gutter pairs	3.00	–
First day cover	–	1.25
Stamp cards	2.50	3.50
Miniature sheet (one of each value)	1.00	1.20
Miniature sheet first day cover	–	1.25

(* The miniature sheet was sold at 53½p, the extra 10p being donated to assist the finances of staging the International Stamp Exhibition. London 1980, which the sheet itself publicised.)

State Coach (9p)
St. Edward's Crown (10½p)
Sovereign's Orb (11p)
Imperial State Crown (13p)

■ 1978, May 31. 25th Anniversary of the Coronation
Des: J. Matthews.

Set	0.75	0.75
Gutter pairs	1.60	–
Traffic light gutter pairs	3.00	–
First day cover	–	1.25
Stamp cards	2.50	3.50

Shire horse (9p)
Shetland pony (10½p)
Welsh pony (11p)
Thoroughbred (13p)

■ 1978, July 5. Horses
Des: P. Oxenham.

Set	0.70	0.75
Gutter pairs	1.50	–
Traffic light gutter pairs	3.00	–
First day cover	–	1.25
Stamp cards	5.50	3.50

Penny Farthing and Safety Bicycle, 1884 (9p)
Touring bicycles, 1920 (10½p)
Modern small-wheel bicycles (11p)
Road racers, 1978 (13p)

■ 1978, August 2. Cycling
Des: F. Wegner.

Set	0.70	0.75
Gutter pairs	1.60	–
Traffic light gutter pairs	3.00	–
First day cover	–	1.25
Stamp cards	4.00	3.50

Singing carols around a Christmas tree (7p)
The waits (9p)
18th-century carol singers (11p)
The boar's head carol (13p)

■ 1978, November 22. Christmas
Des: Faith Jaques. 7p has one phosphor band.

Set	0.70	0.70
Gutter pairs	1.25	–
Traffic light gutter pairs	3.00	–
First day cover	–	1.25
Stamp cards	2.50	3.00

Old English sheepdog (9p)
Welsh springer spaniel (10½p)
West Highland terrier (11p)
Irish setter (13p)

■ 1979, February 7. British Dogs
Des: P. Barrett.

Set	0.70	0.75
Gutter pairs	1.25	–
Traffic light gutter pairs	2.25	–
First day cover	–	1.25
Stamp cards	2.50	3.50

Primrose (9p)
Daffodil (10½p)
Bluebell (11p)
Snowdrop (13p)

■ 1979, March 21. Spring Wild Flowers

Des: P. Newcombe.

Set	0.70	0.75
Gutter pairs	1.50	–
Traffic light gutter pairs	2.25	–
First day cover	–	1.25
Stamp cards	3.50	3.50

Hands placing flags into ballot boxes (9p, 10½p, 11p, 13p)

■ 1979, May 9. First Direct Elections to the European Assembly

Des: S. Cliff.

Set	0.70	0.75
Gutter pairs	1.50	–
Traffic light gutter pairs	2.25	–
First day cover	–	1.25
Stamp cards	2.50	3.00

Saddling Mahmoud for the Derby, 1936 (9p)
Liverpool Great National Steeplechase, 1839 (10½p)
First Spring Meeting at Newmarket, 1793 (11p)
Racing at Dorsett Ferry, Windsor, 1684 (13p)

■ 1979, June 6. Horse Racing Paintings

Des: S. Rose.

Set	0.70	0.75
Gutter pairs	1.50	–
Traffic light gutter pairs	2.25	–
First day cover	–	1.25
Stamp cards	2.50	3.00

'The Tale of Peter Rabbit' by Beatrix Potter (9p)
'The Wind in the Willows' by Kenneth Grahame (10½p)
'Winnie the Pooh' by A. A. Milne (11p)
'Alice's Adventures in Wonderland' by Lewis Carroll (13p)

■ 1979, July 11. International Year of the Child

Des: E. Hughes.

Set	0.85	0.85
Gutter pairs	1.75	–
Traffic light gutter pairs	2.25	–
First day cover	–	1.25
Stamp cards	3.50	4.00

Sir Rowland Hill (10p)
General Post, 1839 (11½p)
London Post, 1839 (13p)
Uniform Penny Post, 1840 (15p)

■ 1979, August 22. Centenary of the Death of Sir Rowland Hill

Des: E. Stemp (set) and J. Matthews (miniature sheet).

Set	0.75	0.75
Gutter pairs	1.60	–
Traffic light gutter pairs	2.25	–
First day cover	–	1.25
Stamp cards	2.50	3.50
Miniature sheet (one of each value)	0.80	0.80
Miniature sheet first day cover		1.25

(* The miniature sheet, issued on October 24, 1979, was sold at 59½p, the extra 10p being donated towards the finances of staging the International Stamp Exhibition, London 1980, which the sheet itself publicised.)

Policeman talking to two children (10p)
Street patrol (11½p)
Policewoman on horseback (13p)
River police (15p)

■ 1979, September 26. 150th Anniversary of the Metropolitan Police

Des: B. Sanders.

Set	0.80	0.85
Gutter pairs	1.60	–
Traffic light gutter pairs	2.25	–
First day cover	–	1.25
Stamp cards	2.50	3.00

Three kings following the star (8p)
Angel appearing to shepherds (10p)
Nativity (11½p)
Joseph and Mary travelling to Bethlehem (13p)
Annunciation (15p)

■ 1979, November 21. Christmas

Des: F. Wegner. 8p has one phosphor band.

Set	0.90	0.90
Gutter pairs	1.80	–
Traffic light gutter pairs	2.25	–
First day cover	–	2.00
Stamp cards	2.75	3.00

Kingfisher (10p)
Dipper (11½p)
Moorhen (13p)
Yellow wagtail (15p)

■ 1980, January 16. Water Birds

Des: Michael Warren.

Set	0.80	0.80
Gutter pairs	2.00	–
First day cover	–	1.25
Stamp cards	2.50	3.50

George Stephenson's Rocket (12p)
First and second class carriages (12p)
Third class carriage and cattle truck (12p)
Open coach on truck and horsebox (12p)
Goods wagon and mail coach (12p)

■ 1980, March 12. 150th Anniversary of the Liverpool & Manchester Railway

Des: D. Gentleman.

Se-tenant strip of five	1.00	1.00
Gutter pairs	2.25	–
First day cover	–	1.50
Stamp cards	3.00	3.50

(* The gutter pairs comprise two horizontal se-tenant strips of the stamps separated by a horizontal gutter.)

Montage of London buildings and monuments (50p)

■ **1980, April 9. London 1980 International Stamp Exhibition**
Des: J. Matthews. Printed in recess by Harrisons. No phosphor.

50p	0.80	0.75
Gutter pair	2.00	–
First day cover	–	1.25
Stamp card	1.50	1.75
Miniature sheet	1.00	1.25
Miniature sheet first day cover	–	1.75

(* The miniature sheet, issued on May 7, 1980, was sold at 75p, the extra 25p being donated towards the finances of staging the International Stamp Exhibition, London 1980. The stamp is known to exist in shades of green, caused by the speed of the ink-drying operation, and fakes of these shades exist.)

Buckingham Palace (10½p)
Albert Memorial (12p)
Royal Opera House (13½p)
Hampton Court (15p)
Kensington Palace (17½p)

■ **1980, May 7. London Landmarks**
Des: Sir Hugh Casson.

Set	1.00	1.00
Gutter pairs	2.50	–
First day cover	–	1.50
Stamp cards	3.00	3.00

Charlotte Brontë and 'Jane Eyre' (12p)
George Eliot and 'The Mill on the Floss' (13½p)
Emily Brontë and 'Wuthering Heights' (15p)
Elizabeth Gaskell and 'North and South' (17½p)

■ **1980, July 9. Famous Authoresses (Europa)**
Des: Barbara Brown.

Set	0.90	0.90
Gutter pairs	2.50	–
First day cover	–	1.50
Stamp cards	2.50	3.00

Queen Elizabeth, the Queen Mother (12p)

■ **1980, August 4. Queen Mother's 80th Birthday**
Des: Jeffery Matthews.

12p	0.40	0.30
Gutter pair	1.00	–
First day cover	–	1.25
Stamp card	1.50	1.75

Sir Henry Wood (12p)
Sir Thomas Beecham (13½p)
Sir Malcolm Sargent (15p)
Sir John Barbirolli (17½p)

■ 1980, September 10. British Conductors
Des: Peter Gauld.

Set	0.90	0.90
Gutter pairs	2.25	–
First day cover	–	1.50
Stamp cards	2.50	2.75

(* These stamps exist on paper which reveals differences in the degree of 'shine' on the surface.)

Athletics (12p)
Rugby (13½p)
Boxing (15p)
Cricket (17½p)

■ 1980, October 10. Sport Centenaries
Des: Robert Goldsmith. Printed in litho by Questa.

Set	0.90	1.00
Gutter pairs	2.25	–
First day cover	–	1.50
Stamp cards	2.50	2.75

Christmas tree (10p)
Candles, ivy and ribbon (12p)
Mistletoe and apples (13½p)
Paper chains with crown and bell (15p)
Holly wreath and ornaments (17½p)

■ 1980, November 10. Christmas
Des: Jeffery Matthews. 10p has one phosphor band.

Set	1.00	1.00
Gutter pairs	2.50	–
First day cover	–	1.50
Stamp cards	2.50	3.00

(* These stamps exist on paper which reveals differences in the degree of 'shine' on the surface.)

St. Valentine's Day (14p)
Morris dancers (18p)
Lammastide (22p)
Medieval mummers (25p)

■ 1981, February 6. Folklore (Europa)
Des: Fritz Wegner.

Set	1.25	1.25
Gutter pairs	3.00	–
First day cover	–	2.00
Stamp cards	2.50	2.75

Blind man walking with guide dog (14p)
'Deaf' spelt in sign language (18p)
Man in wheelchair (22p)
Disabled artist foot painting (25p)

■ 1981, March 25. International Year of Disabled People
Des: John Gibbs.

Set	1.20	1.20
Gutter pairs	3.00	–
First day cover	–	1.75
Stamp cards	2.50	2.75

Small Tortoiseshell

Small tortoiseshell (14p)
Large blue (18p)
Peacock (22p)
Chequered skipper (25p)

■ 1981, May 13. British Butterflies
Des: Gordon Beningfield.

Set	1.25	1.25
Gutter pairs	3.50	–
First day cover	–	1.75
Stamp cards	2.50	3.00

Glenfinnan, Scotland (14p)
Derwentwater, England (18p)
Stackpole Head, Wales (20p)
Giant's Causeway, Northern Ireland (22p)
St. Kilda, Scotland (25p)

■ 1981, June 24. British Landscapes
Des: Michael Fairclough.

Set	1.45	1.40
Gutter pairs	3.50	–
First day cover	–	2.00
Stamp cards	3.00	3.00

Prince Charles and Lady Diana Spencer (14p, 25p)

■ 1981, July 22. Wedding of Prince Charles and Lady Diana Spencer
Des: Jeffery Matthews, from a portrait by Lord Snowdon.

Set	0.80	0.75
Gutter pair	2.00	
First day cover	–	2.00
Stamp cards	2.50	3.00

Expeditions (14p)
Skills (18p)
Service (22p)
Recreation (25p)

■ 1981, August 12. 25th Anniversary of the Duke of Edinburgh's Award Scheme
Des: Philip Sharland. Printed in litho by Waddingtons.

Set	1.25	1.25
Gutter pairs	3.50	–
First day cover	–	2.00
Stamp cards	2.50	2.75

Cockle dredging (14p)
Hauling side trawl net (18p)
Lobster potting (22p)
Hauling Seine net (25p)

■ 1981, September 23. Fishing Industry
Des: Brian Sanders.

Set	1.25	1.25
Gutter pairs	3.50	–
First day cover	–	1.75
Stamp cards	2.50	2.75

Father Christmas with sacks of toys (11½p)
Jesus Christ (14p)
Angel in flight (18p)
Joseph and Mary with donkey (22p)
Three wise men on camels following the star (25p)

■ **1981, November 18. Christmas**
Des: Samantha Brown (11½p), Tracy Jenkins (14p), Lucinda
Blackmore (18p), Stephen Moore (22p), Sophie Sharp (25p). The
11½p has one phosphor band.

Set	1.20	1.35
Gutter pairs	3.00	–
First day cover	–	2.00
Stamp cards	3.00	3.00

Darwin and giant tortoises (15½p)
Darwin and marine iguanas (19½p)
Darwin and finches (26p)
Darwin and prehistoric skulls (29p)

■ **1982, February 10. Centenary of the Death of Charles Darwin.**
Des: David Gentleman.

Set	1.40	1.30
Gutter pairs	3.50	–
First day cover	–	2.00
Stamp cards	2.50	3.50

Boys' Brigade (15½p)
Girls' Brigade (19½p)
Boy Scouts (26p)
Girl Guides and Brownies (29p)

■ **1982, March 24. Youth Organisations**
Des: Brian Sanders.

Set	1.40	1.40
Gutter pairs	3.50	–
First day cover	–	2.00
Stamp cards	2.50	3.50

Ballet (15½p)
Pantomime (19½p)
Shakespearean drama (26p)
Opera (29p)

■ **1982, April 28. British Theatre (Europa)**
Des: Adrian George.

Set	1.35	1.35
Gutter pairs	3.50	–
First day cover	–	2.00
Stamp cards	2.50	3.50

King Henry VIII and Mary Rose (15½p)
Admiral Blake and Triumph (19½p)
Lord Nelson and H.M.S. Victory (24p)
Lord Fisher and H.M.S. Dreadnought (26p)
Viscount Cunningham and H.M.S. Warspite (29p)

■ **1982, June 16. Maritime Heritage**
Des: Marjorie Seynor. Printed in recess and photogravure by
Harrison.

Set	1.75	1.80
Gutter pairs	5.00	–
First day cover	–	2.25
Stamp cards	3.00	3.50

'Strawberry Thief', 1883, by William Morris (15½p)
Untitled work 1906, by F. Steiner and Co (19½p)
'Cherry Orchard', 1930, by Paul Nash (26p)
'Chevrons', 1973, by Andrew Foster (29p)

■ 1982, July 23. British Textiles
Des: Peter Hatch Patnership.

Set	1.50	1.50
Gutter pairs	3.00	–
First day cover	–	2.25
Stamp cards	2.50	3.50

History of communications (15½p)
Modern technology (26p)

■ 1982, September 8. Information Technology Year
Des: Brian Delaney and Darrell Ireland.

Set	0.75	0.90
Gutter pair	2.00	–
First day cover	–	1.25
Stamp cards	1.75	3.50

Austin Seven and Metro (15½p)
Ford Model T and Escort (19½p)
Jaguar SS1 and XJ6 (26p)
Rolls Royce Silver Ghost and Silver Spirit (29p)

■ 1982, October 13. British Motor Cars
Des: Stanley Paine. Printed in litho by Questa.

Set	1.50	1.50
Gutter pairs	3.50	–
First day cover	–	2.00
Stamp cards	2.50	3.50

'While Shepherds Watched' (12½p)
'The Holly and the Ivy' (15½p)
'I Saw Three Ships' (19½p)
'We Three Kings' (26p)
'Good King Wenceslas' (29p)

■ 1982, November 17. Christmas
Des: Barbara Brown. 12½p has one phosphor band.

Set	1.50	1.50
Gutter pairs	3.50	–
First day cover	–	2.00
Stamp cards	3.00	3.50

Salmon (15½p)
Pike (19½p)
Trout (26p)
Perch (29p)

■ 1983, January 26. British River Fish
Des: Alex Jardine.

Set	1.50	1.50
Gutter pairs	3.50	–
First day cover	–	2.00
Stamp cards	2.50	3.50

Tropical island (15½p)
Arid desert (19½p)
Lush arable land (26p)
Cold mountainous region (29p)

■ 1983, March 9. Commonwealth Day
Des: Donald Hamilton Fraser.

Set	1.50	1.50
Gutter pairs	3.50	–
First day cover	–	2.00
Stamp cards	2.50	3.50

Humber Bridge (16p)
Thames Flood Barrier (20½p)
Iolair oilfield emergency support vessel (28p)

■ 1983, May 25. Engineering Achievements (Europa)
Des: Michael Taylor.

Set	1.25	1.25
Gutter pairs	4.00	–
First day cover	–	1.75
Stamp cards	1.75	3.50

Musketeer and pikeman, Royal Scots, 1633 (16p)
Fusilier and ensign, Royal Welch Fusiliers, 18th century (20½p)
Riflemen, 95th Rifles (Royal Green Jackets), 1805 (26p)
Sergeant and guardsman, Irish Guards, 1900 (28p)
Paratroopers, Parachute Regiment, 1983 (31p)

■ 1983, July 6. British Army Uniforms
Des: Eric Stemp.

Set	1.75	1.75
Gutter pairs	4.50	–
First day cover	–	2.50
Stamp cards	3.00	3.50

Sissinghurst, 20th century (16p)
Biddulph Grange, 19th century (20½p)
Blenheim Palace, 18th century (28p)
Pitmedden, 17th century (31p)

■ 1983, August 24. British Gardens
Des: Liz Butler. Printed in litho by Waddingtons.

Set	1.50	1.50
Gutter pairs	4.00	–
First day cover	–	2.25
Stamp cards	2.50	3.50

Merry-go-round (16p)
Menagerie and fairground rides (20½p)
Side shows (28p)
Produce fair (31p)

■ 1983, October 5. British Fairs
Des: Andrew Restall.

Set	1.40	1.50
Gutter pairs	3.25	–
First day cover	–	2.00
Stamp cards	2.50	3.50

Birds posting Christmas cards (12½p)
Chimney pots with a dove and cat (16p)
Dove and blackbird under an umbrella (20½p)
Dove and blackbird under a street lamp (28p)
Hedge sculpture of dove (31p)

■ **1983, November 16. Christmas**
Des: Tony Meeuwissen. 12½p has one phosphor band.

Set	1.50	1.60
Gutter pairs	3.50	–
First day cover	–	2.25
Stamp cards	3.00	3.50

Arms of The College of Arms (16p)
Arms of King Richard III (20½p)
Arms of the Earl Marshal of England (28p)
Arms of the City of London (31p)

■ **1984, January 17. Quincentenary of the College of Arms**
Des: Jeffery Matthews.

Set	1.50	1.50
Gutter pairs	3.50	–
First day cover	–	1.50
Stamp cards	2.50	3.50

16ᴾ   Highland Cow

Highland cow (16p)
Chillingham wild bull (20½p)
Hereford bull (26p)
Welsh black bull (28p)
Irish moiled cow (31p)

■ **1984, March 6. British Cattle**
Des: Barry Driscoll.

Set	1.75	1.80
Gutter pairs	4.00	–
First day cover	–	1.50
Stamp cards	3.00	3.50

Liverpool: International Garden Festival (16p)
Durham: Milburngate Shopping Centre (20½p)
Bristol: Bush House, City Docks (28p)
Perth: Commercial Street Housing Scheme (31p)

■ **1984, April 19. Urban Renewal**
Des: Trickett and Webb, and Ronald Maddox.

Set	1.60	1.60
Gutter pairs	3.50	–
First day cover	–	1.50
Stamp cards	2.50	3.50

Europa 'bridge' and CEPT emblem (16p, 20½p)
Abduction of Europa and European Parliament emblem (16p, 20½p)

■ **1984, May 15. 25th Anniversary of CEPT and Second Elections to the European Parliament (Europa)**
Des: J. Larriviere (16p), Fritz Wegner (20½p). The two designs of each value were printed in se-tenant pairs.

Set	1.50	1.75
Gutter pairs	3.75	–
First day cover	–	1.50
Stamp cards	2.50	3.50

Lancaster House with flags of participating nations (31p)

1984, June 5. London Economic Summit
Des: Paul Hogarth.

31p	0.70	0.70
Gutter pair	1.75	–
First day cover	–	1.00
Stamp card	1.50	3.50

Earth from space (16p)
Navigational chart of the English Channel (20½p)
Aerial photograph of the Greenwich Observatory (28p)
Sir George Airy's transit telescope (31p)

1984, June 21. Centenary of the Greenwich Meridian
Des: J. Barney and H. Walker. Printed in litho by Questa.

Set	1.60	1.60
Gutter pairs	4.00	–
First day cover	–	1.60
Stamp cards	2.50	3.50

Bath mail coach, 1784 (16p)
Attack on the Exeter mail, 1816 (16p)
Norwich mail coach in a thunderstorm, 1827 (16p)
Holyhead and Liverpool mails leaving London, 1828 (16p)
Edinburgh mail coach snowbound, 1831 (16p)

1984, July31. 200th Anniversary of the First Mail Coach Run from Bristol and Bath to London
Des: Keith Bassford and Stanley Paine. Printed in recess and photogravure by Harrison.

Set	1.50	1.50
Gutter pairs	3.50	–
First day cover	–	1.50
Stamp cards	3.00	3.50

(* Gutter pairs comprise two horizontal se-tenant strips of the five stamps separated by a gutter.)

Education for development, Nigeria (17p)
Promoting the arts, Greece (22p)
Technical training, Sri Lanka (31p)
Language and libraries, Middle East (34p)

1984, September 25. 50th Anniversary of the British Council
Des: Francis Newell, John Sorrell and Brian Sanders.

Set	1.50	1.50
Gutter pairs	3.75	–
First day cover	–	1.50
Stamp cards	2.50	3.50

(* Sheets of these stamps sold at the international stamp exhibition held in Melbourne, Australia, in September 1984 had the gutter margins overprinted with the exhibition logo.)

Holy family (13p)
Arrival in Bethlehem (17p)
Shepherd and lamb (22p)
Virgin and Child (31p)
Offering of frankincense (34p)

1984, November 20. Christmas
Des: Yvonne Gilbert. 13p has one centre phosphor band.

Set	1.75	1.80
13p (stars printed on gummed side)	0.60	–
Gutter pairs	4.00	–
First day cover	–	1.50
Stamp cards	3.00	3.50

(* The 13p with an all-over five-pointed-star pattern printed on the gummed side is from a booklet sold at a discount.)

Flying Scotsman (17p)
Golden Arrow (22p)
Cheltenham Flyer (29p)
Royal Scot (31p)
Cornish Riviera (34p)

■ 1985, January 22. Famous Trains
Des: Terence Cuneo.

Set	2.50	2.50
Gutter pairs	6.50	–
First day cover	–	1.50
Stamp cards	3.50	4.50

Buff-tailed bumble bee (17p)
Seven-spotted ladybird (22p)
Wart-biter bush-cricket (29p)
Stag beetle (31p)
Emperor butterfly (34p)

■ 1985, March 12. Insects
Des: Gordon Beningfield.

Set	2.25	2.25
Gutter pairs	6.00	–
First day cover	–	1.50
Stamp cards	2.75	4.50

'Water Music' by George Handel (17p)
'The Planets Suite' by Gustav Holst (22p)
'The First Cuckoo' by Frederick Delius (31p)
'Sea Pictures' by Edward Elgar (34p)

■ 1985, May 14. European Music Year. British Composers (Europa)
Des: Wilson McLean.

Set	2.25	2.25
Gutter pairs	6.00	–
First day cover	–	1.50
Stamp cards	3.00	4.50

RNLI lifeboat and signal flags (17p)
Beachy Head Lighthouse and chart (22p)
Marecs A communications satellite and aerials (31p)
Trinity House buoyage (34p)

■ 1985, June 18. Safety at Sea
Des: Newell and Sorell. Printed in litho by Waddingtons.

Set	1.60	1.60
Gutter pairs	4.00	–
First day cover	–	1.50
Stamp cards	2.50	4.50

Datapost motorcyclist and plane in London (17p)
Postbus in countryside (22p)
Parcel delivery by van in winter (31p)
Postman delivering letters on foot (34p)

■ 1985, July 30. 350th Anniversary of Royal Mail Service to the Public
Des: Paul Hogarth.

Set	1.75	1.75
17p ('D' pattern on gummed side)	0.60	–
Gutter pairs	4.25	–
First day cover	–	1.50
Stamp cards	2.50	4.50

(* The 17p with a 'D' pattern printed on the gummed side is from a booklet sold at a discount.)

King Arthur and Merlin (17p)
The Lady of the Lake (22p)
Queen Guinevere and Sir Lancelot (31p)
Sir Galahad (34p)

1985, September 3. Arthurian Legend
Des: Yvonne Gilbert.

Set	1.75	1.85
Gutter pairs	4.50	–
First day cover	–	1.50
Stamp cards	2.50	4.50

Peter Sellers, photographed by Bill Brandt (17p)
David Niven, photographed by Cornel Lucas (22p)
Charles Chaplin, photographed by Lord Snowdon (29p)
Vivien Leigh, photographed by Angus McBean (31p)
Alfred Hitchcock, photographed by Howard Coster (34p)

1985, October 8. British Film Year
Des: Keith Bassford.

Set	2.25	2.25
Gutter pairs	6.00	–
First day cover	–	1.50
Stamp cards	3.00	4.50

Principal boy (12p)
Genie (17p)
Pantomime dame (22p)
Good fairy (31p)
Pantomime cat (34p)

1985, November 19. Christmas. Pantomime Characters
Des: Adrian George. 12p has one phosphor band.

Set	1.75	1.75
12p (stars on gummed side)	0.55	–
Gutter pairs	5.00	–
First day cover	–	1.50
Stamp cards	2.75	4.50

(* The 12p with a star pattern printed on the gummed side was from a booklet sold at a discount.)

Energy: light bulb and North Sea oil rig (17p)
Health: thermometer and laboratory (22p)
Manufacture: garden hoe and steelworks (31p)
Agriculture: loaf of bread and cornfield (34p)

1986, January 14. Industry Year
Des: Keith Bassford. Printed in litho by Questa.

Set	1.75	1.75
Gutter pairs	5.00	–
First day cover	–	1.75
Stamp cards	2.50	3.75

Sir Edmond Halley as the comet (17p)
Giotto space probe approaching the comet (22p)
'Maybe twice in a lifetime' (31p)
The comet's orbit (34p)

1986, February 18. Halley's Comet
Des: Ralph Steadman.

Set	1.75	1.75
Gutter pairs	4.75	–
First day cover	–	1.75
Stamp cards	2.50	3.75

The Queen at the age of 2, 16 and 26 (17p and 34p)
The Queen at the age of 32, 47 and 56 (17p and 34p)

■ 1986, April 21. The Queen's 60th Birthday
Des: Jeffery Matthews.

Set	2.25	2.50
Gutter pairs	5.00	–
First day cover	–	1.75
Stamp cards	2.50	3.75

Barn owl (17p)
Pine marten (22p)
Wild cat (31p)
Natterjack toad (34p)

■ 1986, May 20. Nature Conservation (Europa)
Des: Ken Lilly.

Set	1.85	1.90
Gutter pairs	5.00	–
First day cover	–	1.75
Stamp cards	2.50	3.75

Peasants working the land (17p)
Freemen and their crafts (22p)
A knight and his retinue (31p)
A lord at a banquet (34p)

■ 1986, June 17. 900th Anniversary of the Domesday Book
Des: Tayburn.

Set	1.75	1.75
Gutter pairs	5.00	–
First day cover	–	1.75
Stamp cards	2.50	3.75

Athletics (17p)
Rowing (22p)
Weightlifting (29p)
Shooting (31p)
Hockey (34p)

■ 1986, July 15. Commonwealth Games, Edinburgh, and World Hockey Cup, London
Des: Nick Cudworth.

Set	2.25	2.25
Gutter pairs	5.50	–
First day cover	–	1.75
Stamp cards	3.00	3.75

Prince Andrew and Sarah Ferguson (12p, 17p)

■ 1986, July 22. Royal Wedding
Des: Jeffery Matthews.

Set	0.85	0.75
Gutter pairs	2.00	–
First day cover	–	1.75
Stamp cards	1.75	3.75

Cross on ballot paper (34p)

■ 1986, August 19. Commonwealth Parliamentary Association Conference

Des: John Gibbs. Printed in litho by Questa.

34p	0.75	0.80
Gutter pairs	2.00	–
First day cover	–	1.25
Stamp card	1.50	3.75

Lord Dowding and Hawker Hurricane (17p)
Lord Tedder and Hawker Typhoon (22p)
Lord Trenchard and De Havilland DH9A (29p)
Sir Arthur Harris and Avro Lancaster (31p)
Lord Portal and De Havilland Mosquito (34p)

■ 1986, September 16. Royal Air Force

Des: Brian Sanders.

Set	2.50	2.50
Gutter pairs	6.50	–
First day cover	–	2.50
Stamp cards	3.00	3.75

The Glastonbury Thorn (12p), (13p)
The Tanad Valley Plygain (18p)
The Hebrides Tribute (22p)
The Dewsbury Church Knell (31p)
The Hereford Boy Bishop (34p)

■ 1986, November 18. Christmas. Folk Customs

Des: Lynda Gray. 12p has one phosphor band and was issued on December 2, 1986; 13p has one phosphor band

Set	2.00	2.00
13p (stars on gummed side)	0.40	–
Gutter Pairs	4.50	–
First day covers	–	2.75
Stamp cards	3.00	4.00

(* The 13p with a star pattern printed on the gummed side was from a booklet and a pack sold at a discount.)

Gaillardia (18p)
Echinops (22p)
Echeveria (31p)
Colchicum (34p)

■ 1987, January 6. Flowers

Des: Jeffery Matthews from photographs by Alfred Lammer.

Set	1.75	1.75
Gutter pairs	4.50	–
First day cover	–	2.00
Stamp cards	2.50	3.50

(* A card with a Flowers design, stamped and cancelled with the 31p and 34p stamps, was made available at several stamp exhibitions, starting with Capex 87 in Toronto in June 1987.)

'Principia Mathematica': apple (18p)
Motion of bodies in ellipses: planets orbiting around sun (22p)
'Optick Treatise': flask of water refracting light (31p)
'The System of the World': Earth and artificial satellite (34p)

■ 1987, March 24. Sir Isaac Newton

Des: Sarah Goodwin.

Set	1.75	1.75
Gutter pairs	4.50	–
First day cover	–	2.00
Stamp cards	2.50	3.50

Willis Faber Dumas Building, Ipswich (18p)
Pompidou Centre, Paris (22p)
Staatgalerie, Stuttgart (31p)
European Investment Bank, Luxembourg (34p)

■ **1987, May 12. British Architects in Europe (Europa)**
Des: Minale Tattersfield Studio.

Set	1.75	1.75
Gutter pairs	4.50	–
First day cover	–	1.75
Stamp cards	2.50	3.50

First aid duties, 1887 (18p)
First aid in wartime, 1940 (22p)
First aid at events, 1965 (31p)
Transporting transplant organs by air, 1987 (34p)

■ **1987, June 16. St John Ambulance Centenary**
Des: Debbie Cook. Printed in litho by Questa.

Set	1.75	1.75
Gutter pairs	4.50	–
First day cover	–	1.75
Stamp cards	2.50	3.50

Arms of the Lord Lyon, King of Arms (18p)
Arms of the Duke of Rothesay (22p)
Arms of the Royal Scottish Academy of Painting,
Sculpture and Architecture (31p)
Arms of the Royal Society of Edinburgh (34p)

■ **1987, July 21. 300th Anniversary of the Revival of the Order of the Thistle**
Des: Jeffery Matthews.

Set	1.75	1.75
Gutter pairs	4.50	–
First day cover	–	1.75
Stamp cards	2.50	3.50

Landseer's painting 'Monarch of the Glen', the Great Exhibition,
Grace Darling (18p)
Brunel's S.S. Great Eastern, Mrs Beeton's 'Book of Household
Management', Prince Albert (22p)
Albert Memorial, Benjamin Disraeli, the first ballot box (31p)
Marconi's broadcast to Paris, the Diamond Jubilee, the Relief of
Mafeking (34p)

■ **1987, September 8. 150th Anniversary of the Accession of Queen Victoria**
Des: Carroll and Dempsey Studio. Printed in recess and
photogravure by Harrison.

Set	1.75	1.75
Gutter pairs	4.50	–
First day cover	–	1.75
Stamp cards	3.00	3.50

Pot by Bernard Leach (18p)
Pot by Elizabeth Fritsch (26p)
Pot by Lucie Rie (31p)
Pot by Hans Coper (34p)

■ 1987, October 13. Studio Pottery
Des: Tony Evans.

Set	1.75	1.75
Gutter pairs	4.50	–
First day cover	–	1.75
Stamp cards	2.50	3.50

Child decorating a Christmas tree (13p)
Child looking out of a window (18p)
Child sleeping, and Father Christmas in his sleigh (26p)
Child reading a book surrounded by toys (31p)
Child playing a recorder, watched by snowman (34p)

■ 1987, November 17. Christmas
Des: M. Foreman. 13p has one phosphor band.

Set	1.75	1.75
13p (stars on gummed side)	0.50	–
Gutter pairs	4.50	–
First day cover	–	1.75
Stamp cards	3.00	3.50

(* The 13p with a star pattern printed on the gummed side was from a pack sold at a discount.)

Short-spined sea scorpion (18p)
Yellow waterlily (26p)
Bewick's swan (31p)
Morel mushroom (34p)

■ 1988, January 19. Bicentenary of the Linnean Society
Des: E. Hughes.

Set	1.75	1.75
Gutter pairs	4.50	–
First day cover	–	2.00
Stamp cards	2.50	3.50

Reverend William Morgan, Bible translator 1588 (18p)
William Salesbury, New Testament translator 1567 (26p)
Bishop Richard Davies, New Testament translator 1567 (31p)
Bishop Richard Parry, Welsh Bible editor 1620 (34p)

■ 1988, March 1. 400th Anniversary of the Welsh Bible
Des: K. Bowen.

Set	1.75	1.75
Gutter pairs	4.50	–
First day cover	–	1.75
Stamp cards	2.50	3.50

Gymnastics: British Amateur Gymnastics Association (18p)
Skiing: Ski Club of Great Britain (26p)
Tennis: Lawn Tennis Association (31p)
Football: Football League (34p)

■ 1988, March 22. Sports Organisations
Des: J. Sutton.

Set	1.75	1.75
Gutter pairs	4.50	–
First day cover	–	1.75
Stamp cards	2.50	3.50

Mallard train and mailbags (18p)
Queen Elizabeth liner and transatlantic mail (26p)
Glasgow tram and pillar box (31p)
Imperial Airways Handley Page HP45 and airmail (34p)

■ **1988, May 10. Transport and Mail Services (Europa)**
Des: M. Dempsey.

Set	1.75	1.75
Gutter pairs	4.50	–
First day cover	–	1.75
Stamp cards	2.50	3.50

(* A set of four airmail cards was issued on March 2, 1993, with the Handley Page design as an imprinted 33p value; price £5 mint.)

Early settler and sailing clipper (18p)
British and Australian parliaments and Queen Elizabeth II (18p)
W. G. Grace and tennis racquet (34p)
Shakespeare, John Lennon and Sydney Opera House (34p)

■ **1988, June 21. Bicentenary of Australian Settlement**
Des: G. Emery. Printed in litho by Questa.

Set (two se-tenant pairs)	1.70	2.20
Gutter pairs	4.00	–
First day cover	–	1.75
Stamp cards	2.50	3.50

Spanish ship off The Lizard (18p)
English fleet leaving Plymouth (18p)
Engagement off the Isle of Wight (18p)
English fire-ships attack off Calais (18p)
Spanish ships in North Sea storm (18p)

■ **1988, July 19. 400th anniversary of the Spanish Armada**
Des: G. Evernden.

Set (se-tenant strip of five)	1.60	1.90
Gutter pairs	4.00	–
First day cover	–	1.75
Stamp cards	3.00	3.50

'The owl and the pussy cat went to sea' (19p)
Self-portrait of Edward Lear as a bird (27p)
'Cat' (32p)
'There was a young lady whose bonnet...' (35p)

■ **1988, September 6. Centenary of the Death of Edward Lear**
Des: M. Swatridge and S. Dew.

Set	2.00	2.00
Gutter pairs	5.00	–
First day cover	–	1.75
Stamp cards	2.50	3.50
Miniature sheet (one of each value)	4.50	4.50
Miniature sheet first day cover	–	3.50

(* The miniature sheet, issued on September 27, 1988, was sold with a surcharge to help fund the international stamp exhibition, Stamp World London 90.)

Carrickfergus Castle (£1)
Caernarfon Castle (£1.50)
Edinburgh Castle (£2)
Windsor Castle (£5)

■ **1988, October 18. Castle high value definitives**
Engraved by C. Matthews from photographs by Prince Andrew.
Recess-printed by Harrison.

Set	16.00	4.50
Gutter pairs	35.00	–
Gutter blocks of four (centre cross)	75.00	–
First day cover	–	20.00

Journeying to Bethlehem (14p)
Shepherds following the star (19p)
Three wise men (27p)
Nativity (32p)
Annunciation (35p)

■ **1988, November 15. Christmas. Christmas Cards**
Des: L. Trickett. 14p has one phosphor band.

Set	1.75	2.20
Gutter pairs	4.00	–
First day cover	–	1.75
Stamp cards	3.00	3.50

Atlantic puffin (19p)
Avocet (27p)
Oystercatcher (32p)
Northern gannet (35p)

■ **1989, January 17. Centenary of the Royal Society for the Protection of Birds**
Des: D. Cordery.

Set	1.75	1.75
Gutter pairs	5.00	–
First day cover	–	1.75
Stamp cards	2.50	3.75

Teddy bear (19p)
Rose (19p)
Cupid (19p)
Yachts (19p)
Fruit (19p)

■ **1989, January 31. Greetings**
Des: P. Sutton. Se-tenant strip of five. Issued in booklets in panes of ten containing two of each design.

Set (se-tenant strip of five)	10.00	11.00
Booklet pane (of 10)	23.00	–
Booklet	25.00	–
First day cover	–	6.00
Stamp cards	5.00	10.00

Fruit and vegetables (19p)
Meat products (27p)
Dairy products (32p)
Cereal products (35p)

■ **1989, March 7. Food and Farming Year**
Des: Sedley Place Ltd.

Set	2.00	2.00
Gutter pairs	5.00	–
First day cover	–	1.75
Stamp cards	2.50	3.75

150th anniversary of public education: mortar board (19p)
Third elections to European Parliament: cross on ballot (19p)
26th Postal, Telegraph and Telephone Congress: posthorn (35p)
Inter-Parliamentary Union Conference: globe (35p)

■ **1989, April 11. Anniversaries and Events**
Des: Lewis Moberly. 19p and 35p issued in se-tenant pairs.

Set (two se-tenant pairs)	2.00	2.00
Gutter pairs	5.00	–
First day cover	–	1.75
Stamp cards	2.50	3.75

Toy aeroplane and locomotive (19p)
Building bricks (27p)
Board games and dice (32p)
Toy robot, boat and doll's house (35p)

■ **1989, May 16. Games and Toys (Europa)**
Des: D. Fern.

Set	2.00	2.00
Gutter pairs	5.00	–
First day cover	–	1.75
Stamp cards	2.50	3.75

Ironbridge, Shropshire (19p)
Tin mine, St Agnes Head, Cornwall (27p)
Cotton Mills, New Lanark, Strathclyde (32p)
Pontcysyllte Aqueduct, Clwyd (35p)

■ **1989, July 4. Industrial Archaeology**
Des: R. Maddox.

Set	2.00	2.00
Gutter pairs	5.00	–
First day cover	–	1.75
Stamp cards	2.50	3.75
Miniature sheet	3.00	3.00
Miniature sheet first day cover	–	1.75

(* The miniature sheet, issued on July 25, 1989, contained one of each value but with the designs in a horizontal format, with a surcharge to help fund the international stamp exhibition, Stamp World London 90.)

Snowflake (19p)
Fly (27p)
Blood cells (32p)
Microchip (35p)

■ **1989, September 5. 150th Anniversary of the Royal Microscopical Society**
Des: K. Bassford. Printed in litho by Questa.

Set	2.00	2.00
Gutter pairs	5.00	–
First day cover	–	1.75
Stamp cards	2.50	3.75

Royal Mail coach (20p)
Escort of the Blues and Royals (20p)
Lord Mayor's coach (20p)
St Paul's Cathedral (20p)
Blues and Royals drum horse (20p)

■ **1989, October 17. Lord Mayor's Show, London**
Des: P. Cox.

Set (se-tenant strip of five)	1.70	1.70
Gutter pairs	4.50	–
First day cover	–	1.70
Stamp cards	3.00	3.75

(* The Royal Mail Coach design also appears in the Treasures of the Archive prestige stamp book issued on August 18, 2009, printed in litho.)

14th century peasants, from stained glass window (15p)
Arches and roundels from West Front (15p+1p)
Octagon Tower (20p+1p)
Arcade from West Transept (34p+1p)
Triple arch from West Front (37p+1p)

■ **1989, November 14. Christmas. 800th Anniversary of Ely Cathedral**
Des: D. Gentleman. 15p and 15p+1p have one phosphor band.

Set	2.25	2.25
Gutter pairs	5.00	–
First day cover	–	1.75
Stamp cards	3.00	3.75

(* Four of the stamps carried a surcharge for charity.)

■ **1990, January 10. 150th Anniversary of the Penny Black**
See under Decimal Machin definitives.

Kitten (20p)
Rabbit (29p)
Duckling (34p)
Puppy (37p)

■ **1990, January 23. 150th Anniversary of the Royal Society for the Prevention of Cruelty to Animals**
Des: T. Evans. Printed in litho by Questa.

Set	2.00	2.00
Gutter pairs	5.00	–
First day cover	–	1.75
Stamp cards	2.50	4.00

Teddy Bear (20p)
Dennis the Menace (20p)
Punch (20p)
Cheshire Cat (20p)
The Man in the Moon (20p)
The Laughing Policeman (20p)
Clown (20p)
Mona Lisa (20p)
Queen of Hearts (20p)
Stan Laurel (20p)

■ **1990, February 6. Greetings: Smiles**
Des: Michael Peters and Partners. Issued se-tenant in booklet panes of ten comprising one of each design.

Booklet pane (of 10)	12.50	14.00
Booklet	15.00	–
First day cover	–	8.00

Alexandra Palace, London (20p)
School of Art, Glasgow (20p)
British Philatelic Bureau, Edinburgh (29p)
Templeton Carpet Factory, Glasgow (37p)

■ **1990, March 6. Glasgow 1990 European City of Culture and Stamp World Exhibition (Europa)**
Des: P. Hogarth.

Set	1.75	1.75
Gutter pairs	4.25	–
First day cover	–	1.75
Stamp cards	2.50	4.00

(* The two 20p designs were issued in separate sheets, not as se-tenant pairs. The 20p Alexandra Palace design also appears as a pane of four in the £5 London Life prestige stamp book issued on March 20, 1990.)

Export Achievement Award (20p and 37p)
Technological Achievement Award (20p and 37p)

■ 1990, April 10. 25th Anniversary of The Queen's Awards for Export and Technology
Des: S. Broom. Printed in litho by Questa.

Set (two se-tenant pairs)	2.00	2.00
Gutter pairs	5.00	–
First day cover	–	1.80
Stamp cards	2.50	4.00

Portraits of Queen Victoria and Queen Elizabeth II (20p)

■ 1990, May 3. Stamp World London 90 International Exhibition
Des: Sedley Place Design; engraved by C. Matthews. Printed in recess and photogravure by Harrison.

Miniature sheet	2.50	2.50
First day cover	–	2.00

(* The border illustrates the 1840 Penny Black, and Britannia from the 1913–1934 Seahorses series. The sheets were sold at £1 each, the surcharge being used to help fund the exhibition.)

Cycad and Sir Joseph Banks Building (20p)
Stone pine and Princess of Wales Conservatory (29p)
Willow tree and Palm House (34p)
Cedar tree and Pagoda (37p)

■ 1990, June 5. 150th Anniversary of Kew Gardens
Des: P. Leith.

Set	1.90	1.90
Gutter pairs	4.75	–
First day cover	–	1.75
Stamp cards	2.50	4.00

Thomas Hardy and Clyffe Clump, Dorset (20p)

■ 1990, July 10. 150th Anniversary of the Birth of Thomas Hardy
Des: J. Gibbs.

20p	0.40	0.40
Gutter pair	1.00	–
First day cover	–	1.00
Stamp card	1.50	4.00

Queen Elizabeth as The Queen Mother (20p)
Queen Elizabeth as Queen (29p)
Queen Elizabeth as Duchess of York (34p)
Queen Elizabeth as Lady Elizabeth Bowes–Lyon (37p)

■ **1990, August 2. 90th Birthday of Queen Elizabeth, The Queen Mother**

Des: J. Gorham from photographs by Norman Parkinson, Dorothy Wilding, B. Park and Rita Martin.

Set	2.75	2.75
Gutter pairs	7.00	–
First day cover	–	2.50
Stamp cards	2.50	4.00

(* The same designs were used in the Queen Mother Memorial issue of April 2002 but with the borders changed to black.)

Victoria Cross (20p)
George Cross (20p)
Distinguished Service Cross, Distinguished Service Medal (20p)
Military Cross and Military Medal (20p)
Distinguished Flying Cross, Distinguished Flying Medal (20p)

■ **1990, September 11. Gallantry Awards**

Des: J. Gibbs and J. Harwood.

Set	1.75	1.75
Gutter pairs	4.50	–
First day cover	–	2.00
Stamp cards	3.00	4.00

(* The 20p also appears on the miniature sheet and in the prestige stamp book for the Victoria Cross issued on September 21, 2006.)

Armagh Observatory, Jodrell Bank & La Palma telescopes (22p)
Early telescope and moon and tides diagram by Newton (26p)
Greenwich Old Observatory and astronomical equipment (31p)
Stonehenge, gyroscope and navigation by the stars (37p)

■ **1990, October 16. Astronomy**

Des: J. Fisher. Printed in litho by Questa.

Set	1.75	1.75
Gutter pairs	4.50	–
First day cover	–	2.00
Stamp cards	2.50	4.00

Building a snowman (17p)
Fetching a Christmas tree (22p)
Carol singers (26p)
Tobogganing (31p)
Ice-skating (37p)

■ **1990, November 13. Christmas**

Des: J. Gorham and A. Davidson. The 17p has one phosphor band.

Set	2.00	2.00
Gutter pairs	5.00	–
First day cover	–	2.00
Stamp cards	3.00	4.00

(* The 17p was also sold in booklets.)

'King Charles Spaniel' (22p)
'A Pointer' (26p)
'Two Hounds in a Landscape' (31p)
'A Rough Dog' (33p)
'Fino and Tiny' (37p)

■ **1991, January 8. Dogs. Paintings by George Stubbs**

Des: Carroll, Dempsey and Thirkell.

Set	2.25	2.25
Gutter pairs	5.50	–
First day cover	–	2.50
Stamp cards	3.00	4.00

Thrush's nest (1st)
Shooting star and rainbow (1st)
Magpies and charm bracelet (1st)
Black cat (1st)
Kingfisher and key (1st)
Mallard and frog (1st)
Four-leaf clover, boot and matchbox (1st)
Pot of gold at the end of the rainbow (1st)
Butterflies (1st)
Wishing well and sixpence (1st)

■ 1991, February 5. Greetings: Good Luck
Des: J. Meeuwissen. Issued se-tenant in booklet panes of ten containing one of each design.

Booklet pane (of 10)	10.00	10.00
Booklet	10.00	–
First day cover	–	8.00

Michael Faraday, electricity (22p)
Charles Babbage, computer (22p)
Robert Watson Watt, radar (31p)
Frank Whittle, jet engine: Gloster Whittle E28/39 aircraft (37p)

■ 1991, March 5. Scientific Achievements
Des: P. Till (22p, 22p), J. Harwood (31p, 37p).

Set	2.25	2.25
Gutter pairs	5.00	–
First day cover	–	2.50
Stamp cards	2.50	4.00

■ 1991, March 26. Greetings: Smiles
Designs as for the Greetings stamps of February 6, 1990, but with all values changed to 1st class. Issued se-tenant in booklet panes of ten containing one of each design.

Booklet pane (of 10)	9.00	8.00
Booklet	9.00	–
First day cover	–	7.50

(* These designs were also used for Smilers sheets in 2000 and 2001.)

Man looking at space (22p, 22p)
Space looking at man (37p, 37p)

■ 1991, April 23. Europe in Space (Europa)
Des: J-M. Folon.

Set (two se-tenant pairs)	2.25	2.25
Gutter pairs	6.00	–
First day cover	–	2.50
Stamp cards	2.50	4.00

Fencing (22p)
Hurdling (26p)
Diving (31p)
Rugby (37p)

■ 1991, June 11. World Student Games, Sheffield, and Rugby World Cup
Des: Huntley Muir Partners.

Set	2.25	2.25
Gutter pairs	6.00	–
First day cover	–	2.50
Stamp cards	2.50	4.00

Silver Jubilee rose (22p)
Madame Alfred Carrière rose (26p)
Rosa Moyesii rose (31p)
Harvest Fayre rose (33p)
Mutabilis rose (37p)

■ 1991, July 16. World Congress of Roses, Belfast
Des: Yvonne Skargon. Printed in litho by Questa.

Set	2.40	2.25
Gutter pairs	6.00	–
First day cover	–	2.50
Stamp cards	3.00	4.00

Iguanodon (22p)
Stegosaurus (26p)
Tyrannosaurus (31p)
Protoceratops (33p)
Triceratops (37p)

■ 1991, August 20. 150th Anniversary of the Identification of Dinosaurs by Richard Owen
Des: B. Kneale.

Set	2.50	2.50
Gutter pairs	6.00	–
First day cover	–	2.50
Stamp cards	3.00	4.00

Map of Hamstreet, Kent, in 1816 (24p)
Map of Hamstreet, Kent, in 1906 (28p)
Map of Hamstreet, Kent, in 1959 (33p)
Map of Hamstreet, Kent, in 1991 (39p)

■ 1991, September 17. Bicentenary of Ordnance Survey
Des: H. Brown. Printed in recess and litho by Harrison (24p), in litho by Harrison (28p), and in litho by Questa (33p, 39p).

Set	2.25	2.25
Gutter pairs	6.00	–
First day cover	–	2.50
Stamp cards	2.50	4.00

(* Examples of the 28p are known with the denomination of 26p, from supplies printed before an increase in postage rates affected the denominations of this set.)

Adoration of the Magi (18p)
Mary with Jesus in stable (24p)
Holy family and angel (28p)
Annunciation (33p)
Flight into Egypt (39p)

■ 1991, November 12. Christmas
Des: D. Driver, from the Acts Of Mary & Jesus illuminated manuscript. The 18p has one phosphor band.

Set	2.25	2.25
Gutter pairs	6.00	–
First day cover	–	2.50
Stamp cards	3.00	4.00

(* The 18p was also sold in booklets.)

Fallow deer in Scottish forest (18p)
Hare on North Yorkshire moors (24p)
Fox in the Fens (28p)
Redwing in the Home Counties (33p)
Welsh mountain sheep in Snowdonia (39p)

■ 1992, January 14. The Four Seasons: Wintertime
Des: J. Gorham and K. Bowen. 18p has one phosphor band.

Set	2.50	2.25
Gutter pairs	6.00	–
First day cover	–	2.25
Stamp cards	3.00	3.75

(* The 39p also appears as a pane of four in the Cymru Wales prestige stamp booklet issued on February 25, 1992.)

Spray of flowers (1st)
Double locket (1st)
Key (1st)
Toy car and cigarette cards (1st)
Compass and map (1st)
Pocket watch (1st)
Penny Red stamp and pen (1st)
Pearl necklace (1st)
Marbles (1st)
Starfish and a bucket and spade (1st)

■ 1992, January 28. Greetings: Memories
Des: Trickett and Webb Ltd. Issued se-tenant in booklet panes of ten,containing one of each design.

Booklet pane (of 10)	9.00	8.00
Booklet	9.00	–
First day cover	–	7.50

Queen Elizabeth II, in Coronation robes (24p)
Queen Elizabeth II, in Garter robes (24p)
Queen Elizabeth II, with Prince Andrew as a baby (24p)
Queen Elizabeth II, at Trooping of the Colour (24p)
Queen Elizabeth II, with emblem of the Commonwealth (24p)

■ 1992, February 6. 40th Anniversary of the Accession
Des: Why Not Associates. Printed in litho by Questa.

Set (se-tenant strip of five)	3.00	3.50
Gutter pairs	7.50	–
First day cover	–	2.50
Stamp cards	3.00	3.75

Tennyson in 1888 and 'The Beguiling of Merlin' by Burne-Jones (24p)
Tennyson in 1856 and 'April Love' by Hughes (28p)
Tennyson in 1864 and 'I Am Sick Of The Shadows' by Waterhouse (33p)
Tennyson as a young man and 'Mariana' by Rossetti (39p)

■ 1992, March 10. Centenary of the Death of Alfred, Lord Tennyson
Des: Irene von Treskow.

Set	2.25	2.25
Gutter pairs	5.00	–
First day cover	–	2.25
Stamp cards	2.50	3.75

Barcelona Olympics: British Olympic Association logo (24p)
Barcelona Paralympics: British Paralympic Association logo (24p)
Discovery of America by Columbus: 'Santa Maria' (24p)
Operation Raleigh Grand Regatta: 'Kaisei' (39p)
Expo '92 in Seville: British Pavilion (39p)

■ 1992, April 7. International Events (Europa)
Des: K. Bassford (Olympics, Paralympics and Expo), K. Bassford and S. Paine (Columbus and Raleigh). Printed in litho by Questa (Olympics, Paralympics and Expo) or in recess and litho by Harrison (Columbus and Raleigh). The Olympics and Paralympics designs were issued as a se-tenant pair.

Set	2.25	2.60
Gutter pairs	6.00	–
First day cover	–	2.25
Stamp cards	3.00	3.75

Carrickfergus Castle (£1)
Caernarfon Castle (£1.50)
Edinburgh Castle (£2)
Windsor Castle (£5)

■ 1992, March 24. Castle high value definitives

As issue of October 18, 1988, but with the Queen's head in silhouette, printed in optically variable ink which changes colour from gold to green depending on the angle at which it is viewed, and with an elliptical perforation along each side.

Set	19.50	4.00
Gutter pairs	70.00	–
Gutter blocks of four (centre cross)	£140	–
First day cover	–	15.00
Stamp cards	8.00	55.00

(* The £1.50, £2 and £5 exist with either blue–tinted PVAD gum or white PVA gum.)

Pikeman (24p)
Drummer (28p)
Musketeer (33p)
Standard bearer (39p)

■ 1992, June 16. 350th Anniversary of the Civil War

Des: J. Sancha.

Set	2.25	2.25
Gutter pairs	6.00	–
First day cover	–	2.25
Stamp cards	2.50	3.75

'The Yeoman of the Guard' (18p)
'The Gondoliers' (24p)
'The Mikado' (28p)
'The Pirates of Penzance' (33p)
'Iolanthe' (39p)

■ 1992, July 21. Gilbert and Sullivan Operas

Des: Lynda Gray. 18p has one phosphor band.

Set	2.20	2.25
Gutter pairs	5.50	–
First day cover	–	2.25
Stamp cards	3.00	3.75

Acid rain kills (24p)
Ozone layer (28p)
Greenhouse effect (33p)
Bird of hope (39p)

■ 1992, September 15. Protection of the Environment

Des: C. Hall (24p), L. Fowler (28p), S. Warren (33p) and A. Newton-Mold (39p). All paintings by children, in conjunction with the BBC Television programme 'Blue Peter'.

Set	2.20	2.25
Gutter pairs	5.50	–
First day cover	–	2.25
Stamp cards	2.50	3.75

European star (24p)

■ 1992, October 13. Single European Market

Des: D. Hockney.

24p	0.50	0.45
Gutter pair	1.50	–
First day cover	–	1.00
Stamp card	1.75	2.00

Angel Gabriel, from St. James's, Pangbourne (18p)
Madonna and Child, from St. Mary's, Bilbury (24p)
King with gold, from Our Lady and St. Peter, Leatherhead (28p)
Shepherds, from All Saints, Porthcawl (33p)
Kings with gifts, from Our Lady and St. Peter, Leatherhead (39p)

■ 1992, November 10. Christmas. Stained-Glass Windows
Des: Carroll, Dempsey and Thirkell. The 18p has one phosphor band.

Set	2.25	2.25
Gutter pairs	6.00	–
First day cover	–	2.25
Stamp cards	3.00	3.75

(* The 18p was also sold in booklets.)

Mute swan cob and St. Catherine's Chapel (18p)
Cygnet and decoy (24p)
Swans and cygnet (28p)
Eggs in nest and Tithe Barn (33p)
Young swan (39p)

■ 1993, January 19. 600th Anniversary of Abbotsbury Swannery
Des: David Gentleman. The 18p has one phosphor band.

Set	4.00	3.25
Gutter pairs	10.00	–
First day cover	–	2.50
Stamp cards	3.00	5.00

William (1st)
Long John Silver (1st)
Tweedledum and Tweedledee (1st)
Mole and Toad (1st)
Teacher and Wilfred (1st)
Peter Rabbit and Mrs Rabbit (1st)
Snowman and Father Christmas (1st)
The Big Friendly Giant and Sophie (1st)
Bill Badger and Rupert Bear (1st)
Aladdin and the Genie (1st)

■ 1993, February 2. Greetings: Gift Giving
Des: Newell and Sorell. Issued se-tenant in booklet panes of ten containing one of each design.

Booklet pane (of 10)	9.00	8.00
Booklet	9.00	–
First day cover	–	7.50
Stamp cards	8.00	15.50

(* The Peter Rabbit and Mrs Rabbit design also appears in the Story of Beatrix Potter prestige stamp book issued on August 10, 1993.)

H4 chronometer: decorated enamel dial (24p)
H4 chronometer: escapement, remontoire and fusée (28p)
H4 chronometer: balance and spring (33p)
H4 chronometer: movement seen from back (39p)

■ 1993, February 16. 300th Anniversary of the Birth of John Harrison
Des: H. Brown and D. Penny. Printed in litho by Questa.

Set	2.25	2.25
Gutter pairs	5.50	–
First day cover	–	2.25
Stamp cards	2.50	5.00

Britannia (£10)

1993, March 2. £10 definitive

Des: M. Denney and B. Craddock. Printed in litho by Questa, with die-stamping and braille embossing.

£10	20.00	8.50
First day cover	–	15.00
Stamp card	4.50	50.00

Dendrobium hellwigianum (18p)
Paphiopedilum Maudiae 'Magnificum' (24p)
Cymbidium lowianum (28p)
Vanda Rothschildiana (33p)
Dendrobium vexillarius var. albiviride (39p)

1993, March 16. World Orchid Conference, Glasgow

Des: Pandora Sellars. The 18p has one phosphor band.

Set	2.50	2.50
Gutter pairs	5.50	–
First day cover	–	2.25
Stamp cards	3.00	5.00

'Family Group' by Henry Moore (24p)
'Kew Gardens' by Edward Bawden (28p)
'St Francis and the Birds' by Stanley Spencer (33p)
'Still Life: Odyssey 1' by Ben Nicholson (39p)

1993, May 11. Contemporary Art (Europa)

Des: A. Dastor.

Set	2.25	2.25
Gutter pairs	6.00	–
First day cover	–	2.25
Stamp cards	2.50	5.00

Emperor Claudius, from gold coin (24p)
Emperor Hadrian, from bronze head (28p)
Goddess Roma, from gemstone (33p)
Christ, from mosaic at Hinton St. Mary (39p)

1993, June 15. Roman Britain

Des: J. Gibbs.

Set	2.25	2.25
Gutter pairs	6.00	–
First day cover	–	2.25
Stamp cards	2.50	5.00

Narrowboats on Grand Junction Canal (24p)
Humber keels on Stainforth and Keadby Canal (28p)
Horse-drawn barges on Brecknock and Abergavenny Canal (33p)
Steam barges and fishing boats on Crinan Canal (39p)

1993, July 20. Inland Waterways

Des: T. Lewery. Printed in litho by Questa.

Set	2.00	2.00
Gutter pairs	5.00	–
First day cover	–	2.25
Stamp cards	3.50	5.00

Horse chestnut (18p)
Blackberry (24p)
Hazel (28p)
Rowan (33p)
Pear (39p)

1993, September 14. The Four Seasons: Autumn

Des: Charlotte Knox. The 18p has one phosphor band.

Set	2.25	2.25
Gutter pairs	6.00	–
First day cover	–	2.25
Stamp cards	3.00	5.00

'The Reigate Square' (24p)
'The Hound of the Baskervilles' (24p)
'The Six Napoleons' (24p)
'The Greek Interpreter' (24p)
'The Final Problem' (24p)

■ 1993, October 12. Sherlock Holmes
Des: A. Davidson. Printed in litho by Questa.

Set (se-tenant strip of five)	2.25	2.25
Gutter pairs	6.00	–
First day cover	–	2.25
Stamp cards	5.00	4.50

Bob Cratchit and Tiny Tim (19p)
Mr. and Mrs. Fezziwig (25p)
Mr. Scrooge (30p)
The prize turkey (35p)
Mr. Scrooge's nephew (41p)

■ 1993, November 9. Christmas. 150th Anniversary of 'A Christmas Carol' by Charles Dickens
Des: Q. Blake. The 19p has one phosphor band.

Set	2.25	2.50
Gutter pairs	6.00	–
First day cover	–	2.25
Stamp cards	3.50	5.00

(* The 19p and 25p were also sold in booklets.)

Class 5 and Class B1 on the West Highland Line (19p)
Class A1 at Kings Cross (25p)
Class 4 at Blythe North (30p)
Class 4 near Wigan Central (35p)
Castle class crossing Worcester & Birmingham Canal (41p)

■ 1994, January 18. The Age of Steam
Des: B. Delaney, from photographs by Colin Gifford. The 19p has one phosphor band.

Set	2.25	2.50
Gutter pairs	6.00	–
First day cover	–	2.50
Stamp cards	4.00	5.50

Dan Dare (1st)
The Three Bears (1st)
Rupert Bear (1st)
Alice in Wonderland (1st)
Noggin and the Ice Dragon (1st)
Peter Rabbit (1st)
Little Red Riding Hood (1st)
Orlando the Marmalade Cat (1st)
Biggles (1st)
Paddington Bear (1st)

■ 1994, February 1. Greetings: Messages
Des: Newell and Sorell. Issued se-tenant in booklet panes of ten containing one of each design.

Booklet pane (of 10)	9.00	8.50
Booklet	9.00	–
First day cover	–	7.50
Stamp cards	8.00	15.50

Castell Y Waun / Chirk Castle, Clwyd, Cymru / Wales

Chirk Castle, Clwyd, Wales (19p)
Ben Arkle, Sutherland, Scotland (25p)
Mourne Mountains, County Down, Northern Ireland (30p)
Dersingham, Norfolk, England (35p)
Dolwyddelan, Gwynedd, Wales (41p)

■ **1994, March 1. 25th Anniversary of the Investiture of The Prince of Wales**
Des: paintings by the Prince of Wales. The 19p has one phosphor band.

Set	2.25	2.50
Gutter pairs	6.00	–
First day cover	–	2.50
Stamp cards	3.00	5.50

(* The 30p also appears as a pane of four in the Northern Ireland prestige stamp book issued on July 26, 1994.)

Bathing at Blackpool (19p)
'Where's my little lad?' (25p)
'Wish you were here' (30p)
Punch and Judy show (35p)
Tower Crane machine (41p)

■ **1994, April 12. Centenary of Picture Postcards**
Des: M. Dempsey and B. Dare. Printed in litho by Questa. The 19p has one phosphor band, and the other values have two.

Set	2.25	2.50
Gutter pairs	6.50	–
First day cover	–	2.50
Stamp cards	3.00	5.50

British lion and French cockerel (25p, 41p)
Hands over a train (25p, 41p)

■ **1994, May 3. Opening of the Channel Tunnel**
Des: G. Hardie (lion and cockerel), J.–P. Cousin (hands and train).

Set (two se–tenant pairs)	2.50	2.50
Gutter pairs	6.50	–
First day cover	–	2.50
Stamp cards	3.00	5.50

Ground crew servicing Douglas Boston aircraft (25p)
HMS Warspite (25p)
Commandos on Gold Beach (25p)
Infantry on Sword Beach (25p)
Tank and infantry at Ouistreham (25p)

■ **1994, June 6. 50th Anniversary of D–Day**
Des: K. Bassford. Printed in litho by Questa.

Set (se–tenant strip of five)	2.50	2.25
Gutter pairs	6.00	–
First day cover	–	2.50
Stamp cards	3.50	5.50

St. Andrew's, old course (19p)
Muirfield, 18th hole (25p)
Carnoustie, 15th hole (30p)
Royal Troon, 8th hole (35p)
Turnberry, 9th hole (41p)

■ **1994, July 5. Scottish Golf Courses**
Des: P. Hogarth. The 19p has one phosphor band.

Set	2.50	2.50
Gutter pairs	6.50	–
First day cover	–	2.50
Stamp cards	3.50	5.50

Royal Welsh Show, Llanelwedd (19p)
All England Tennis Championships, Wimbledon (25p)
Cowes Week (30p)
Test Match, Lord's (35p)
Braemar Gathering (41p)

■ **1994, August 2. The Four Seasons: Summertime**
Des: M. Cook. The 19p has one phosphor band.

Set	2.25	2.50
Gutter pairs	6.00	–
First day cover	–	2.50
Stamp cards	3.25	5.50

Ultrasonic imaging (25p)
Scanning electron microscopy (30p)
Magnetic resonance imaging (35p)
Computed tomography (41p)

■ 1994, September 27. Medical Discoveries (Europa)

Des: P. Vermier and J.–P. Tibbles. Printed in photogravure by Enschedé.

Set	2.25	2.25
Gutter pairs	6.00	–
First day cover	–	2.50
Stamp cards	2.50	5.50

Mary and Joseph (19p)
Three wise men (25p)
Mary with doll (30p)
Shepherds (35p)
Angels (41p)

■ 1994, November 1. Christmas. Children's Nativity Plays

Des: Yvonne Gilbert. The 19p has one phosphor band.

Set	2.25	2.50
Gutter pairs	6.00	–
First day cover	–	2.50
Stamp cards	3.00	5.50

(* The 19p and 25p were also sold in booklets.)

Black cat (19p)
Siamese and tabby cat (25p)
Ginger cat (30p)
Tortoiseshell and Abyssinian cat (35p)
Black and white cat (41p)

■ 1995, January 17. Cats

Des: Elizabeth Blackadder. Printed in litho by Questa. The 19p has one phosphor band, other values two phosphor bands.

Set	2.40	2.40
Gutter pairs	6.00	–
First day cover	–	2.50
Stamp cards	3.50	6.50

Dandelions (19p)
Chestnut leaves (25p)
Garlic leaves (30p)
Hazel leaves (35p)
Spring grass (41p)

■ 1995, March 14. The Four Seasons: Springtime

Des: plant sculptures by Andy Goldsworthy. The 19p has one phosphor band, other values two phosphor bands.

Set	2.25	2.40
Gutter pairs	6.00	–
First day cover	–	2.50
Stamp cards	3.00	6.50

'La Danse à la Campagne' by Pierre–Auguste Renoir (1st)
'Troilus and Criseyde' by Peter Brookes (1st)
'The Kiss' by Auguste Rodin (1st)
'Girls on the Town' by Beryl Cook (1st)
'Jazz' by Andrew Mockett (1st)
'Girls Performing a Kathak Dance' (1st)
'Alice Keppel With Her Daughter' by Alice Hughes (1st)
'Children Playing' by L. S. Lowry (1st)
'Circus Clowns' by Emily Firmin and Justin Mitchell (1st)
'All the Love Poems of Shakespeare' by Eric Gill (1st)

■ 1995, March 21. Greetings: Art

Des: Newell and Sorell. Printed in litho by Walsall. Issued se–tenant in booklet panes of ten containing one of each design.

Booklet pane (of 10)	9.00	9.00
Booklet	9.00	–
First day cover	–	7.00
Stamp cards	10.00	15.50

Fireplace decoration (19p)
Oak seedling (25p)
Carved table leg (30p)
St David's Head, Dyfed, Wales (35p)
Elizabethan window (41p)

■ 1995, April 11. Centenary of The National Trust

Des: T. Evans. The 19p has one phosphor band, the 25p and 35p two phosphor bands, the 30p and 41p phosphor paper.

Set	2.25	2.25
Gutter pairs	6.00	–
First day cover	–	2.50
Stamp cards	3.00	6.50

(* The 25p also appeared in a pane of six in the National Trust prestige stamp book issued on April 25, 1995.)

British troops and French civilians (19p)
Symbolic hands and Red Cross emblem (19p)
Searchlights in a 'V' over St. Paul's Cathedral (25p)
Hand releasing dove of peace (25p)
Symbolic hands and United Nations (30p)

■ 1995, May 2. Peace & Freedom (Europa)

Des: J–M. Folon (Red Cross 19p, Dove 25p, 30p), J. Gorham (Troops 19p, Searchlights 25p). The 19p has one phosphor band, other values two phosphor bands.

Set	2.25	2.25
Gutter pairs	6.00	–
First day cover	–	2.50
Stamp cards	3.00	6.50

(* The design with St Paul's Cathedral was also used as a 1st class stamp in the End of the War miniature sheet in 2005.)

'The Time Machine' (25p)
'The First Men in the Moon' (30p)
'The War of the Worlds' (35p)
'The Shape of Things to Come' (41p)

■ 1995, June 6. Novels of H. G. Wells

Des: Siobhan Keaney. Printed in litho by Questa.

Set	2.25	2.25
Gutter pairs	6.00	–
First day cover	–	2.50
Stamp cards	3.00	6.50

The Swan Theatre, 1595 (25p)
The Rose Theatre, 1592 (25p)
The Globe Theatre, 1599 (25p)
The Hope Theatre, 1613 (25p)
The Globe Theatre, 1614 (25p)

■ 1995, August 8. Reconstruction of Shakespeare's Globe Theatre

Des: C. Hodges. Printed in litho by Walsall.

Set (se–tenant strip of five)	2.50	2.50
Gutter pairs	6.00	–
First day cover	–	2.50
Stamp cards	3.50	6.50

■ 1995, August 22. Castle high-value definitive

Des: as issue of March 24, 1992, but new value, replacing the £1.

£3	8.50	1.75
Gutter pair	20.00	–
Gutter block of four (centre cross)	40.00	–
First day cover	–	5.00
Stamp card	8.00	21.00

(* This stamp exists with either blue tinted PVAD gum or white PVA gum.)

Sir Rowland Hill and Uniform Penny Postage petition (19p)
Sir Rowland Hill and Penny Black (25p)
Guglielmo Marconi and early wireless (41p)
Guglielmo Marconi and the sinking of the 'Titanic' (60p)

■ 1995, September 5. Pioneers of Communications

Des: The Four Hundred; engraved by C. Slania. Printed in recess and litho by Harrison. The 19p has one phosphor band.

Set	2.25	2.50
Gutter pairs	6.00	–
First day cover	–	2.50
Stamp cards	2.50	6.50

Harold Wagstaff (19p)
Gus Risman (25p)
Jim Sullivan (30p)
Billy Batten (35p)
Brian Bevan (41p)

■ 1995, October 3. Centenary of Rugby League

Des: C. Birmingham. The 19p has one phosphor band, other values two phosphor bands.

Set	2.40	2.50
Gutter pairs	6.00	–
First day cover	–	2.50
Stamp cards	3.00	6.50

Robin in letter box (19p)
Robin on railings (25p)
Robin on milk bottles (30p)
Robin on road sign (41p)
Robin on door handle (60p)

■ 1995, October 30. Christmas. Robins

Des: K. Lilly. The 19p has one phosphor band, other values two phosphor bands.

Set	2.70	2.70
Gutter pairs	7.00	–
First day cover	–	2.50
Stamp cards	3.25	6.50

(* The 19p, 25p and 60p were also sold in booklets, and the 19p was used in Smilers sheets in 2000 and 2001.)

'Wee, fleeket, cowran, tim'rous beastie' (19p)
'O, my love's like a red, red rose' (25p)
'Scots, wha hae wi Wallace bled' (41p)
'Should auld acquaintance be forgot' (60p)

■ 1996, January 25. Bicentenary of the Death of Robert Burns

Des: Tayburn Consultancy. Printed in litho by Questa. The 19p has one phosphor band, other values two phosphor bands.

Set	2.25	2.25
Gutter pairs	5.50	–
First day cover	–	2.50
Stamp cards	3.50	6.50

'I'm writing to you because you don't listen to a word I say' (1st)
'More! Love' (1st)
'Sincerely' (1st)
'Do you have something for the human condition?' (1st)
'Mental floss' (1st)
'4:55pm. Don't ring' (1st)
'Dear lottery prize winner' (1st)
'Fetch this, fetch that. Let the cat do it' (1st)
'My day starts before I'm ready for it' (1st)
'The cheque in the post' (1st)

■ **1996, February 26. Greetings: Cartoons**
Des: M. Wolff. Printed in litho by Walsall. All-over phosphor.
Issued se-tenant in booklet panes of ten containing one of each
design.

Booklet pane (of 10)	9.00	9.00
Booklet	9.00	–
First day cover	–	7.00
Stamp cards	10.00	16.00

Muscovy duck (19p)
Lapwing (25p)
White-front goose (30p)
Bittern (35p)
Whooper swan (41p)

■ **1996, March 12. 50th Anniversary of the Wildfowl and
Wetlands Trust**
Des: Moseley Webb, from paintings by C. F. Tunnicliffe. The 19p
has one phosphor band.

Set	2.25	2.50
Gutter pairs	6.00	–
First day cover	–	2.75
Stamp cards	3.00	6.50

Odeon, Harrogate (19p)
Laurence Olivier and Vivien Leigh in 'Lady Hamilton' (25p)
Cinema ticket (30p)
Pathé News (35p)
Cinema sign, Odeon, Manchester (41p)

■ **1996, April 16. Centenary of Cinema**
Des: The Chase. The 19p has one phosphor band, other values
two phosphor bands.

Set	2.40	2.50
Gutter pairs	6.00	–
First day cover	–	2.75
Stamp cards	3.50	6.50

Dixie Dean (19p)
Bobby Moore (25p)
Duncan Edwards (30p)
Billy Wright (35p)
Danny Blanchflower (41p)

■ **1996, May 14. European Football Championship**
Des: H. Brown. Printed in litho by Questa. The 19p has one
phosphor band, other values two phosphor bands.

Set	2.50	2.75
Gutter pairs	6.50	–
First day cover	–	2.75
Stamp cards	3.50	6.50

(* All five values also appeared in the European Football
Championship prestige stamp book, issued on May 14, 1996.)

Athlete on starting blocks (26p)
Throwing the javelin (26p)
Basketball (26p)
Swimming (26p)
Athlete and Olympic rings (26p)

■ 1996, July 9. Olympic and Paralympic Games, Atlanta, USA
Des: N. Knight. Printed in litho by Questa.

Set (se-tenant strip of five)	2.25	2.40
Gutter pairs	6.00	–
First day cover	–	2.75
Stamp cards	3.00	6.50

Dorothy Hodgkin (20p)
Margot Fonteyn (26p)
Elizabeth Frink (31p)
Daphne du Maurier (37p)
Marea Hartman (43p)

■ 1996, August 6. Famous Women (Europa)
Des: Stephanie Nash. The 20p has one phosphor band, other values two phosphor bands.

Set	2.50	2.60
Gutter pairs	6.50	–
First day cover	–	2.75
Stamp cards	3.00	6.50

Muffin the Mule (20p)
Sooty (26p)
Stingray (31p)
The Clangers (37p)
Dangermouse (43p)

■ 1996, September 3. 50th Anniversary of Children's Television
Des: Tutssels. Printed in photogravure by Enschedé. The 20p has one phosphor band, other values two phosphor bands.

Set	2.50	2.75
Gutter pairs	6.50	–
First day cover	–	2.75
Stamp cards	3.00	6.50

(* The 20p also appeared in the 75th Anniversary of the BBC prestige stamp booklet issued on September 23, 1997, printed in photogravure by Harrison; price £1.00 mint or used.)

Triumph TR3 (20p)
MG TD (26p)
Austin Healey 100 (37p)
Jaguar XK120 (43p)
Morgan Plus 4 (63p)

■ 1996, October 1. Classic Sports Cars
Des: S. Clay. The 20p has one phosphor band, other values two phosphor bands.

Set	3.00	3.00
Gutter pairs	8.50	–
First day cover	–	2.75
Stamp cards	3.50	6.50

Three kings (2nd)
Annunciation (1st)
Journey to Bethlehem (31p)
Nativity (43p)
Shepherds (63p)

■ **1996, October 28. Christmas**
Des: Laura Stoddart. The 2nd class has one phosphor band, other values two phosphor bands.

Set	3.00	3.00
Gutter pairs	8.50	–
First day cover	–	2.75
Stamp cards	3.50	6.50

(* The 2nd class and 1st class were also sold in booklets.)

■ **1996, November 11. Greetings: Cartoons**
As issue of February 26, but with two phosphor bands. Issued se-tenant in booklet panes of ten containing one of each design.

Booklet pane (of 10)	25.00	25.00
Booklet	25.00	–

(* These designs were also used for Smilers sheets in 2001 and 2002.)

Iris latifolia (1st)
Gentiana acaulis (1st)
Magnolia grandiflora (1st)
Camellia japonica (1st)
Tulipa (1st)
Fuchsia 'Princess of Wales' (1st)
Tulipa gesneriana (1st)
Gazania splendens (1st)
Hippeastrum rutilum (1st)
Passiflora coerulea (1st)

■ **1997, January 6. Greetings: 19th–Century Flower Paintings**
Des: Tutssels. Printed in litho by Walsall. Two phosphor bands. Issued se-tenant in booklet panes of ten containing one of each design.

Booklet pane (of 10)	9.00	8.00
Booklet	9.00	–
First day cover	–	8.00
Stamp cards	12.00	20.00

(* The *Gentiana acaulis*, *Tulipa* and *Iris latifolia* designs also appear in the Glory of the Garden prestige stamp book of 2004, and the *Tulipa* and *Iris latifolia* designs in the 50th Anniversary of NAFAS booklet of May 21, 2009, in self adhesive form. All the designs were also used for a Smilers sheet issued in 2003.)

King Henry VIII (26p)
Catherine of Aragon (26p)
Anne Boleyn (26p)
Jane Seymour (26p)
Anne of Cleves (26p)
Catherine Howard (26p)
Catherine Parr (26p)

■ **1997, February 21. 450th Anniversary of the Death of King Henry VIII**
Des: Kate Stephens. Two phosphor bands. The wives designs were issued in a se-tenant strip of six.

Set	3.50	3.50
Gutter pairs	9.00	–
First day cover	–	3.50
Stamp cards	6.00	6.50

St Columba in boat (26p)
St Columba on Iona (37p)
St Augustine with King Ethelbert (43p)
St Augustine with a model of cathedral (63p)

■ **1997, March 11. Religious Anniversaries**
Des: Claire Melinsky. Printed in photogravure by Enschedé. Two phosphor bands.

Set	2.75	2.75
Gutter pairs	7.00	–
First day cover	–	3.00
Stamp cards	2.50	6.50

Dracula (26p)
Frankenstein (31p)
Dr Jekyll and Mr Hyde (37p)
The Hound of the Baskervilles (43p)

■ 1997, May 13. Horror Stories (Europa)

Des: J. Pollock. Printed in photogravure by Walsall. Two phosphor bands and features printed in fluorescent ink which are visible only under ultra-violet light.

Set	2.75	2.75
Gutter pairs	6.50	–
First day cover	–	3.00
Stamp cards	2.50	6.50

Supermarine Spitfire MkIIA and Reginald Mitchell (20p)
Avro Lancaster MkI and Roy Chadwick (26p)
De Havilland Mosquito B MkXVI and Ronald Bishop (37p)
Gloster Meteor T Mk7 and George Carter (43p)
Hawker Hunter FGA Mk9 and Sir Sydney Camm (63p)

■ 1997, June 10. British Aircraft Designers

Des: Turner Duckworth. The 20p has one phosphor band, other values two phosphor bands.

Set	3.25	3.25
Gutter pairs	8.00	–
First day cover	–	3.00
Stamp cards	3.50	6.50

(* The 20p also appears in the Pilot To Plane: RAF Uniforms prestige stamp book issued on September 18, 2008.)

Carriage horse (20p)
Lifeguards horse (26p)
Blues and Royals drum horse (43p)
Duke of Edinburgh's horse (63p)

■ 1997, July 8. All The Queen's Horses. 50th Anniversary of the British Horse Society

Des: J.-L. Benard. Printed in litho by Walsall. The 20p has one phosphor band, other values two phosphor bands.

Set	2.50	2.75
Gutter pairs	7.00	–
First day cover	–	3.00
Stamp cards	2.50	6.50

Caernarfon Castle (£1.50)
Edinburgh Castle (£2)
Carrickfergus Castle (£3)
Windsor Castle (£5)

■ 1997, July 29. Castle high-value definitives

Des: as the issues of March 24, 1992, and August 22, 1995, but re-engraved by Inge Madlé. Printed in recess and silk screen (for Queen's portrait) by Enschedé.

Set	45.00	10.00
Gutter pairs	£125	–
Gutter blocks of four (centre cross)	£275	–
First day cover	–	25.00

Haroldswick, Shetland (20p)
Painswick, Gloucestershire (26p)
Beddgelert, Gwynedd (43p)
Ballyroney, County Down (63p)

1997, August 12. Sub Post Offices

Des: T. Millington. Printed in photogravure by Enschedé. The 20p has one phosphor band, other values two phosphor bands.

Set	2.50	2.75
Gutter pairs	7.00	–
First day cover	–	3.00
Stamp cards	2.50	6.50

'Noddy' (20p)
'Famous Five' (26p)
'Secret Seven' (37p)
'Faraway Tree' (43p)
'Malory Towers' (63p)

1997, September 9. Centenary of the Birth of Enid Blyton

Des: C. Birmingham. Printed in photogravure by Enschedé. The 20p has one phosphor band, other values two phosphor bands.

Set	2.75	3.00
Gutter pairs	7.00	–
First day cover	–	3.00
Stamp cards	4.00	6.50

Father Christmas and children pulling a cracker (2nd)
Father Christmas holding a cracker (1st)
Father Christmas riding on a cracker (31p)
Father Christmas riding on a snowball (43p)
Father Christmas on a chimney (63p)

1997, October 27. Christmas. 150th Anniversary of the Christmas Cracker

Des: M. Thomas (1st) and J. Gorham (others). The 2nd class has one phosphor band, other values two phosphor bands.

Set	3.00	3.00
Gutter pairs	8.00	–
First day cover	–	3.00
Stamp cards	3.25	6.50

(* The 2nd class and 1st class also appeared in booklets, and the 1st class appeared in Smilers sheets in 2000 and 2001.)

Queen Elizabeth II and Prince Philip, wedding photograph of 1947 (20p, 43p)
Queen Elizabeth II and Prince Philip, photographed in 1997 (26p, 63p)

1997, November 13. Royal Golden Wedding

Des: D. Driver (20p, 43p), Lord Snowdon (26p, 63p). The 20p has one phosphor band, other values two phosphor bands.

Set	3.00	3.00
Gutter pairs	8.50	–
First day cover	–	3.00
Stamp cards	3.50	6.50

Common dormouse (20p)
Lady's slipper orchid (26p)
Song thrush (31p)
Shining ram's-horn snail (37p)
Mole cricket (43p)
Devil's bolette (63p)

1998, January 20. Endangered Species

Des: R. Maude. Printed in litho by Questa. The 20p has one phosphor band, other values two phosphor bands.

Set	3.75	4.00
Gutter pairs	9.00	–
First day cover	–	3.00
Stamp cards	3.50	6.50

Princess Diana wearing necklace, 1997 (26p)
Princess Diana dressed in blue, 1997 (26p)
Princess Diana wearing tiara, 1991 (26p)
Princess Diana dressed in black and white checks, 1995 (26p)
Princess Diana wearing black evening dress, 1987 (26p)

■ 1998, February 3. Diana, Princess of Wales Memorial
Des: B. Robinson. Two phosphor bands.

Set (se-tenant strip of five)	2.25	2.25
Gutter pairs	6.00	–
First day cover	–	3.00

Lion of England and Griffin of Edward III (26p)
Falcon of Plantagenet and Bull of Clarence (26p)
Lion of Mortimer and Yale of Beaufort (26p)
Greyhound of Richmond and Dragon of Wales (26p)
Unicorn of Scotland and Horse of Hanover (26p)

■ 1998, February 24. The Queen's Beasts. 650th Anniversary of the Order of the Garter
Des: Jeffery Matthews. Printed in recess and litho by Harrison. Two phosphor bands.

Set (se-tenant strip of five)	2.40	2.50
Gutter pairs	6.00	–
First day cover	–	3.00
Stamp cards	3.00	6.50

Wilding design of 1952–67 (20p, 26p, 37p)

■ 1998, March 10. Wilding definitives
Des: Dew Gibbons Design Group, from original design by G. Knipe. Printed in gravure by Walsall. Issued only in the Wilding Definitives prestige stamp book.

20p light green (phos band at left)	0.70	0.75
20p light green (phos band at right)	0.70	0.75
26p red-brown	0.75	0.80
37p light purple	1.75	1.85

St John's Point lighthouse (20p)
Smalls lighthouse (26p)
Needles Rock lighthouse (37p)
Bell Rock lighthouse (43p)
Eddystone lighthouse (63p)

■ 1998, March 24. Lighthouses
Des: D. Davis and J. Boon. Printed in litho by Questa. The 20p has one phosphor band, other values two phosphor bands.

Set	3.00	3.00
Gutter pairs	8.50	–
First day cover	–	3.25
Stamp cards	4.50	6.50

Tommy Cooper (20p)
Eric Morecambe (26p)
Joyce Grenfell (37p)
Les Dawson (43p)
Peter Cook (63p)

■ 1998, April 23. Comedians
Des: Gerald Scarfe. Printed in litho by Questa. The 20p has one phosphor band, other values two phosphor bands.

Set	2.75	3.25
Gutter pairs	6.00	–
First day cover	–	3.25
Stamp cards	3.50	6.50

(* Examples exist of the 37p design but with a denomination of 30p, printed before an increase in postal rates, and issued in error; price £1,500 mint.)

Hands forming the shape of a heart (20p)
Adult holding the hand of a child (26p)
Hands forming a cradle (43p)
Hand taking a pulse (63p)

■ **1998, June 23. 50th Anniversary of the National Health Service**
Des: V. Frost, using photographs by A. Wilson. Printed in litho by Questa. The 20p has one phosphor band, other values two phosphor bands.

Set	2.50	2.50
Gutter pairs	7.00	–
First day cover	–	3.25
Stamp cards	3.00	6.50

'The Hobbit' by J. R. R. Tolkien (20p)
'The Lion, The Witch and The Wardrobe' by C. S. Lewis (26p)
'The Phoenix and the Carpet' by E. Nesbit (37p)
'The Borrowers' by Mary Norton (43p)
'Through The Looking Glass' by Lewis Carroll (63p)

■ **1998, July 21. Children's Fantasy Novels**
Des: P. Malone. Printed in photogravure by De La Rue. The 20p has one phosphor band, other values two phosphor bands.

Set	3.00	3.00
Gutter pairs	7.50	–
First day cover	–	3.25
Stamp cards	6.00	6.50

Woman in costume of yellow feathers (20p)
Woman in blue costume (26p)
Children in white and gold robes (43p)
Child dressed as a tree (63p)

■ **1998, August 25. Notting Hill Carnival (Europa)**
Des: T. Hazael. Printed in photogravure by Walsall. The 20p has one phosphor band, other values two phosphor bands.

Set	2.75	2.75
Gutter pairs	7.00	–
First day cover	–	3.25
Stamp cards	3.00	6.50

Bluebird of Sir Malcolm Campbell, 1925 (20p)
Sunbeam of Sir Henry Segrave, 1926 (26p)
Babs of John Parry Thomas, 1926 (30p)
Railton Mobil Special of John Cobb, 1947 (43p)
Bluebird CN7 of Donald Campbell, 1964 (63p)

■ **1998, September 29. British Land Speed Records**
Des: Roundel Design Group. Printed in photogravure by De La Rue. The 20p has one phosphor band, other values two phosphor bands.

Set	3.00	3.25
Gutter pairs	7.50	–
First day cover	–	3.25
Stamp cards	4.00	6.50

(* The 20p also appears in the Breaking Barriers prestige stamp book issued on October 13, 1988, but printed in photogravure by Walsall, and with one phosphor band printed on the left or right of the stamp; price £1.00 each mint or used)

Angel with hands in blessing (20p)
Angel praying (26p)
Angel playing lute (30p)
Angel playing flute (43p)
Angel praying (63p)

■ **1998, November 2. Christmas. Angels**

Des: Irene von Treskow. Printed in photogravure by De La Rue. The 20p has one phosphor band, other values two phosphor bands.

Set	3.25	3.25
Gutter pairs	9.00	–
First day cover	–	3.25
Stamp cards	4.00	6.50

(* The 20p and 26p were also sold in booklets.)

During 1999 and 2000 Royal Mail produced a series of special stamp issues to mark the new millennium. Each design includes the inscription 'Millennium', the year of issue and a serial number. The designs for 1999 looked back over the previous millennium under 12 different themes. The designs for 2000 highlighted projects undertaken to celebrate the millennium.

Timekeeping: Greenwich Meridian and clock face (20p)
Steam Power: worker and blast furnace (26p)
Photography: photograph of leaves (43p)
Computers: computer inside head (63p)

■ **1999, January 12. The Inventors' Tale**

Des: David Gentleman (20p), P. Howson (26p), Z. and B. Baran (43p), E. Paolozzi (63p). Printed in photogravure by Enschedé (26p), or De La Rue (20p, 43p, 63p). The 20p has one phosphor band, other values two phosphor bands.

Set	3.00	3.00
Gutter pairs	7.50	–
First day cover	–	3.75
Stamp cards	3.00	6.50

(* The 63p also appears in the World Changers prestige stamp book issued on September 21, 1999, but printed in photogravure by Questa; price £2.25 mint or used.)

Jet Travel: globe surrounded by aircraft (20p)
Liberation By Bike: woman on bicycle (26p)
Linking The Nation: railway station (43p)
Cook's Endeavour: Captain Cook and man (63p)

■ **1999, February 2. The Travellers' Tale**

Des: G. Hardie (20p), S. Fanelli (26p), J. Lawrence (43p), A. Klimowski (63p). Printed in photogravure by Enschedé (20p, 63p) or De La Rue (26p), or litho by Enschedé (43p). The 20p has one phosphor band, other values two phosphor bands.

Set	3.00	3.00
Gutter pairs	7.50	–
First day cover	–	3.75
Stamp cards	3.00	6.50

Jenner's Vaccination: cow with markings of vaccinated child (20p)
Nursing Care: patient on trolley (26p)
Fleming's Penicillin: penicillin mould (43p)
Test Tube Baby: sculpture of baby (63p)

■ 1999, March 2. The Patients' Tale
Des: P. Brookes (20p), S. Macfarlane (26p), M. Dempsey (43p), A. Gormley (63p. Printed in photogravure by Questa. The 20p has one phosphor band, other values two phosphor bands.

Set	3.00	3.00
Gutter pairs	7.50	–
First day cover	–	3.75
Stamp cards	3.00	6.50

(* The 20p also appears in the World Changers prestige stamp book issued on September 21, 1999.)

Migration To Scotland: Norman settler and dove (20p)
Pilgrim Fathers: settlers and Red Indian (26p)
Destination Australia: sailing ship and aspects of settlement (43p)
Migration To UK: face superimposed on hummingbird (63p)

■ 1999, April 6. The Settlers' Tale
Des: J. Byrne (20p), W. McLean (26p), J. Fisher (43p), G. Powell (63p). Printed in litho (20p) or photogravure (26p, 43p, 63p) by Walsall. The 20p has one phosphor band, other values two phosphor bands.

Set	3.00	3.00
Gutter pairs	7.50	–
First day cover	–	3.75
Stamp cards	3.00	6.50

(* The 26p also appears in a booklet issued on May 12, 1999.)

Weaver's Craft: woven threads (19p)
Mill Towns: Salts Mill, Saltaire (26p)
Shipbuilding: hull on slipway (44p)
City Finance: Lloyd's Building, London (64p)

■ 1999, May 4. The Workers' Tale
Des: P. Collingwood (19p), D. Hockney (26p), R. Sanderson (44p), B. Neiland (64p). Printed in litho (19p) or photogravure (26p, 44p, 64p) by De La Rue. The 19p has one phosphor band, other values two phosphor bands.

Set	3.00	3.00
Gutter pairs	7.50	–
First day cover	–	3.75
Stamp cards	3.00	6.50

(* The 26p also appears in a booklet issued on May 12, 1999, printed in photogravure by Walsall; price £1.75 mint or used.)

Mercury's Magic: Freddie Mercury of Queen on stage (19p)
World Cup: Bobby Moore holding the trophy (26p)
Doctor Who: dalek (44p)
Chaplin's Genius: Charlie Chaplin (64p)

■ 1999, June 1. The Entertainers' Tale
Des: P. Blake (19p), M. White (26p), Lord Snowdon (44p), R. Steadman (64p). Printed in photogravure by Enschedé. The 19p has one phosphor band, other values two phosphor bands.

Set	3.00	3.00
Gutter pairs	7.50	–
First day cover	–	3.75
Stamp cards	5.00	6.50

Prince Edward and Miss Sophie Rhys-Jones facing front (26p)
Prince Edward and Miss Sophie Rhys-Jones facing sideways (64p)

■ 1999, June 15. Royal Wedding
Des: J. Gibbs, from photographs by John Swannell. Printed in photogravure by De La Rue.

Set	1.50	1.75
Gutter pairs	4.00	–
First day cover	–	2.50
Stamp cards	2.50	3.50

Equal Rights: suffragette behind bars (19p)
Right To Health: tap (26p)
Right To Learn: children at school (44p)
First Rights: Magna Carta (64p)

■ 1999, July 6. The Citizens' Tale

Des: N. Kerr (19p), M. Craig-Martin (26p), A. Drummond (44p), A. Kitching (64p). Printed in photogravure by De La Rue. The 19p has one phosphor band, other values two phosphor bands.

Set	3.00	3.00
Gutter pairs	7.50	–
First day cover	–	3.75
Stamp cards	3.00	6.50

Decoding DNA: molecular structures (19p)
Darwin's Theory: Galapagos finch and skeleton (26p)
Faraday's Electricity: light polarised by magnetism (44p)
Newton: Saturn, from Hubble Space Telescope (64p)

■ 1999, August 3. The Scientists' Tale

Des: M. Curtis (19p), R. Harris Ching (26p), C. Gray (44p), photograph (64p). Printed in photogravure (19p, 64p) or litho (26p, 44p) by Questa. The 19p has one phosphor band, other values two phosphor bands.

Set	3.00	3.00
Gutter pairs	7.50	–
First day cover	–	3.75
Stamp cards	3.00	6.50

(* The 26p and 44p also appear in the World Changers prestige stamp book of September 21, 1999; price £3.50 for the pair. The 64p also appears on a miniature sheet of August 11.)

Saturn, from Hubble Space Telescope (64p)

■ 1999, August 11. Solar Eclipse

Des: four 64p values from the issue of August 3. Printed in photogravure by De La Rue.

Miniature sheet	10.00	10.00
First day cover	–	12.50

Strip Farming: upland landscape (19p)
Mechanical Farming: horse-drawn seed drill (26p)
Food From Afar: peeling potato (44p)
Satellite Agriculture: combine harvester in field (64p)

■ 1999, September 7. The Farmers' Tale

Des: D. Tress (19p), C. Wormell (26p), T. Traeger (44p), R. Cooke (64p). Printed in photogravure by De La Rue. The 19p has one phosphor band, other values two phosphor bands.

Set	2.75	2.75
Gutter pairs	6.50	–
First day cover	–	3.75
Stamp cards	3.00	6.50

(* The 26p also appears in a booklet issued on September 21, 1999, printed in gravure by Walsall; price £2.00 mint or used.)

Bannockburn: Robert the Bruce (19p)
Civil War: cavalier and horse (26p)
World Wars: war graves (44p)
Peace-Keeping: soldiers with boy (64p)

■ 1999, October 5. The Soldiers' Tale

Des: A. Davidson (19p), R. Kelly (26p), D. McCullin (44p), C. Corr (64p). Printed in litho (19p) or photogravure (26p, 44p, 64p) by Walsall. The 19p has one phosphor band, other values two phosphor bands.

Set	2.75	2.75
Gutter pairs	6.50	–
First day cover	–	3.75
Stamp cards	3.00	6.50

Wesley: 'Hark the Herald Angels Sing' (19p)
King James Bible: King James I and Authorised Version (26p)
St. Andrews Pilgrimage: St. Andrews Cathedral, Fife (44p)
First Christmas: nativity (64p)

■ **1999, November 2. The Christians' Tale**
Des: B. Neuenschwander (19p), C. Melinsky (26p), C. Yass (44p),
C. Aitchison (64p). Printed in photogravure by De La Rue. The 19p
has one phosphor band, other values two phosphor bands.

Set	3.00	3.00
Gutter pairs	7.50	–
First day cover	–	3.75
Stamp cards	3.00	6.50

(* The 19p and 26p were also sold in booklets.)

World Of The Stage: dancers behind curtain (19p)
World Of Music: coloured stripes (26p)
World Of Literature: untitled book (44p)
New Worlds: rainbow abstract (64p)

■ **1999, December 7. The Artists' Tale**
Des: A. Jones (19p), B. Riley (26p), L. Milroy (44p), Sir H. Hodgkin
(64p). Printed in photogravure by Walsall. The 19p has one
phosphor band, other values two phosphor bands.

Set	3.00	3.00
Gutter pairs	7.00	–
First day cover	–	3.75
Stamp cards	3.00	6.50

Clock face and globe showing North America (64p)
Clock face and globe showing Asia (64p)
Clock face and globe showing Middle East (64p)
Clock face and globe showing Europe (64p)

■ **1999, December 14. Millennium Timekeeper**
Des: David Gentleman. Printed in gravure by De La Rue.

Miniature sheet	12.00	12.00
First day cover	–	12.50
Stamp cards	8.00	19.00

(* The miniature sheet also exists with the margin overprinted
'Earls Court, London 22–28 May 2000 The Stamp Show 2000',
sold at £10 with tickets to the exhibition from March 1, 2000;
price £18.00 mint.)

Third Millennium, Muncaster: barn owl (19p)
National Space Centre, Leicester: night sky (26p)
Torrs Walkway, New Mills: River Goyt and textile mills (44p)
Seabird Centre, North Berwick: cape gannets (64p)

■ **2000, January 18. Above and Beyond**
Printed in litho (44p) and gravure (19p, 26p, 64p) by Questa. The
19p has one phosphor band, other values two phosphor bands.

Set	3.00	3.00
Gutter pairs	7.50	–
First day cover	–	3.75
Stamp cards	3.00	6.50

(* The 26p also appears as a 1st class value in a £2.70 stamp
booklet issued on May 26, 2000, printed in gravure by Walsall;
price £3.00 mint.)

Beacons Across The Land: millennium beacon (19p)
Rheilffordd Eryri, Snowdonia: Garratt locomotive and train (26p)
Dynamic Earth Centre, Edinburgh: lightning (44p)
Lighting Croydon's Skyline: floodlighting (64p)

■ **2000, February 1. Fire and Light**
Printed in gravure by De La Rue. The 19p has one phosphor band,
other values two phosphor bands.

Set	3.00	3.00
Gutter pairs	7.50	–
First day cover	–	3.75
Stamp cards	3.00	6.50

Turning The Tide, Durham: beach pebbles (19p)
National Pondlife Centre, Merseyside: frog's legs and lilies (26p)
Parc Arfordirol, Llanelli: cliff boardwalk (44p)
Portsmouth Harbour: reflections in water (64p)

2000, March 7. Water and Coast

Printed in litho (44p) or gravure (19p, 26p, 64p) by Walsall. The 19p has one phosphor band, other values two phosphor bands.

Set	3.00	3.00
Gutter pairs	8.50	–
First day cover	–	4.00
Stamp cards	3.00	6.50

ECOS, Ballymena: River Braid reed beds (2nd)
Web Of Life, London Zoo: leaf-cutter ants (1st)
Earth Centre, Doncaster: solar sensors (44p)
Project Suzy, Teesside: hydroponic leaves (64p)

2000, April 4. Life and Earth

Printed in gravure by De La Rue. The 2nd class has one phosphor band, other values two phosphor bands.

Set	3.50	3.50
Gutter pairs	9.50	–
First day cover	–	4.00
Stamp cards	3.00	6.50

(* The 1st class also appears in a booklet of May 26, 2000.)

Ceramica Museum, Stoke-on-Trent: pottery glaze (2nd)
Tate Modern, London: bankside galleries (1st)
Cycle Network: road markings for bicycles (45p)
Lowry Centre, Salford: people in Salford (65p)

2000, May 2. Art and Craft

Printed in gravure by Enschedé. The 2nd class has one phosphor band, other values two phosphor bands.

Set	3.50	3.50
Gutter pairs	9.50	–
First day cover	–	4.00
Stamp cards	3.00	6.50

Coronation design of 1953 (£1)
Definitives (1st, 1st. 1st, 1st)

2000, May 23. Her Majesty's Stamps. Stamp Show 2000

Des: Delaney Design Consultants, the £1 based on the 1953 Coronation 1/3 design by Edmund Dulac. Printed in gravure by De La Rue.

Miniature sheet	9.00	9.00
First day cover	–	20.00
Stamp cards	9.50	35.00

Millennium Greens Project: children playing (2nd)
Millennium Bridge, Gateshead: bridge (1st)
Mile End Park, London: daisies (45p)
On The Meridian Line: African hut and thatched cottage (65p)

2000, June 6. People and Places

Printed in gravure (2nd, 45p) or litho (1st, 65p) by Walsall. The 2nd class has one phosphor band, other values two bands.

Set	3.50	3.50
Gutter pairs	9.50	–
First day cover	–	4.00
Stamp cards	3.00	6.50

Strangford Stone, Killyleagh: raising the stone (2nd)
Trans-Pennine Trail, Derbyshire: horse's hooves (1st)
Kingdom Of Fife Cycle Ways: cyclist and reflection (45p)
Groundwork's Changing Places: bluebell wood (65p)

■ 2000, July 4. Stone and Soil
Printed in gravure in Enschedé. The 2nd class has one phosphor band, other values two phosphor bands.

Set	3.50	3.50
Gutter pairs	9.50	–
First day cover	–	4.00
Stamp cards	3.00	6.50

(* The 1st also appears in a £2.70 stamp booklet issued on September 5, 2000, printed in gravure by Walsall; price 75p mint. The 65p also appears in the Treasury of Trees prestige stamp book issued on September 18, 2000, printed in gravure by Walsall; price £1.50 mint.)

Yews For The Millennium: tree roots (2nd)
Eden Project, St. Austell: sunflower (1st)
Millennium Seed Bank, Ardingly: sycamore seeds (45p)
Forest For Scotland: highland forest (65p)

■ 2000, August 1. Tree and Leaf
Printed in gravure in De La Rue. The 2nd class has one phosphor band, other values two phosphor bands.

Set	3.50	3.50
Gutter pairs	9.50	–
First day cover	–	4.00
Stamp cards	3.00	6.50

(* The 2nd, 45p and 65p also appear in the Treasury of Trees prestige stamp book issued on September 18, 2000, printed in gravure by Walsall; price £3 each mint.)

Queen Elizabeth II (27p)
Prince William (27p)
The Queen Mother (27p)
Prince Charles (27p)

■ 2000, August 4. 100th Birthday of The Queen Mother
Des: J. Gibbs. Photograph by J. Swannell. Printed in gravure by De La Rue.

Miniature sheet	6.50	6.50
First day cover	–	8.50
Stamp cards	9.00	11.50

(* The Queen Mother design, and the entire miniature sheet but in a slightly larger size, also appeared in the Life Of The Century prestige stamp book issued on August 4, 2000, printed in gravure; price £1.50 mint or used.)

Wildscreen At Bristol: head of ant (2nd)
Norfolk & Norwich Project: gathering water lilies on Broads (1st)
Millennium Point, Birmingham: X-ray of hand on mouse (45p)
Scottish Cultural Resources Network: tartan wool holder (65p)

■ 2000, September 5. Mind and Matter
Printed in litho by Walsall. The 2nd class has one phosphor band, other values two phosphor bands.

Set	3.50	3.50
Gutter pairs	9.50	–
First day cover	–	4.00
Stamp cards	3.00	6.50

Body Zone, Millennium Dome: acrobats (2nd)
Hampden Park, Glasgow: footballers (1st)
Bath Spa Project: bather (45p)
Centre For Life, Newcastle: hen's egg under magnification (65p)

■ 2000, October 3. Body and Bone
Printed in litho (2nd) or gravure (1st, 45p, 65p) by Questa. The 2nd class has one phosphor band, other values two phosphor bands.

Set	3.50	3.50
Gutter pairs	9.50	–
First day cover	–	4.00
Stamp cards	3.00	6.50

St. Edmundsbury Cathedral, Suffolk: stained glass window (2nd)
Church Floodlighting: St. Peter and St. Paul, Overstowey (1st)
St. Patrick Centre, Downpatrick: Latin gradual (45p)
Mystery Plays, York Minster: Chapter House ceiling (65p)

■ 2000, November 7. Spirit and Faith
Printed in gravure by De La Rue. The 2nd class has one phosphor band, other values two phosphor bands.

Set	3.50	3.50
Gutter pairs	9.50	–
First day cover	–	4.00
Stamp cards	3.00	6.50

(* The 2nd class and 1st class also appear in booklets.)

Ringing In The Millennium: church bells (2nd)
Year Of The Artist: eye (1st)
Canolfan Mileniwm, Cardiff: top of a harp (45p)
Talent & Skills 2000: figure in latticework (65p)

■ 2000, December 5. Sound and Vision
Printed in gravure by De La Rue. The 2nd class has one phosphor band, other values two phosphor bands.

Set	3.25	3.25
Gutter pairs	9.00	–
First day cover	–	4.00
Stamp cards	3.00	6.50

Children's face painting: flower (2nd)
Children's face painting: tiger (1st)
Children's face painting: owl (45p)
Children's face painting: butterfly (65p)

■ 2001, January 16. Rights of the Child
Des: Why Not Associates. Printed in gravure by De La Rue. The 2nd class has one phosphor band, other values two phosphor bands.

Set	3.00	3.00
Gutter pairs	7.50	–
First day cover	–	3.75
Stamp cards	3.25	6.50

Hallmark: 'Love' (1st)
Hallmark: 'Thanks' (1st)
Hallmark: 'ABC' (1st)
Hallmark: 'Welcome' (1st)
Hallmark: 'Cheers' (1st)

■ 2001, February 6. Occasions
Des: Springpoint Design. Printed in gravure by Enschedé.

Set	4.75	4.75
Gutter pairs	12.00	–
First day cover	–	5.50
Stamp cards	4.50	7.50

(* These designs were also used for Smilers sheets in 2001.)

Dog in bath (1st)
Dog and man on a bench (1st)
Dog at dog show (1st)
Cat in handbag (1st)
Cat on gate (1st)
Dog in car (1st)
Dog looking over fence (1st)
Cat watching bird (1st)
Cat in wash basin (1st)

■ 2001, February 13. Cats and Dogs
Des: Johnson Banks. Printed in gravure by Walsall. Self-adhesive. Issued as a sheetlet which could be folded to form a booklet, containing one of each of the ten designs.

Sheetlet	10.00	10.00
First day cover	–	9.50
Stamp cards	7.00	16.00

(* The ten designs, along with two 1st class definitives, also appear in a retail booklet issued on February 13, 2001.)

Quadrant of a barometer: rain (19p)
Quadrant of a barometer: fair (27p)
Quadrant of a barometer: stormy (45p)
Quadrant of a barometer: very dry (65p)

■ 2001, March 13. The Weather

Des: H. Brown and T. Meeuwissen. Printed in gravure by De La Rue. The 19p has one phosphor band, other values two phosphor bands.

Set	3.00	3.00
Gutter pairs	7.50	–
First day cover	–	3.50
Miniature sheet (one of each value)	7.00	7.00
Miniature sheet first day cover	–	8.00
Stamp cards	3.50	9.00

Vanguard class submarine (2nd)
Swiftsure class submarine (1st)
Unity class submarine (45p)
Holland class submarine (65p)

■ 2001, April 10. Centenary of Royal Navy Submarine Service

Des: D. Davis. Printed in gravure by Questa. Perf: 15x14. PVA gum. The 2nd class has one phosphor band, other values two phosphor bands.

Set	3.75	3.75
Gutter pairs	9.50	–
First day cover	–	4.00
Stamp cards	4.00	6.50

(* The four stamps also appear in the Unseen And Unheard prestige stamp book issued on October 22, 2001, perf: 15x15; price £10.00 mint or used. The 1st class design also appears in self-adhesive form in a retail booklet issued on April 17, 2001; price £35 mint or used. See also the issue of October 22.)

Leyland X2, B Type, Leyland Titan TD1, AEC Regent I (1st)
AEC Regent I, Daimler COG5, Guy Arab II, AEC Regent III (1st)
AEC Regent III, Bristol K, AEC Routemaster, Bristol Lodekka FSF (1st)
Bristol Lodekka FSF, Leyland PD3, Leyland Atlantean, Daimler Fleetline (1st)
Daimler Fleetline, MCW Metrobus, Leyland Olympian, Dennis Trident (1st)

■ 2001, May 15. 150th Anniversary of the Double–Decker Bus

Des: M. English. Printed in gravure by Questa. The illustrations extend into the sheet margins, and across the sheet, so that some of the illustrations span two stamps.

Set (se–tenant strip of five)	4.75	4.75
Gutter pairs	11.50	–
First day cover	–	5.00
Miniature sheet (one of each value)	7.50	7.50
Miniature sheet first day cover	–	8.50
Stamp cards	7.50	16.00

Toque hat by Pip Hackett(1st)
Butterfly hat by Dai Rees (E)
Top hat by Stephen Jones (45p)
Spiral hat by Philip Treacy (65p)

■ 2001, June 19. Fashion Hats

Des: Rose Design, from photographs by N. Knight. Printed in litho by Enschedé.

Set	3.50	3.50
Gutter pairs	9.00	–
First day cover	–	4.50
Stamp cards	3.50	6.50

Common frog (1st)
Great diving beetle (E)
Three-spined stickleback (45p)
Southern hawker dragonfly (65p)

■ 2001, July 10. Pond Life (Europa)
Des: J. Gibbs. Printed in gravure by De La Rue.

Set	3.75	3.75
Gutter pairs	9.00	–
First day cover	–	4.75
Stamp cards	3.50	6.50

Policeman (1st)
Mr Punch (1st)
Clown (1st)
Judy (1st)
Beadle (1st)
Crocodile (1st)

■ 2001, September 4. Punch and Judy Puppets
Des: K. Bernstein, from puppets made by Bryan Clarkez. Printed in gravure by Walsall. PVA gum. Perf: 14x15.

Set (se-tenant strip of six)	4.75	4.75
Gutter pairs	12.00	–
First day cover	–	5.50
Stamp cards	4.75	8.50

(* The Mr Punch and Judy designs also appear in self-adhesive form in a booklet issued on September 4, 2001, printed in gravure by Questa, perf: 14x15½; price £15 mint per pair.)

Carbon molecule, printed in litho and silk screen (2nd)
Globe, printed in litho and recess (1st)
Dove, printed in litho and embossing (E)
Crosses, printed in litho (40p)
'The Addressing of Cats' by T. S. Eliot, printed in litho (45p)
Boron molecule, printed in litho with hologram (65p)

■ 2001, October 2. Nobel Prizes
Des: P. Vermier, with engraving by Inge Madle (1st). Printed by Enschedé. The 2nd class has one phosphor band, other values a phosphor frame around the design.

Set	8.50	8.50
Gutter pairs	22.00	–
First day cover	–	5.50
Stamp cards	7.50	8.50

White Ensign (1st)
Union Flag (1st)
Jolly Roger (1st)
Flag of Chief of Defence Staff (1st)

■ 2001, October 22. Centenary of Royal Navy Submarine Service. Flags and Ensigns
Des: D. Davis. Printed in gravure by Questa. PVA gum.

Miniature sheet	4.00	4.00
First day cover	–	5.00
Stamp cards	7.00	14.00

(* The White Ensign and Jolly Roger designs also appear in self-adhesive form in a booklet issued on October 22, 2001; price £16 mint or used per pair. The Union Jack and White Ensign designs appear in Smilers sheets from 2005, and also appear in the Ian Fleming's James Bond prestige stamp book issued on January 8, 2008. See also the issue of April 10.)

Robins with snowman (2nd)
Robins on bird table (1st)
Robins skating on bird bath (E)
Robins with Christmas pudding hanging from tree (45p)
Robins in nest made of paper chains (65p)

■ 2001, November 6. Christmas. Robins

Des: A. Robins and H. Brown. Printed in gravure by De La Rue.
Self-adhesive.

Set	4.00	4.25
First day cover	–	4.50
Stamp cards	3.50	7.50

(* The 2nd and 1st class values also appear in booklets, and were
used for Smilers stamps in 2003 and 2005.)

'The Elephant's Child' (1st)
'How the Whale got his Throat' (1st)
'How the Camel got his Hump' (1st)
'How the Rhinoceros got his Skin' (1st)
'How the Leopard got his Spots' (1st)
'The Sing Song of Old Man Kangaroo' (1st)
'The Beginning of the Armadillos' (1st)
'The Crab that Played with the Sea' (1st)
'The Cat that Walked by Himself' (1st)
'The Butterfly that Stamped' (1st)

■ 2002, January 15. Centenary of the Just So Stories by Rudyard Kipling

Des: I. Cohen. Printed in gravure by Walsall. Self-adhesive.
Issued as a sheetlet which could be folded to form a booklet,
containing one of each of the ten designs.

Sheetlet	9.00	9.00
First day cover	–	7.00
Stamp cards	6.00	21.00

Queen Elizabeth II in 1952, by Dorothy Wilding (2nd)
Queen Elizabeth II in 1968, by Cecil Beaton (1st)
Queen Elizabeth II in 1978, by Lord Snowdon (E)
Queen Elizabeth II in 1984, by Yousef Karsh (45p)
Queen Elizabeth II in 1996, by Tim Graham (65p)

■ 2002, February 6. Golden Jubilee

Des: Kate Stephens. Printed in gravure by De La Rue. Wmk: 50
(sideways). The 2nd class has one phosphor band, other values
two phosphor bands.

Set	4.50	4.50
Gutter pairs	12.00	–
First day cover	–	4.50
Stamp cards	3.25	7.00

(* The stamps also appear in the Gracious Accession prestige
book, but with the Wmk upright; price £13 mint, £13 used.)

Wilding design of 1952–67 (2nd)
Wilding design of 1952–67 (1st)

■ 2002, February 6. Wilding definitives

Des: M. Farrar-Bell (2nd), Enid Marx (1st). Printed in gravure by
Enschedé. Wmk: 50. The 2nd class has one phosphor band, the
1st class two phosphor bands. Issued only in the £7.29 Gracious
Accession prestige stamp book. One pane had a tilted stamp,
resulting in a diagonal watermark.

2nd carmine-red	1.50	1.50
2nd carmine-red (Wmk diagonal)	2.50	2.50
1st green	1.25	1.25

Love (1st)
Rabbits, inscribed 'a new baby' (1st)
'Hello' written in sky (1st)
Bear pulling topiary tree in shape of house (1st)
Flowers inscribed 'best wishes' (1st)

■ 2002, March 5. Occasions

Des: I. Bilbey (Rabbits and Flowers), A. Kitching (Love), Hoop
Associates (Hello), G. Percy (Bear). Printed in litho by Questa.

Set	4.75	4.75
Gutter pairs	12.00	–
First day cover	–	4.50
Stamp cards	3.25	7.00

(* The Hello design also appears in self-adhesive form in a
booklet issued on March 4, 2003; price £3.50 mint or used. All
designs also appear in Smilers sheets.)

Studland Bay, Dorset (27p)
Luskentyre, South Harris (27p)
Cliffs of Dover, Kent (27p)
Padstow Harbour, Cornwall (27p)
Broadstairs, Kent (27p)
St Abb's Head, Berwickshire (27p)
Dunster Beach, Somerset (27p)
Newquay Beach, Cornwall (27p)
Portrush, County Antrim (27p)
Sand spit, Conwy, (27p)

■ 2002, March 19. British Coastlines

Des: R. Cooke. Printed in litho by Walsall.

Set (se–tenant block of ten)	4.75	5.00
Gutter pairs	13.00	–
First day cover	–	4.50
Stamp cards	5.00	13.50

Slack wire act (2nd)
Lion tamer (1st)
Trick tricyclists (E)
Krazy kar (45p)
Equestrienne (65p)

■ 2002, April 10. Circus (Europa)

Des: R. Fuller. Printed in gravure by Questa. The 2nd class has one phosphor band, other values two phosphor bands.

Set	3.75	3.75
Gutter pairs	10.00	–
First day cover	–	4.25
Stamp cards	3.25	7.50

Queen Mother: 20p design from the 1990 issue (1st)
Queen Mother: 29p design from the 1990 issue (E)
Queen Mother: 34p design from the 1990 issue (45p)
Queen Mother: 37p design from the 1990 issue (65p)

■ 2002, April 25. Queen Mother Memorial

Des: J. Gorham, as the issue of August 2, 1990, but with frames and Queen's head in black. Printed in gravure by De La Rue.

Set	3.75	3.75
Gutter pairs	10.00	–
First day cover	–	4.25

Airbus A340–600, 2002 (2nd)
Concorde, 1976 (1st)
Trident, 1964 (E)
VC10, 1964 (45p)
Comet, 1952 (65p)

■ 2002, May 2. Airliners

Des: Roundel. Printed in gravure by De La Rue. The 2nd class has one phosphor band, other values two phosphor bands.

Set	5.00	5.00
Gutter pairs	17.50	–
First day cover	–	4.25
Miniature sheet (one of each value)	8.00	8.00
Miniature sheet first day cover	–	6.00
Stamp cards	3.50	14.00

(* The 1st class design also appears in self-adhesive form in a booklet issued on May 2, 2002, printed in gravure; price £3.50 mint or used. It also appears in the British Design Classics prestige stamp book issued on January 13, 2009)

Lion with shield of St. George (1st)
Top left quarter of English flag with football (1st)
Top right quarter of English flag with football (1st)
Bottom left quarter of English flag with football (1st)
Bottom right quarter of English flag with football (1st)

■ 2002, May 21. Football World Cup, Japan and Korea

Des: Sedley Place (lion), H. Brown (flag). Printed in gravure by Walsall. The St. George design was issued in counter sheets, and all five designs in a miniature sheet.

1st (St. George design)	1.25	1.25
Gutter pair (St. George design)	3.00	–
First day cover	–	2.75
Miniature sheet	5.00	5.00
Miniature sheet first day cover		4.50
Stamp cards (set of six)	3.50	11.00

(* The 1st class designs showing the top left and top right of the flag also appear in self-adhesive form in a booklet issued on May 21, 2002; price £5.50 per pair. The 1st class design showing the bottom right of the flag also appears in Smilers sheets.)

Swimming (2nd)
Running (1st)
Cycling (E)
Long jump (47p)
Wheelchair racing (68p)

■ 2002, July 16. 17th Commonwealth Games, Manchester

Des: Madeleine Bennett. Printed in gravure by Enschedé. The 2nd class has one phosphor band, other values two phosphor bands.

Set	4.25	4.25
Gutter pairs	11.00	–
First day cover	–	4.50
Stamp cards	3.50	10.00

Tinkerbell (2nd)
Wendy, John and Michael Darling flying past Big Ben (1st)
Crocodile and the alarm clock (E)
Captain Hook (47p)
Peter Pan (68p)

■ 2002, August 20. Peter Pan

Des: Tutsells. Printed in gravure by De La Rue. The 2nd class has one phosphor band, other values two phosphor bands.

Set	4.25	4.25
Gutter pairs	11.00	–
First day cover	–	4.50
Stamp cards	5.00	8.00

Millennium Bridge, 2001 (2nd)
Tower Bridge, 1894 (1st)
Westminster Bridge, 1864 (E)
Blackfriars Bridge, 1800 (47p)
London Bridge, 1670 (68p)

■ 2002, September 10. Bridges of London

Des: Sarah Davies and Robert Maude. Printed in litho by Questa. The 2nd class has one phosphor band, other values two phosphor bands.

Set	6.50	4.50
Gutter pairs	17.00	–
First day cover	–	4.50
Stamp cards	4.00	10.00

(* The 1st class design also appears in self-adhesive form in a booklet issued on September 10, 2002, printed in gravure by Questa; price £3.50 mint or used.)

Planetary nebula in Aquila (1st)
Seyfert 2 galaxy in Pegasus (1st)
Planetary nebula in Norma (1st)
Seyfert 2 galaxy in Circinus (1st)

■ 2002, September 24. Astronomy

Des: Rose. Printed in gravure by Questa.

Miniature sheet	3.50	3.50
First day cover	–	4.50
Stamp cards	4.00	10.00

(* The miniature sheet also appears in a larger format in the Across The Universe prestige stamp book issued on September 21, 2002.)

Green pillar box, 1857 (2nd)
Horizontal-aperture pillar box, 1874 (1st)
Blue air mail box, 1934 (E)
Double-aperture pillar box, 1939 (47p)
Modern pillar box, 1980 (68p)

■ 2002, October 8. 150th Anniversary of the First Pillar Box

Des: Silk Pearce; engraved by C. Slania. Printed in recess and litho by Enschedé. The 2nd class has one phosphor band, other values two phosphor bands.

Set	4.50	4.50
Gutter pairs	12.00	–
First day cover	–	4.50
Stamp cards	4.00	7.50

Blue spruce (2nd)
Holly (1st)
Ivy (E)
Mistletoe (47p)
Pine cone (68p)

■ 2002, November 5. Christmas

Des: Rose. Printed in gravure by De La Rue. Self-adhesive. The 2nd class has one phosphor band, other values two phosphor bands.

Set	4.50	4.50
First day cover	–	4.50
Stamp cards	3.50	7.50

(* The 2nd and 1st class stamps also appear in booklets.)

The Wilding definitives collection I ~ 1952 - 1953

Wilding designs of 1952–67 (1p, 2p, 5p, 2nd, 1st, 33p, 37p, 47p, 50p)

■ 2002, December 5. 50th Anniversary of the Wilding Definitives (1st issue)

Des: Rose (based on the original designs of 1952). Printed in gravure by De La Rue. Wmk: 50. The 2nd class has one phosphor band, other values two phosphor bands.

Miniature sheet	5.00	5.00
First day cover	–	5.00
Stamp cards	5.00	15.50

(* The 47p value also appears in the Perfect Coronation prestige stamp book issued on June 2, 2003.)

Barn owl in flight, five different views (1st, 1st, 1st, 1st, 1st)
Kestrel in flight, five different views (1st, 1st, 1st, 1st, 1st)

■ 2003, January 14. Birds of Prey

Des: J. Gibbs, from photographs by S. Dalton. Printed in litho by Walsall.

Set (se-tenant block of ten)	8.50	8.50
Gutter pairs	22.00	–
First day cover	–	6.50
Stamp cards	5.50	15.00

Gold star, See me, Playtime (1st)
I 'love' U, XXXX, S.W.A.L.K. (1st)
Angel, Poppet, Little terror (1st)
Yes, No, Maybe (1st)
Oops! Sorry, Will try harder (1st)
I did it! You did it! We did it! (1st)

■ 2003, February 4. Occasions

Des: UNA, S. Wiegand and M. Exon. Printed in litho by Questa.

Set (se–tenant block of six)	5.50	5.50
Gutter pairs	21.00	
First day cover	–	5.00
Stamp cards	3.50	9.00

(* These designs also appear in Smilers sheets.)

Genome The End of the Beginning

The genetic jigsaw (2nd)
Ape looking at scientist behind bars (1st)
DNA snakes and ladders (E)
Animals dressed as scientists (47p)
Looking into a DNA crystal ball (68p)

■ 2003, February 25. 50th Anniversary of the Discovery of DNA

Des: William Murray Hamm and P. Brookes. Printed in litho by Enschedé. The 2nd class has one phosphor band, other values two phosphor bands.

Set	4.25	4.25
Gutter pairs	11.00	–
First day cover	–	5.00
Stamp cards	3.00	8.50

(* The 2nd and E designs also appear in the Microcosmos prestige stamp book issued on February 25, 2003.)

Red pepper (1st)
Strawberry (1st)
Potato (1st)
Apple (1st)
Pear (1st)
Orange (1st)
Tomato (1st)
Lemon (1st)
Brussels sprout (1st)
Aubergine (1st)

■ 2003, March 25. Fruit and Vegetables

Des: Johnson Banks. Printed in gravure by Walsall. Issued as a self-adhesive sheetlet containing one each of the ten designs.

Sheetlet	9.00	9.00
First day cover	–	7.00
Stamp cards	7.50	22.00

(* This sheetlet came with a pane of self-adhesive stickers, such as of eyes, ears and mouths, so that the fruit and vegetables could be customised to resemble faces. These designs also appear in Smilers sheets.)

Amy Johnson with biplane (2nd)
The 1953 Everest team in the Himalayas (1st)
Freya Stark in the Arabian desert (E)
Ernest Shackleton in the Antarctic (42p)
Francis Chichester with 'Gipsy Moth IV' (47p)
Robert Falcon Scott at the South Pole (68p)

■ 2003, April 29. Extreme Endeavours

Des: H. Brown. Printed in gravure by Questa. The 2nd class has one phosphor band, other values two phosphor bands. Perf: 15x14½.

Set	5.00	5.00
Gutter pairs	13.00	–
First day cover	–	5.00
Stamp cards	3.50	10.00

(* The 1st class design also appears, in self adhesive form, in a booklet issued on April 29, 2003, printed in gravure by De La Rue, Perf: 14½; price £3.50 mint, £3.50 used.)

The Wilding definitives collection II ~ 1953 - 1959

Wilding designs of 1952–67 (4p, 8p, 10p, 20p, 28p, 34p, E, 42p, 68p)

■ 2003, May 20. 50th Anniversary of the Wilding Definitives (2nd issue)

Des: Rose (based on the original designs of 1952). Printed in gravure by De La Rue. Wmk: 50. The 20p has one phosphor band, other values two phosphor bands.

Miniature sheet	5.00	5.50
First day cover	–	6.50

(* The 68p value also appears in the Perfect Coronation prestige stamp book issued on June 2, 2003.)

Coronation procession (1st)
Children reading poster (1st)
Queen seated in the Coronation Chair (1st)
Children producing royal montage (1st)
Queen in Coronation robes, by Cecil Beaton (1st)
Children racing during street party (1st)
Coronation Coach passing through Admiralty Arch (1st)
Children in fancy dress (1st)
Coronation Coach outside Buckingham Palace (1st)
Children at street party (1st)

■ 2003, June 2. 50th Anniversary of the Coronation

Des: Kate Stephens. Printed in gravure by De La Rue.

Set (se–tenant block of ten)	9.00	9.00
Gutter pairs	23.00	–
First day cover	–	6.50
Stamp cards	6.00	20.00

(* Eight of these designs also appear in the Perfect Coronation prestige stamp book issued on June 2, 2003.)

Photograph of Prince William by Brendan Beirne (28p)
Photograph of Prince William by Tim Graham (E)
Photograph of Prince William by Camera Press (47p)
Photograph of Prince William by Tim Graham (68p)

■ 2003, June 17. 21st Birthday of Prince William

Des: Madeleine Bennett. Printed in gravure by Walsall.

Set	6.00	5.50
Gutter pairs	15.00	–
First day cover	–	5.00
Stamp cards	4.50	20.00

Loch Assynt, Sutherland (2nd)
Ben More, Isle of Mull (1st)
Rothiemurchus, Cairngorms (E)
Dalveen Pass, Lower Hills (42p)
Glenfinnan Viaduct, Lochaber (47p)
Papa Little, Shetland Islands (68p)

■ 2003, July 15. A British Journey: Scotland

Des: Phelan Barker. Printed in gravure by De La Rue. The 2nd class has one phosphor band, other values two phosphor bands.

Set	4.50	4.50
Gutter pairs	12.00	–
First day cover	–	5.00
Stamp cards	3.50	9.50

(* The 1st class design also appears in self adhesive form in a booklet issued on July 15, 2003; price £3.00 mint or used.)

The Station (1st)
Black Swan (E)
The Cross Keys (42p)
The Mayflower (47p)
The Barley Sheaf (68p)

■ 2003, August 12. Pub Signs (Europa)

Des: Elmwood. Printed in gravure by De La Rue.

Set	5.00	4.50
Gutter pairs	12.50	–
First day cover	–	5.00
Stamp cards	3.50	7.50

(* The 1st class design also appears in the Letters By Night prestige stamp book issued on March 16, 2004.)

MECCANO
Constructor Biplane c 1931

Meccano constructor biplane, 1931 (1st)
Wells–Brimtoy clockwork double–decker bus, 1938 (E)
Hornby M1 clockwork locomotive, 1948 (42p)
Dinky Toys Ford Zephyr, 1956 (47p)
Mettoy friction–drive Eagle space ship, 1960 (68p)

■ 2003, September 18. Classic Transport Toys
Des: Trickett and Webb. Printed in gravure by Enschedé.

Set	4.75	4.75
Gutter pairs	12.00	–
First day cover	–	4.75
Miniature sheet (one of each value)	4.50	4.50
Miniature sheet first day cover	–	5.00
Stamp cards	3.50	13.50

(* The 1st class design also appears, in self–adhesive form, in a booklet issued on September 18, 2003, printed in gravure by De La Rue; price £3.25 mint or used.)

Coffin of Denytenamun, Egypt, c.900 BC (2nd)
Sculpture of Alexander the Great, Greece, c.200 BC (1st)
Anglo–Saxon helmet, Sutton Hoo, c.600 AD (E)
Sculpture of Parvati, India, c.1550 AD (42p)
Aztec mask of Xiuhtecuhtli, Mexico, c.1500 AD (47p)
Statue of Hoa Hakananai'a, Easter Island, c.1000 AD (68p)

■ 2003, October 7. 250th Anniversary of the British Museum
Des: Rose. Printed in gravure by Walsall. The 2nd class has one centre phosphor band, the 42p and 68p one phosphor band at right, other values two phosphor bands.

Set	5.50	5.50
Gutter pairs	14.00	–
First day cover	–	5.00
Stamp cards	3.75	9.50

Ice spiral (2nd)
Icicle star (1st)
Wall of ice blocks (E)
Ice ball (53p)
Ice hole (68p)
Snow pyramids (£1.12)

■ 2003, November 4. Christmas. Ice Sculptures
Des: D. Davis, from ice sculptures by Andy Goldsworthy. Printed in gravure by De La Rue. Self–adhesive. The 2nd class has one phosphor band, other values two phosphor bands.

Set	6.00	6.00
First day cover	–	5.00
Stamp cards	4.00	12.00

(* The 1st class and 2nd class designs also appear in booklets, and in Smilers sheets.)

England fans and England flag (1st)
England team huddled in a circle before the final (1st)
Rugby World Cup held aloft (68p)
England team members from the back after the final (68p)

■ 2003, December 19. England's Victory in the Rugby World Cup
Des: Why Not Associates. Printed in litho by Walsall.

Miniature sheet	10.00	10.00
First day cover	–	10.00

'Dolgoch' on the Rheilffordd Talyllyn Railway (20p)
CR 439 on the Bo'ness and Kinneil Railway (28p)
GCR 8K on the Grand Central Railway (E)
GWR Manor on the Severn Valley Railway (42p)
SR West Country on the Bluebell Railway (47p)
BR Standard on the Keighley and Worth Valley Railway (68p)

■ 2004, January 13. Classic Locomotives

Des: Roundel. Printed in litho by De La Rue. The 2nd class has one phosphor band, other values two phosphor bands.

Set	5.50	5.50
Gutter pairs	14.00	–
First day cover	–	6.00
Miniature sheet (one of each value)	6.00	6.00
Miniature sheet first day cover	–	15.00
Stamp cards	6.00	25.00

(* The 28p, E and 42p designs also appear in the Letters by Night prestige stamp book issued on March 16, 2004.)

Postman (1st)
Face (1st)
Duck (1st)
Baby (1st)
Aircraft (1st)

■ 2004, February 3. Occasions.

Des: S. Kambayashi. Printed in litho by De La Rue.

Set (se-tenant strip of five)	4.25	4.25
Gutter pairs	11.00	–
First day cover	–	4.50
Stamp cards	3.50	7.50

(* These designs also appear in Smilers sheets.)

J.R.R. TOLKIEN · THE LORD OF THE RINGS

Middle Earth (1st)
Forest of Lothlórien (1st)
The Fellowship of the Ring (1st)
Rivendell (1st)
The Hall at Bag End (1st)
Orthanc (1st)
Doors of Durin (1st)
Barad-dûr (1st)
Minas Tirith (1st)
Fangorn Forest (1st)

■ 2004, February 26. The Lord of The Rings by J. R. R. Tolkien

Des: HGV Design. Printed in litho by Walsall.

Set (se-tenant block of ten)	9.00	8.00
Gutter pairs	22.00	–
First day cover	–	8.50
Stamp cards	8.00	15.00

Ely Island, Lower Lough Erne (2nd)
Giant's Causeway, Antrim (1st)
Slemish, Antrim (E)
Banns Road, Mourne Mountains (42p)
Glenelly Valley, Sperrins (47p)
Islandmore, Strangford Lough (68p)

■ 2004, March 16. A British Journey: Northern Ireland

Des: Phelan Barker. Printed in gravure by Enschedé. The 2nd class has one phosphor band, other values two phosphor bands.

Set	4.50	5.50
Gutter pairs	12.00	–
First day cover	–	6.00
Stamp cards	3.50	9.50

(* The 28p design also appears in self-adhesive form in a booklet issued on March 16, 2004; price £3.00 mint or used.)

'Lace 1 (trial proof) 1968' by Sir Terry Frost (28p)
'Coccinelle' by Sonia Delaunay (57p)

2004, April 6. Centenary of the Entente Cordiale

Des: Rose. Printed in gravure by Walsall.

Set	1.75	1.75
Gutter pairs	4.50	–
Traffic light gutter pairs	11.00	–
First day cover	–	3.50
Stamp cards	3.00	4.00

(* This was a joint issue with La Poste of France.)

RMS 'Queen Mary 2', 2004 (1st)
SS 'Canberra', 1961 (E)
RMS 'Queen Mary', 1936 (42p)
RMS 'Mauretania', 1907 (47p)
SS 'City of New York', 1888 (57p)
PS 'Great Western', 1838 (68p)

2004, April 13. Ocean Liners

Des: J. Gibbs. Printed in gravure by De La Rue.

Set	5.00	5.00
Gutter pairs	12.50	–
First day cover	–	5.50
Miniature sheet (one of each value)	8.00	8.50
Miniature sheet first day cover	–	10.00
Stamp cards	4.00	16.50

(* The 1st class also appears in self-adhesive form, in a booklet issued on April 13, 2004; price £3.00 mint or used.)

Dianthus Allwoodii group (2nd)
Dahlia 'Garden Princess' (1st)
Clematis 'Arabella' (E)
Miltonia 'French Lake' (42p)
Lilium 'Lemon Pride' (47p)
Delphinium 'Clifford Sky' (68p)

2004, May 25. Bicentenary of the Royal Horticultural Society

Des: Rose. Printed in gravure by Enschedé. The 2nd class has one phosphor band, other values two phosphor bands.

Set	5.00	5.00
Gutter pairs	12.50	–
First day cover	–	5.00
Miniature sheet (one of each value)	7.50	7.50
Miniature sheet first day cover	–	7.50
Stamp cards	4.00	16.50

(* All values also appear in the Glory of the Garden prestige book of May 25, 2004, and the 1st class in Smilers sheets.)

Barmouth Bridge (2nd)
Hyddgen, Plynlimon (1st)
Brecon Beacons (40p)
Pen-pych, Rhondda Valley (43p)
Rhewl, Dee Valley (47p)
Marloes Sands, Pembrokeshire (68p)

2004, June 15. A British Journey: Wales (Europa)

Des: Phelan Barker. Printed in gravure by De La Rue. The 2nd class has one phosphor band, other values two phosphor bands.

Set	4.25	4.50
Gutter pairs	12.00	–
First day cover	–	5.50
Stamp cards	3.50	9.50

(* The 1st class design also appears in self-adhesive form in a booklet of June 15, 2004; price £3.00 mint or used.)

Penny Black and citation to Sir Rowland Hill (1st)
William Shipley, founder of the RSA (40p)
R, S and A as typewriter keys and shorthand notation (43p)
George Smart's brush for sweeping chimneys (47p)
Eric Gill's typeface (57p)
'Zero Waste' manifesto (68p)

2004, August 10. 250th Anniversary of the Royal Society of Arts

Des: D. Birdsall. Printed in litho by Walsall.

Set	6.25	6.25
Gutter pairs	15.00	–
First day cover	–	6.50
Stamp cards	3.50	9.50

Pine marten (1st)
Roe deer (1st)
Badger (1st)
Yellow-necked mouse (1st)
Wild cat (1st)
Red squirrel (1st)
Stoat (1st)
Natterer's bat (1st)
Mole (1st)
Fox (1st)

■ 2004, September 16. Woodland Animals
Des: Kate Stephens. Printed in gravure by Enschedé.

Set (se-tenant block of ten)	10.50	10.00
Gutter pairs	25.00	–
Traffic light gutter blocks	45.00	–
First day cover	–	10.00
Stamp cards	5.00	15.00

Scotland definitives (40p, 1st, 2nd, 1st, 40p)

■ 2004, October 5. Opening of the Scottish Parliament Building, Edinburgh
Des: H. Brown. Printed in gravure by De La Rue.

Miniature sheet	4.50	4.50
First day cover	–	5.00

Private McNamara, 5th Dragoon Guards (2nd)
Piper Muir, 42nd Regiment of Foot (1st)
Sergeant Major Edwards, Scots Fusilier Guards (40p)
Sergeant Powell, 1st Regiment of Foot Guards (57p)
Sergeant Major Poole, Royal Sappers and Miners (68p)
Sergeant Glasgow, Royal Artillery (£1.12)

■ 2004, October 12. The Crimean War
Des: Atelier Works, from period photographs. Printed in litho by Walsall. The 2nd class has one phosphor band, other values two phosphor bands.

Set	6.00	6.50
Gutter pairs	15.00	–
Traffic light gutter pairs	40.00	–
First day cover	–	7.50
Stamp cards	3.50	9.50

Father Christmas on roof (2nd)
Father Christmas welcoming the sunrise (1st)
Father Christmas battling against the wind (40p)
Father Christmas holding an umbrella (57p)
Father Christmas holding a torch (68p)
Father Christmas sheltering behind a chimney (£1.12)

■ 2004, November 2. Christmas
Des: R. Briggs. Printed in gravure by De La Rue. Counter stamps self-adhesive, miniature sheet gummed. The 2nd class has one phosphor band, other values two phosphor bands.

Set	6.00	5.75
First day cover	–	7.50
Miniature sheet (one of each value)	6.00	6.00
Miniature sheet first day cover	–	8.00
Stamp cards	4.50	15.00

(* The 1st class and 2nd class designs also appear in booklets, and in Smilers sheets.)

Emden geese (1st)
British saddleback pigs (1st)
Khaki Campbell ducks (1st)
Clydeside mare and foal (1st)
Dairy shorthorn cattle (1st)
Border collie dog (1st)
Light Sussex chickens (1st)
Suffolk sheep (1st)
Bagot goat (1st)
Norfolk black turkeys (1st)

■ 2005, January 11. Farm Animals

Des: Rose, from illustrations by C. Wormell. Printed in gravure by Enschedé.

Set (se-tenant block of ten)	9.00	9.00
Gutter pairs	23.00	–
Traffic light gutter blocks	35.00	–
First day cover	–	7.00
Stamp cards	5.50	15.50

Old Harry Rocks, Studland Bay, Dorset (2nd)
Wheal Coates, St Agnes, Cornwall (1st)
Start Point, Start Bay, Devon (40p)
Horton Down, Wiltshire (43p)
Chiselcombe, Exmoor, Devon (57p)
St James's Stone, Lundy Island (68p)

■ 2005, February 8. A British Journey: South–West England

Des: J. Phelan and L. Barker. Printed in gravure by De La Rue. The 2nd class has one phosphor band, other values two phosphor bands.

Set	4.75	4.75
Gutter pairs	12.50	–
First day cover	–	5.50
Stamp cards	3.75	9.50

Scene from 'Jane Eyre': Mr. Rochester (2nd)
Scene from 'Jane Eyre': come to me (1st)
Scene from 'Jane Eyre': in the comfort of her bonnet (40p)
Scene from 'Jane Eyre': La Ligne des Rats (57p)
Scene from 'Jane Eyre': refectory (68p)
Scene from 'Jane Eyre': inspection (£1.12)

■ 2005, February 24. 150th Anniversary of the Death of Charlotte Brontë

Des: P. Willberg, from illustrations by Paula Rego. Printed in litho by Walsall. The 2nd class has one phosphor band, other values two phosphor bands.

Set	6.00	6.00
Gutter pairs	15.00	–
Traffic light gutter blocks	45.00	–
First day cover	–	5.50
Miniature sheet (one of each value)	6.00	6.00
Miniature sheet first day cover	–	6.00
Stamp cards	4.00	15.00

(* All designs also appear in the Brontë Sisters prestige stamp book issued on February 24, 2005.)

Spinning coin trick (1st)
Rabbit and top hat trick (40p)
Knotted scarf trick (47p)
Card trick (68p)
Pyramids under fezzes trick (£1.12)

■ 2005, March 15. Centenary of the Magic Circle

Des: Tathem Design, from illustrations by G. Hardie. Printed in gravure by Walsall. Rubbing the 1st class stamp with a coin reveals either the head or tail of a coin; parts of the 47p and £1.12 designs fade temporarily when exposed to heat.

Set	5.75	5.75
Gutter pairs	15.00	–
First day cover	–	5.50
Stamp cards	3.50	7.50

(* The 1st class design also appears in Smilers sheets.)

Carrickfergus Castle (50p)
Caernarvon Castle (£1)
Edinburgh Castle (£1)
Windsor Castle (50p)

■ 2005, March 22. The Castles Definitives of 1955

Des: Sedley Place, based on designs of 1955–58 by Lynton Lamb but with new values. Printed by intaglio and litho by Enschedé.

Miniature sheet	4.75	5.00
First day cover	–	6.00
Stamp cards	7.00	15.00

(* The 50p design also appears in the First UK Aerial Post prestige stamp book issued on September 9, 2011.)

The couple at the Mey Games (30p, 30p)
The couple at Birkhall (68p, 68p)

■ 2005, April 8. The Wedding of Prince Charles and Camilla Parker Bowles

Des: Rose, from photographs by Christopher Furlong (30p) and Carolyn Robb (68p). Printed in litho by Enschedé.

Miniature sheet	3.75	3.75
First day cover	–	5.50

(* Whilst the miniature sheet and first day handstamps are dated April 8, the wedding took place on April 9.)

Hadrian's Wall, England (2nd)
Uluru Kata Tjuta National Park, Australia (2nd)
Stonehenge, England (1st)
Wet Tropics of Queensland, Australia (1st)
Blenheim Palace, England (47p)
Greater Blue Mountains, Australia (47p)
Heart of Neolithic Orkney, Scotland (68p)
Pumululu National Park, Australia (68p)

■ 2005, April 21. World Heritage Sites

Des: Jason Godfrey from photographs by Peter Marlow. Litho printed by Enschedé. The 2nd class has one phosphor band, other values two phosphor bands.

Set (four se-tenant pairs)	6.50	6.50
Gutter pairs	16.00	–
Traffic light gutter blocks	35.00	–
First day cover	–	5.50
Stamp cards	4.50	12.50

(* This was a joint issue with Australia Post.)

Ensign of the Scots Guards (2nd)
The Queen taking the salute, 1983 (1st)
Trumpeter of the Household Cavalry (42p)
Welsh Guardsmann (60p)
The Queen on horseback, 1972 (68p)
The Queen and Duke of Edinburgh in carriage, 2004 (£1.12)

■ 2005, June 7. Trooping the Colour

Des: Why Not Associates. Printed in litho by Walsall. The 2nd class has one phosphor band, other values two phosphor bands.

Set	6.00	6.00
Gutter pairs	16.00	–
First day cover	–	5.50
Miniature sheet (one of each value)	6.50	6.00
Miniature sheet first day cover	–	6.00
Stamp cards	4.25	17.50

Searchlights in a 'V' over St. Paul's Cathedral (1st)
Definitives (1st, 1st, 1st, 1st, 1st)

■ **2005, July 5. 60th Anniversary of the End of World War II**
Des: Jeffery Matthews, using the St. Paul's stamp designed by J. Gorham and originally issued on May 2, 1995. Printed in gravure by Enschedé.

Miniature sheet	6.00	6.00
First day cover	–	5.00

1991 **Norton F.1** road version of a race winner

Norton F1, 1991 (1st)
BSA Rocket 3, 1969 (40p)
Vincent Black Shadow, 1949 (42p)
Triumph Speed Twin, 1938 (47p)
Brough Superior, 1930 (60p)
Royal Enfield, 1914 (68p)

■ **2005, July 19. Motorcycles**
Des: Atelier Works, with illustrations by Michael English. Printed in litho by Walsall.

Set	5.00	5.00
Gutter pairs	12.50	–
First day cover	–	5.50
Stamp cards	4.25	9.50

Athletes (1st, 1st, 1st, 1st, 1st, 1st)

■ **2005, August 12. London 2012**
Des: one of each of the five designs issued on July 9, 1996, plus a second of one design, but with Olympic rings omitted and new values. Printed in litho by Walsall.

Miniature sheet	6.00	6.00
First day cover	–	5.50

Woman eating rice (2nd)
Woman drinking tea (1st)
Boy eating sushi (42p)
Woman eating pasta (47p)
Woman eating chips (60p)
Boy eating apple (68p)

■ **2005, August 23. Changing Tastes in Britain (Europa)**
Des: Rose, with illustrations by Catell Ronca. Printed in gravure by Enschedé. The 2nd class has one phosphor band, other values two phosphor bands.

Set	5.00	5.00
Gutter pairs	12.50	–
First day cover	–	5.50
Stamp cards	4.25	10.00

'Inspector Morse' (2nd)
'Emmerdale' (1st)
'Rising Damp' (42p)
'The Avengers' (47p)
'The South Bank Show' (60p)
'Who Wants To Be A Millionaire?' (68p)

■ **2005, September 15. Classic ITV Programmes**
Des: Kate Stephens. Printed in litho by De La Rue. The 2nd class has one phosphor band, other values two phosphor bands.

Set	5.00	5.00
Gutter pairs	12.00	–
First day cover	–	5.50
Stamp cards	4.25	9.00

(* The 1st class design also appears in Smilers sheets.)

Gazania splendens (1st)
Hello (1st)
Love (1st)
Union flag (1st)
Teddy bear (1st)
Robin looking through pillar box slit (1st)

2005, October 4. Smilers
Printed by litho by Walsall. Self-adhesive. Issued in booklets containing one of each of the six designs.

Booklet (without PiP information)	10.00	–
Booklet (with PiP information)	9.00	–
First day cover	–	8.00

(* These designs also appear in Smilers sheets. For the same designs with elliptical perforations, see the issues of January 16, 2007, and February 28, 2008.)

THE ASHES ENGLAND WINNERS 2005

England team celebrating with Ashes trophy (1st)
Kevin Pietersen, Michael Vaughan and Andrew Flintoff (1st)
Michael Vaughan batting (68p)
Action from Second Test at Edgbaston (68p)

2005, October 6. The Ashes
Des: Why Not Associates. Printed in litho by Cartor.

Miniature sheet	4.00	4.00
First day cover	–	4.50

HMS 'Entreprenante' and HMS 'Belle Isle' (1st)
Nelson wounded on HMS 'Victory' (1st)
HMS 'Entreprenante' and burning French ship 'Achille' (42p)
HMS 'Pickle' and cutter (42p)
British fleet attacking in two columns (68p)
Franco-Spanish fleet putting to sea from Cadiz (68p)

2005, October 18. Bicentenary of the Battle of Trafalgar
Des: Dick Davis from a painting by William Heath. Printed in litho by Walsall. Issued in se-tenant pairs.

Set (three se-tenant pairs)	5.25	5.50
Gutter pairs	14.00	–
First day cover	–	5.50
Stamp cards	5.50	25.00
Miniature sheet (one of each value)	5.00	5.25
Miniature sheet first day cover	–	6.00

(* The stamps also appear in the Battle of Trafalgar prestige stamp book issued on October 18, 2005.)

Madonna and Child painting, Haitian (2nd)
Madonna and Child painting, European (1st)
Madonna and Child painting, European (42p)
Madonna and Child painting, North American Indian (60p)
Madonna and Child painting, Indian (68p)
Madonna and Child painting, Australian Aboriginal (£1.12)

2005, November 1. Christmas
Des: Irene von Treskow. Printed in gravure by De La Rue. Counter stamps self-adhesive, miniature sheet gummed. The 2nd class has one phosphor band, other values two phosphor bands.

Set	6.00	6.00
First day cover	–	5.50
Miniature sheet (one of each value)	5.50	6.00
Miniature sheet first day cover	–	5.50
Stamp cards	5.00	18.50

(* The 2nd class and 1st class stamps also appear in booklets.)

'The Tale of Mr Jeremy Fisher' by Beatrix Potter(2nd)
'Kipper' by Mick Inkpen (2nd)
'The Enormous Crocodile' by Roald Dahl (1st)
'More About Paddington' by Michael Bond (1st)
'Comic Adventures of Boots' by Satoshi Kitamura (42p)
'Alice's Adventures in Wonderland' by Lewis Carroll (42p)
'The Very Hungry Caterpillar' by Eric Carle (68p)
'Maisy's ABC' by Lucy Cousins (68p)

2006. January 10. Animal Tales
Des: Rose. Printed in litho by De La Rue. Issued in se-tenant pairs.

Set (four se-tenant pairs)	6.25	6.50
Gutter pairs	15.00	–
Traffic light gutter blocks	55.00	–
First day cover	–	7.50
Stamp cards	5.00	12.50

Carding Mill Valley, Shropshire (1st)
Beachy Head, Sussex (1st)
St. Paul's Cathedral, London (1st)
Brancaster, Norfolk (1st)
Derwent Edge, Peak District (1st)
Robin Hood's Bay, Yorkshire (1st)
Buttermere, Lake District (1st)
Chipping Campden, Cotswolds (1st)
St Boniface Down, Isle of Wight (1st)
Chamberlain Square, Birmingham (1st)

■ 2006, February 7. A British Journey: England
Des: Phelan Parker Design Consultants. Printed in gravure by De La Rue.

Set (se-tenant block of 10)	10.00	10.00
Gutter pairs	25.00	–
First day cover	–	10.00
Stamp cards	4.50	15.00

Royal Albert Bridge (1st)
Box Tunnel (40p)
Paddington Station (42p)
PSS 'Great Britain' (47p)
Clifton Suspension Bridge (60p)
Maidenhead Bridge (68p)

■ 2006, February 23. Bicentenary of the Birth of Isambard Kingdom Brunel
Des: Hat-Trick Design. Printed in litho by Enschedé.

Set	5.00	5.00
Gutter pairs	12.50	–
First day cover	–	6.00
Miniature sheet (one of each value)	5.50	5.50
Miniature sheet first day cover	–	6.00
Stamp cards	5.50	25.00

Wales definitives (68p, 1st, 2nd, 1st, 68p)

■ 2006, March 1. Opening of the Welsh Assembly Building, Cardiff
Des: Silk Pearce. Printed in gravure by De La Rue.

Miniature sheet	4.50	4.50
First day cover	–	5.00

Sabre-tooth cat (1st)
Giant deer (42p)
Woolly rhino (47p)
Woolly mammoth (68p)
Cave bear (£1.12)

■ 2006, March 21. Ice Age Animals
Des: Howard Brown from illustrations by Andrew Davidson. Printed in litho by Enschedé.

Set	5.25	5.25
Gutter pairs	14.00	–
First day cover	–	6.00
Stamp cards	4.00	8.50

The Queen in 1972 (2nd)
The Queen in 1985 (2nd)
The Queen in 1931 with Duchess of York (1st)
The Queen in 2001 (1st)
The Queen in 1951 (44p)
The Queen in 1960 (44p)
The Queen in 1940 (72p)
The Queen in 1951 with Duke of Edinburgh (72p)

■ 2006, April 18. The Queen's 80th Birthday
Des: Sedley Place. Printed in gravure by Enschedé.

Set	6.50	6.50
Gutter pairs	17.00	–
First day cover	–	7.50
Stamp cards	5.00	16.00

England (1st)
Italy (42p)
Argentina (44p)
Germany (50p)
France (64p)
Brazil (72p)

■ 2006, June 6. World Cup Winners
Des: Getty Images. Printed in litho by Walsall.

Set	5.50	5.50
Gutter pairs	14.00	–
First day cover	–	6.50
Stamp cards	4.50	11.00

30 St Mary Axe, London (1st)
Maggie's Centre, Dundee (42p)
Selfridges, Birmingham (44p)
Downland Gridshell, Chichester (50p)
An Turas, Isle of Tiree (64p)
The Deep, Hull (72p)

■ 2006, June 20. Modern Architecture
Des: Roundel. Printed in gravure by Walsall.

Set	5.75	5.75
Gutter pairs	14.00	–
First day cover	–	6.25
Stamp cards	4.00	10.00

T. S. Eliot by Patrick Heron (1st)
Sir Winston Churchill by Walter Sickert (1st)
Sir Joshua Reynolds, self-portrait (1st)
Emmeline Pankhurst by Georgina Brackenbury (1st)
Virginia Woolf by George Beresford (1st)
Sir Walter Scott by Sir Francis Chantry (1st)
Mary Seacole by Albert Challen (1st)
William Shakespeare by John Taylor (1st)
Dame Cicely Saunders by Catherine Goodman (1st)
Charles Darwin by John Collier (1st)

■ 2006, July 18. 150th Anniversary of the National Portrait Gallery
Des: Peter Willberg. Printed in gravure by De La Rue.

Set (se-tenant block of 10)	8.50	8.50
Gutter pairs	22.00	–
Traffic light gutter blocks	35.00	–
First day cover	–	9.00
Stamp cards	5.00	15.00

Definitive (£3)

■ 2006, August 31. The Year of the Three Kings
Des: Together Design. Printed in gravure by De La Rue.

Miniature sheet	5.75	5.75
First day cover	–	6.50

(* The border illustrates the 1d stamps of the reigns of King George V, King Edward VIII and King George VI.)

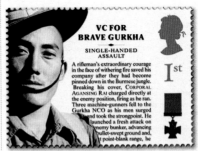

Corporal Agansing Rai (1st)
Boy Seaman First Class Jack Cornwell (1st)
Midshipman Charles Lucas (64p)
Captain Noel Chavasse (64p)
Captain Alan Ball (72p)
Captain Charles Upham (72p)

2006, September 21. Victoria Cross
Des: Atelier Works. Printed in litho by Enschedé.

Set	6.00	6.00
Gutter pairs	15.00	–
First day cover	–	7.00
Miniature sheet (one of each value, plus the 20p Victoria Cross from September 1990)	6.00	6.00
Miniature sheet first day cover	–	8.00
Press sheet	75.00	–
Stamp cards	5.00	20.00

Asian sitar and dancer (1st)
Caribbean base guitar and drum (42p)
Irish fiddle and harp (50p)
Black American saxophone and blues guitar (72p)
Latin American maracas and salsa dancers (£1.19)

2006, October 3. Sounds of Britain (Europa)
Des: CDT. Printed in litho by Cartor

Set	5.00	5.75
Gutter pairs	15.00	–
Traffic light gutter blocks	30.00	–
First day cover	–	6.00
Stamp cards	4.00	8.00

New baby (1st)
Best wishes (1st)
Thank you (1st)
Balloons (1st)
Firework (1st)
Champagne, flowers and butterflies (1st)

2006, October 17. Smilers
Des: NB Studio. Printed by litho by Walsall. Self-adhesive. Issued in booklets containing one of each of the six designs.

Booklet	8.00	–
First day cover	–	12.50
Stamp cards	7.00	21.00

(*These designs also appear in Smilers sheets. For the same designs with elliptical perforations, see the issue of February 28, 2008.)

Poppies on barbed wire (1st)
Country definitives (72p, 72p, 72p, 72p)

2006, November 6. Lest We Forget (issue 1)
Des: Hat-Trick Design. Printed in gravure by De La Rue.

Miniature sheet	6.00	6.00
First day cover	–	6.50

(* The 1st class design also appears in Smilers sheets.)

Snowman (2nd, 2nd Large)
Father Christmas sitting on chimney (1st, 1st Large)
Reindeer (72p)
Christmas tree (£1.19)

2006, November 7. Christmas
Des: CDT. Printed in litho by De La Rue. Counter sheets self-adhesive, miniature sheet gummed. The 2nd class has one phosphor band, other values two phosphor bands.

Set	6.50	6.50
Gutter pairs	17.00	–
First day cover	–	7.00
Miniature sheet (one of each value)	6.50	6.50
Miniature sheet first day cover	–	6.75
Stamp cards	4.50	18.00

(* The 2nd class and 1st class also appear in booklets.)

Scotland definitive (1st)
Scottish flag (1st)
St Andrew (72p)
Edinburgh Castle (72p)

2006, November 30. Celebrating Scotland
Des: P. Crowther and C. Melinsky, Silk Pearce. Printed in gravure by De La Rue.

Miniature sheet	4.50	4.50
First day cover	–	5.00
Stamp cards	4.00	15.00

(* The 1st class Scottish Flag design also appears in the Football Heroes prestige stamp book of 2013 and the Classic Locomotives of the UK prestige stamp book of 2014.)

Album cover: 'With The Beatles' (1st)
Album cover: 'Sgt Pepper's Lonely Hearts Club Band' (1st)
Album cover: 'Help!' (64p)
Album cover: 'Abbey Road' (64p)
Album cover: 'Revolver' (72p)
Album cover: 'Let It Be' (72p)

■ 2007, January 9. The Beatles
Des: Johnson Banks, from album sleeve covers. Printed in gravure by Walsall. Self-adhesive, in freeform shape. Available in horizontal pairs.

Set	6.75	7.00
First day cover	–	5.50
Stamp cards (set & miniature sheet)	6.25	25.00

Guitar and badge (1st)
Yellow Submarine lunch box and key rings (1st)
'Love Me Do' vinyl record (1st)
Tea tray and badges (1st)

■ 2007, January 9. The Beatles
Des: Johnson Banks. Printed in litho by Walsall.

Miniature sheet	4.00	4.00
First day cover	–	5.50

■ 2007, January 16. Smilers
Printed in litho by Walsall. Self-adhesive. Design as the 'Love' 1st class stamp of October 4, 2005, but with elliptical perforations along vertical sides. Issued in booklets of six.

Booklet	15.00	–

(* This design also appears in a booklet issued on January 15, 2008, and in Smilers sheets.)

Moon jellyfish (1st)
Common starfish (1st)
Beadlet anemone (1st)
Bass (1st)
Thornback ray (1st)
Lesser octopus (1st)
Common mussels (1st)
Grey seal (1st)
Shore crab (1st)
Common sun star (1st)

■ 2007, February 1. Sea Life
Des: A. Ross. Printed in litho by Cartor.

Set (se-tenant block of ten)	10.00	10.00
Gutter pairs	25.00	–
First day cover	–	5.50
Stamp cards	5.00	16.00

Saturn nebula C55 (1st)
Eskimo nebula C39 (1st)
Cat's Eye nebula C6 (50p)
Helix nebula C63 (50p)
Flaming Star nebula C31 (72p)
The Spindle galaxy C53 (72p)

■ 2007, February 13. The Sky at Night
Des: D. Davis. Printed in gravure by Walsall. Self-adhesive. Available in horizontal pairs. Stamps have description of designs on the backing paper.

Set	7.25	7.25
First day cover	–	5.50
Stamp cards	5.25	13.00

Bridge building: iron bridge in Thomas Telford's imagination (1st)
Railways: locomotive billowing track as steam (1st)
Communications: Britain and Australia close on map (64p)
Television: reporter on camera and viewer with screen (64p)
E-mail and internet: world wide web as globe (72p)
Space tourism: couple carrying suitcases on the Moon (72p)

■ 2007, March 1. World of Invention
Des: P. Willberg. Printed in gravure by De La Rue. Counter stamps self-adhesive, with description of designs on the backing paper. Miniature sheet gummed.

Set	8.50	8.50
Gutter pairs	22.00	–
First day cover	–	5.50
Miniature sheet (one of each value)	8.00	8.00
Miniature sheet first day cover	–	11.00
Stamp cards	4.25	22.00

(* All designs also appear, gummed, in the World of Invention prestige stamp book issued on March 1, 2007.)

William Wilberforce and abolitionist poster (1st)
Olaudah Equiano and map of slave trade routes (1st)
Granville Sharp and slave ship (50p)
Thomas Clarkson and diagram of slave ship (50p)
Hannah More and title page of 'The Sorrows of Yamba' (72p)
Ignatius Sancho and business card (72p)

■ 2007, March 22. Bicentenary of the Abolition of the Slave Trade
Des: Howard Brown. Printed in litho by Cartor. Issued in se-tenant pairs.

Set	6.00	6.00
Gutter pairs	15.50	–
Traffic light gutter blocks	45.00	–
First day cover	–	5.50
Stamp cards	4.00	13.00

England definitive (1st)
English flag (1st)
St. George (78p)
Houses of Parliament (78p)

■ 2007, April 23. Celebrating England
Des: P. Crowther and C. Melinsky, Silk Pearce. Printed in gravure by De La Rue.

Miniature sheet	5.50	5.50
First day cover	–	5.00
Stamp cards	3.75	14.00

(* The 1st class English Flag design also appears in the Football Heroes prestige stamp book of 2013 and the Classic Locomotives of the UK prestige stamp book of 2014.)

Ice cream cone (1st)
Sand castle (46p)
Merry-go-round (48p)
Beach huts (54p)
Deckchairs (69p)
Donkeys (78p)

■ 2007, May 15. Beside the Seaside
Des: Phelan Barker Design Consultants. Printed in gravure by De La Rue.

Set	6.00	6.00
Gutter pairs	15.00	–
First day cover	–	5.50
Stamp cards	4.00	11.00

(* The 1st class design also appears, as a self-adhesive, in a booklet issued on May 13, 2008: price £2.00 mint.)

Lion with shield of St. George (1st)
England definitives (2nd, 2nd, 78p, 78p)

■ 2007, May 17. Opening of the New Wembley Stadium, London
Des: Roundel. Printed in gravure by De La Rue.

Miniature sheet	5.25	5.25
First day cover	–	5.50

(* The 1st class design was previously issued on May 21, 2002, with an inscription, and also appears in Smilers sheets.)

Arnold Machin (1st)
4d Machin olive sepia–brown (1st)
Definitive (£1 bluish–violet)
Definitive (£1 ruby)

2007, June 5. 40th Anniversary of the Machin Definitives

Des: J. Matthews and Together Design. Printed in gravure by De La Rue.

Miniature sheet	5.50	5.50
Press sheet	75.00	–
First day cover	–	5.50
Stamp cards	4.25	16.00

(* The 1st Arnold Machin design also appears in a generic Smilers sheet. The two 1st class designs also appear in The Making of a Masterpiece prestige stamp book.)

'Harry Potter and the Philosopher's Stone' (1st)
'Harry Potter and the Chamber of Secrets' (1st)
'Harry Potter and the Prisoner of Azkaban' (1st)
'Harry Potter and the Goblet of Fire' (1st)
'Harry Potter and the Order of the Phoenix' (1st)
'Harry Potter and the Half–Blood Prince' (1st)
'Harry Potter and the Deathly Hallows' (1st)

2007, July 17. Harry Potter

Des: True North, from book covers. Printed in litho by Walsall.

Set	6.50	6.50
Gutter pairs	17.00	–
Traffic light gutter pairs	35.00	–
First day cover	–	5.50
Stamp cards	11.00	42.00

Symbol of Gryffindor house (1st)
Symbol of Hufflepuff house (1st)
Crest of Hogwarts School (1st)
Symbol of Ravenclaw house (1st)
Symbol of Slytherin house (1st)

2007, July 17. Harry Potter

Des: True North. Printed in litho by Walsall.

Miniature sheet	6.50	6.50
First day cover	–	5.50

(* These designs also appear in a generic Smilers sheet.)

Stirling Moss and Vanwall 2.5L, 1957 (1st)
Graham Hill and BRM P57, 1962 (1st)
Jim Clark and Lotus–Climax 25, 1963 (54p)
Jackie Stewart and Tyrrell–Cosworth 006, 1973 (54p)
James Hunt and McLaren–Cosworth M23, 1976 (78p)
Nigel Mansell and Williams–Honda FW11, 1986 (78p)

2007, July 3. Grand Prix

Des: True North, from photographs by James Callaghan. Printed in litho by Cartor.

Set	6.50	6.50
Gutter pairs	17.00	–
First day cover	–	5.50
Stamp cards	5.00	11.00

Scout looking at the Moon (1st)
Scouts conquering a mountain (46p)
Scout planting a tree (48p)
Scout learning archery (54p)
Scout piloting a glider (69p)
Scouts from many nations (78p)

■ 2007, July 26. Centenary of Scouting (Europa)
Des: The Workroom. Printed in litho by Enschedé.

Set	5.50	6.00
Gutter pairs	14.00	–
First day cover	–	5.50
Stamp cards	4.50	11.00

(* These designs were also issued as a set of six stamped postcards, imprinted with either the 1st class or 54p on the address side: price £7.50 mint.)

White-tailed eagle (1st)
Bearded tit (1st)
Red kite (1st)
Cirl bunting (1st)
Marsh harrier (1st)
Avocet (1st)
Bittern (1st)
Dartford warbler (1st)
Corncrake (1st)
Peregrine (1st)

■ 2007, September 4. Endangered Species. Birds
Des: Kate Stephens. Printed in litho by De La Rue. Issued in a se-tenant block.

Set (se-tenant block of ten)	9.00	9.00
Gutter pairs	23.00	–
First day cover	–	5.50
Stamp cards	5.00	16.00

NCO, British Military Police, 1999 (1st)
Tank Commander, 5th Royal Tank Regiment, 1944 (1st)
Observer, Royal Field Artillery, 1917 (1st)
Rifleman, 95th Rifles, 1813 (78p)
Grenadier, Royal Regiment of Foot of Ireland, 1704 (78p)
Trooper, Earl of Oxford's Horse, 1661 (78p)

■ 2007, September 20. British Army Uniforms
Des: Atelier Works and Graham Turner. Printed in litho by Enschedé. Issued in se-tenant strips of three.

Set (two se-tenant strips of three)	5.75	5.75
Gutter pairs	14.00	–
Traffic light gutter pairs	35.00	–
First day cover	–	5.50
Stamp cards	4.25	11.00

(* All six stamps also appear in the British Army Uniforms prestige stamp book issued on September 20, 2007. The 1st class Observer stamp also appears in the Great War 2015 prestige stamp book.)

The Queen and Prince Philip in 2006 (1st)
The Queen and Prince Philip in 1997 (1st)
The Queen and Prince Philip in 1980 (54p)
The Queen and Prince Philip in 1969 (54p)
The Queen and Prince Philip in 1961 (78p)
The Queen and Prince Philip in 1947 (78p)

■ 2007, October 16. Royal Diamond Wedding Anniversary
Des: Pentagram. Printed in gravure by Walsall. Issued in se-tenant pairs.

Set (three se-tenant pairs)	5.75	5.75
Gutter pairs	15.00	–
First day cover	–	5.50
Stamp cards	6.00	28.00

Photographs of the royal family (1st, 1st, 69p, 78p)

■ 2007, October 16. Royal Diamond Wedding Anniversary
Des: Pentagram. Printed in gravure by Walsall. Self-adhesive. The reverse of the sheet shows photographs of the royal couple leading up to their marriage.

Miniature sheet	5.50	5.50
Press sheet	60.00	–
First day cover	–	5.50

Peace: angel playing trumpet (2nd, 2nd Large)
Goodwill: angel playing lute (1st, 1st Large)
Joy: angel playing flute (78p)
Glory: angel playing tambourine (£1.24)

■ 2007, November 6. Christmas. Angels

Des: Rose, with illustrations by Marco Ventura. Printed in gravure by De La Rue. Counter stamps self-adhesive, miniature sheet gummed.

Set	8.00	8.00
Gutter pairs	20.00	–
First day cover	–	6.50
Miniature sheet (one of each value)	8.00	8.00
Miniature sheet first day cover	–	6.50
Stamp cards	5.00	17.50

(* The 2nd class and 1st class designs also appear in booklets, and the 2nd, 1st and 78p in Smilers sheets.)

'Madonna & Child' by William Dyce (2nd)
'The Madonna of Humility' by Lippo di Dalmasio (1st)

■ 2007, November 6. Christmas. Madonna and Child

Des: Peter Willberg, from paintings. Printed in gravure by De La Rue. Self-adhesive.

Set	1.50	1.50
Gutter pairs	5.00	–
First day cover	–	5.50

(* These stamps were re-issued at Christmas in 2008–2012.)

Soldiers in poppy (1st)
Country definitives (78p, 78p, 78p, 78p)

■ 2007, November 8. Lest We Forget (issue 2)

Des: Hat-Trick Design. Printed in gravure by De La Rue.

Miniature sheet	7.50	7.50
First day cover	–	8.50

(* The 1st class design also appears in a Smilers generic sheet.)

Book covers of 'Casino Royale' (1st)
Book covers of 'Dr No' (1st)
Book covers of 'Goldfinger' (54p)
Book covers of 'Diamonds Are Forever' (54p)
Book covers of 'For Your Eyes Only' (78p)
Book covers of 'From Russia With Love' (78p)

■ 2008, January 8. Centenary of the Birth of Ian Fleming.
James Bond Books

Des: A2. Prined in litho by De La Rue.

Set	6.00	6.00
Gutter pairs	15.00	–
First day cover	–	7.00
Miniature sheet	9.00	9.00
Miniature sheet first day cover	–	10.00
Press sheet	75.00	–
Stamp cards (set and miniature sheet)	7.00	25.00

(* These stamps also appear in the Ian Fleming's James Bond prestige stamp book, issued on January 8, 2008.)

Assistance dog with letter (1st)
Mountain rescue dog (46p)
Police dog (48p)
Customs dog (54p)
Sheepdog (69p)
Guide dog (78p)

■ 2008, February 5. Working Dogs

Des: Redpath Design. Printed in litho by Cartor.

Set	5.50	5.50
Gutter pairs	14.00	–
First day cover	–	6.50
Stamp cards	5.00	14.00

King Henry IV, 1399-1413 (1st)
King Henry V, 1413-22 (1st)
King Henry VI, 1422-61 and 1470-71 (54p)
King Edward IV, 1461-70 and 1471-83 (54p)
King Edward V, 1483 (69p)
King Richard III, 1483-85 (69p)

■ **2008, February 28. Kings and Queens. Houses of Lancaster and York**
Des: Ian Chilvers, Atelier Works. Printed in litho by Walsall.

Set	5.25	5.50
Gutter pairs	14.00	–
Traffic light gutter blocks	35.00	–
First day cover	–	5.50
Stamp cards	6.00	26.00

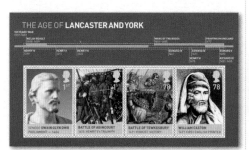

Owain Glyndwr's parliament, 1404 (1st)
Battle of Agincourt, 1415 (1st)
Battle of Tewkesbury, 1471 (78p)
William Caxton, first English printer, 1477 (78p)

■ **2008, February 28. The Age of Lancaster and York**
Des: Ian Chilvers. Printed in litho by Walsall.

Miniature sheet	3.75	3.75
First day cover	–	5.25
Press sheet	90.00	–

■ **2008, February 28. Smilers**
Printed in litho by Walsall. Self-adhesive. As designs of Hello, Gazania splendens and Union flag 1st class of October 4, 2005, and Champagne, flowers and butterfly, Firework and New baby 1st class of October 17, 2006, but with elliptical perforations on vertical sides. Issued in booklets of six.

Booklet	30.00	30.00
First day cover	–	30.00

(* These designs also appear in Smilers sheets.)

Carrickfergus Castle (1st)
Giant's Causeway (1st)
St Patrick (78p)
Queen's Bridge, Belfast (78p)

■ **2008, March 11. Celebrating Northern Ireland**
Des: Silk Pearce (sheet) and David Lyons, Clare Melinsky, Tony Pleavin and Ric Ergenbright (stamps). Printed in litho by De La Rue.

Miniature sheet	5.00	5.00
First day cover	–	5.00
Stamp cards	3.75	15.00

Lifeboat at Barra (1st)
Lifeboat and dinghy at Appledore (46p)
Helicopter rescue at Portland (48p)
Lifeboat at St Ives (54p)
Rescue helicopter at Lee-on-Solent (69p)
Lifeboat at Dinbych-y-Pysgod, Tenby (78p)

■ **2008, March 13. Rescue at Sea**
Des: Hat Trick Design. Printed in litho by Walsall. 'Dot' and 'dash' shaped perforations at top and bottom.

Set	5.50	5.50
Gutter pairs	14.00	–
First day cover	–	7.00
Stamp cards	4.25	13.00

Adonis blue butterfly (1st)
Southern damselfly (1st)
Red-barded ant (1st)
Barberry carpet moth (1st)
Stag beetle (1st)
Hazel pot beetle (1st)
Field cricket (1st)
Silver-spotted skipper (1st)
Purbeck mason wasp (1st)
Noble chafer beetle (1st)

■ **2008, April 15. Endangered Species. Insects**
Des: Andrew Ross. Printed in litho by De La Rue. Issued in se-tenant blocks of ten.

Set	8.50	8.50
Gutter pairs	20.00	–
First day cover	–	9.00
Stamp cards	6.50	22.00

Lichfield Cathedral (1st)
Belfast Cathedral (48p)
Gloucester Cathedral (50p)
St. Davids Cathedral (56p)
Westminster Cathedral (72p)
St. Magnus Cathedral, Kirkwall, Orkney (81p)

■ **2008, May 13. Cathedrals**
Des: Howard Brown. Printed in litho by Enschedé.

Set	7.50	7.50
Gutter pairs	18.00	–
Traffic light gutter pairs	35.00	–
First day cover	–	7.50
Stamp cards	6.00	27.50

Composite view inside St Paul's Cathedral (1st, 1st, 81p, 81p)

■ **2008, May 13. 300th Anniversary of St. Paul's Cathedral**
Des: Howard Brown. Printed in litho by Enschedé.

Miniature sheet	6.00	6.00
First day cover	–	6.50
Press sheet	70.00	–

Poster promoting 'Carry On Sergeant' (1st)
Poster promoting 'Dracula' (48p)
Poster promoting 'Carry on Cleo' (50p)
Poster promoting 'The Curse of Frankenstein' (56p)
Poster promoting 'Carry On Screaming' (72p)
Poster promoting 'The Mummy' (81p)

■ **2008, June 10. Classic Carry On and Hammer Films**
Des: Elmwood Design Group, from film posters. Printed in litho by Walsall.

Set	5.75	5.75
Gutter pairs	14.00	–
First day cover	–	6.50
Postcard and stamp set	40.00	–
Stamp cards	4.75	14.00

(*The postcard and stamp set comprised six cards showing the stamp designs against a brick background, together with a folder containing three 1st class and three 56p values.)

Red Arrows aerobatic display, 2006 (1st)
RAF Falcons parachute display, 2006 (48p)
Spectators watching the Red Arrows, 2006 (50p)
Avro Vulcan prototypes and Avro 707S, 1953 (56p)
Parachutist Robert Wyndham and Avro 504, 1933 (72p)
Hendon air race, 1912 (81p)

■ 2008, July 17. Air Displays
Des: Roundel. Printed in litho by Cartor.

Set	6.50	6.50
Gutter pairs	15.00	–
First day cover	–	7.00
Stamp cards	4.50	14.00

(*The 1st class design also appears in the Pilot To Plane: RAF Uniforms prestige stamp book of September 18, 2008, and in Smilers sheets.)

National Stadium, Beijing (1st)
London Eye (1st)
Tower of London (1st)
Corner Tower the Forbidden City, Beijing (1st)

■ 2008, August 22. Handover of the Olympic Flag from Beijing to London
Des: Why Not Associates. Printed in litho by Walsall, with the Olympic rings in a silk screen varnish.

Miniature sheet	5.00	5.00
First day cover	–	5.50
Stamp cards	5.00	15.00

Drum Major, RAF Central Band, 2007 (1st)
Helicopter rescue winchman, 1984 (1st)
Hawker Hunter pilot, 1951 (1st)
Lancaster air gunner, 1944 (81p)
WAAF plotter, 1940 (81p)
Pilot, 1918 (81p)

■ 2008, September 18. RAF Uniforms
Des: Quentin Newark of Atelier Works and Graham Turner. Printed in litho by Walsall. Issued in se-tenant strips of three.

Set	6.00	6.00
Gutter pairs	15.00	–
Traffic light gutter pairs	27.50	–
First day cover	–	6.50
Stamp cards	4.50	14.00

(* All designs also appear in the Pilot To Plane: RAF Uniforms prestige stamp book issued on September 18, 2008.)

Northern Ireland 3d design, 1958 (1st)
Northern Ireland 6d design, 1958 (1st)
Northern Ireland 1s 3d design, 1958 (1st)
Scotland 3d design, 1958 (1st)
Scotland 6d design, 1958 (1st)
Scotland 1s 3d design, 1958 (1st)
Wales 3d design, 1958 (1st)
Wales 6d design, 1958 (1st)
Wales 1s 3d design, 1958 (1st)

■ 2008, September 29. 50th Anniversary of the Country Definitives
As the 1958 regional stamps of Northern Ireland, Scotland and Wales, with new values. Printed in gravure by De La Rue.

Miniature sheet	9.00	9.00
Press sheet	80.00	–
First day cover	–	9.00
Stamp cards	11.00	35.00

(* All designs also appear in the Heraldry and Symbol prestige stamp book issued on September 29, 2008.)

Millicent Garrett Fawcett: votes for women (1st)
Elizabeth Garrett Anderson: women's health (48p)
Marie Stopes: family planning (50p)
Eleanor Rathbone: family allowance (56p)
Claudia Jones: civil rights (72p)
Barbara Castle: equal pay for women (81p)

■ 2008, October 14. Women of Distinction
Des: Together Design. Printed in gravure by Walsall.

Set	5.75	5.75
Gutter pairs	15.00	–
First day cover	–	7.00
Stamp cards	4.50	14.00

The Ugly Sisters from 'Cinderella' (2nd, 2nd Large)
The Genie from 'Aladdin' (1st, 1st Large)
Captain Hook from 'Peter Pan' (50p)
The Wicked Queen from 'Snow White' (81p)

■ 2008, November 4. Christmas. Pantomime
Des: Steve Haskins, using photographs by Peter Thorpe.
Printed in gravure by De La Rue. Counter stamps self–adhesive, miniature sheet gummed.

Set	6.50	6.50
Gutter pairs	16.00	–
First day cover	–	7.00
Miniature sheet (one of each value)	6.50	6.50
Miniature sheet first day cover	–	7.50
Stamp cards	4.25	19.00

(* The 1st class and 2nd class designs also appear in booklets, and the 2nd, 1st and 81p designs in Smilers sheets.)

Soldier's face in poppy (1st)
Country definitives (81p, 81p, 81p, 81p)

■ 2008, November 6. Lest We Forget (issue 3)
Des: Hat-Trick Design. Printed in litho by De La Rue.

Miniature sheet	7.00	7.00
First day cover	–	8.00

(* The 1st class design also appears in a Smilers generic sheet.)

■ 2008, November 6. Lest We Forget
The Poppy designs of November 6, 2006, November 8, 2007, and November 6, 2008, but in se–tenant strips in counter sheets. Printed in litho by De La Rue.

Set (se–tenant strip of three)	4.00	4.00
Gutter pairs	10.00	–
Traffic light gutter pairs	17.00	–
First day cover	–	4.00
Stamp cards (3 stamps, 3 miniature sheets)	10.00	27.00

London Underground Map
Designed by Harry Beck

Supermarine Spitfire by R. J. Mitchell (1st)
Mini skirt by Mary Quant (1st)
Mini by Sir Alec Issigonis (1st)
Anglepoise lamp by George Carwardine (1st)
Concorde by BAC and Aerospatiale (1st)
K2 telephone kiosk by Sir Giles Gilbert Scott (1st)
Polypropylene chair by Robin Day (1st)
Penguin book cover by Edward Young (1st)
London Underground map by Harry Beck (1st)
Routemaster bus by A.A.M. Durrant (1st)

■ 2009, January 13. British Design Classics

Des: HGV Design. Printed in litho by Cartor. Issued in se-tenant blocks of 10.

Set	9.00	9.00
Gutter pairs	23.00	–
First day cover	–	10.00
Postcards and stamp set	15.00	–
Stamp cards	6.50	22.00

(* The postcard and stamp set comprises 10 cards reproducing the stamp designs against a Union Flag background, and a set of the stamps. All designs also appear in the British Design Classics prestige stamp book issued on January 13, 2009. The Routemaster, Telephone Kiosk, Mini, Concorde, Spitfire and Mini Skirt designs also appear in self-adhesive form in booklets; price £3.00 each mint. The Mini and Concorde designs also appear in Smilers generic sheets.)

'A Man's a Man for a' That' (1st)
Portrait of Burns by Alexander Nasmyth (1st)
Scotland definitives (2nd, 1st, 50p, 81p)

■ 2009, January 22. 250th Anniversary of the Birth of Robert Burns

Des: Tayburn. Printed in gravure by Enschedé.

Miniature sheet	5.25	5.50
First day cover	–	6.00
Press sheet	90.00	–
Stamp cards	3.25	12.50

Charles Darwin (1st)
Marine iguana (48p)
Finches (50p)
Atoll (56p)
Bee orchid (72p)
Orang-utan (81p)

■ 2009, February 12. Bicentenary of the Birth of Charles Darwin

Des: Hat-Trick Design. Printed in gravure by De La Rue. Self-adhesive, in freeform shape to resemble jigsaw pieces.

Set	7.00	7.25
Gutter pairs	17.00	–
First day cover	–	8.00
Stamp cards	7.00	28.00

(* The stamps also appear in the Charles Darwin prestige stamp book issued on February 12, 2009, but with PVA gum.)

Flightless cormorant and Galapagos Islands (1st)
Giant tortoise, cactus finch and Galapagos Islands (1st)
Marine iguana and Galapagos Islands (81p)
Floreana mockingbird and Galapagos Islands (81p)

■ 2009, February 12. Bicentenary of the Birth of Charles Darwin. The Galapagos Islands

Des: Howard Brown. Printed in litho by De La Rue.

Miniature sheet	5.00	5.00
First day cover	–	5.50
Press sheet	55.00	–

(* The miniature sheet also appears as a pane in the Charles Darwin prestige stamp book issued on February 12, 2009.)

Welsh flag (1st)
Wales definitive (1st)
St. David (81p)
National Assembly for Wales, Cardiff (81p)

■ 2009, February 26. Celebrating Wales

Des: Silk Pearce. Printed in litho by De La Rue.

Miniature sheet	4.50	4.75
First day cover	–	6.00
Stamp cards	3.75	15.00

(* The 1st class Welsh Flag design also appears in the Football Heroes prestige stamp book of 2013 and the Classic Locomotive of the UK prestige stamp book of 2014.)

Matthew Boulton, manufacturing (1st)
James Watt, engineering (1st)
Richard Arkwright, textiles (50p)
Josiah Wedgwood, ceramics (50p)
George Stephenson, railways (56p)
Henry Maudslay, machine–making (56p)
James Brindley, canal engineering (72p)
John McAdam, road building (72p)

■ 2009, March 17. Pioneers of the Industrial Revolution

Des: Webb & Webb. Printed in litho by Enschedé. Issued in se–tenant pairs.

Set	8.50	9.50
Gutter pairs	22.00	–
First day cover	–	10.00
Stamp cards	5.00	20.00

King Henry VII, 1485–1509 (1st)
King Henry VIII, 1509–47 (1st)
King Edward VI, 1547–53 (62p)
Lady Jane Grey, 1553 (62p)
Queen Mary 1, 1553–58 (81p)
Queen Elizabeth I, 1558–1603 (81p)

■ 2009, April 21. Kings and Queens. The House of Tudor

Des: Ian Chilvers, Atelier Works. Printed in litho by Walsall.

Set	7.00	7.25
Gutter pairs	17.50	–
Traffic light gutter pairs	32.50	–
First day cover	–	8.00
Stamp cards	6.50	30.00

'Mary Rose' warship, 1510 (1st)
Field of Cloth of Gold conference, 1520 (1st)
Royal Exchange commercial centre, 1565 (90p)
Francis Drake's circumnavigation, 1580 (90p)

■ 2009, April 21. The Age of the Tudors

Des: Ian Chilvers, Atelier Works. Printed in litho by Walsall.

Miniature sheet	4.75	5.00
First day cover	–	6.00
Press sheet	90.00	–

Round–headed leek (1st)
Floating water–plantain (1st)
Lady's slipper orchid (1st)
Dwarf milkwort (1st)
Marsh saxifrage (1st)
Downy woundwort (1st)
Upright spurge (1st)
Plymouth pear (1st)
Sea knotgrass (1st)
Deptford pink (1st)

■ 2009, May 19. Endangered Species: Plants

Des: Studio Dempsey. Printed in litho by Cartor. Issued in se–tenant blocks of ten.

Set	10.00	10.00
Gutter pairs	25.00	–
First day cover	–	11.00
Stamp cards	8.00	35.00

Palm House, Kew Gardens (1st)
Millennium Seed Bank, Wakehurst Place (1st)
Pagoda, Kew Gardens (90p)
Sackler Crossing, Kew Gardens (90p)

■ 2009, May 19. 250th Anniversary of the Royal Botanic Gardens, Kew

Des: Studio Dempsey. Printed in litho by Cartor.

Miniature sheet	4.75	5.00
First day cover	–	6.00
Maximum cards set	12.00	–
Press sheet	70.00	–

(* The maximum cards set comprises four postcards, each with one stamp from the miniature sheet affixed and cancelled on the picture side, sold in a pack with a mint miniature sheet.)

Dragons (1st)
Unicorns (1st)
Giants (62p)
Pixies (62p)
Mermaids (90p)
Fairies (90p)

■ 2009, June 16. Mythical Creatures

Des: Morgan Radcliffe, from illustrations by Dave McKean. Printed in gravure by De La Rue.

Set	8.00	8.00
Gutter pairs	20.00	–
First day cover	–	8.00
Stamp cards	4.50	17.00

George V type B wall box, 1933, at Cookham Rise (1st)
Edward VII Ludlow box, 1901, at Bodiam post office (56p)
Victorian lamp box, 1896, at Hythe (81p)
Elizabeth II type A wall box, 1962, at Slaithwaite sorting office (90p)

■ 2009, August 18. Post Boxes

Des: Elmwood Design Group, from photographs by Peter Marlow. Printed in litho by Cartor.

Miniature sheet	8.00	6.50
First day cover	–	6.50
Press sheet	70.00	–
Stamp cards	4.00	17.00

(* All designs also appear in the Treasures of the Archive prestige stamp book of August 18, 2009, and the 1st class design in a Smilers generic sheet.)

Firefighting (1st)
Chemical fire (54p)
Emergency rescue (56p)
Flood rescue (62p)
Search and rescue (81p)
Fire safety (90p)

■ 2009, September 1. Fire and Rescue Services

Des: Rose. Printed in gravure by De La Rue.

Set	7.00	7.50
Gutter pairs	17.50	–
First day cover	–	8.00
Stamp cards	4.25	17.00

Flight Deck Officer, 2009 (1st)
Captain, 1941 (1st)
Second Officer WRNS, 1918 (1st)
Able Seaman, 1880 (90p)
Royal Marine, 1805 (90p)
Admiral, 1795 (90p)

■ 2009, September 17. Royal Navy Uniforms

Des: Atelier Works, with illustrations by Graham Turner. Printed in litho by Cartor. Issued in se-tenant strips of three.

Set	9.00	9.25
Gutter pairs	23.00	–
Traffic light gutter pairs	32.50	–
First day cover	–	10.00
Stamp cards	4.25	17.00

(* All designs also appear in the Royal Navy Uniforms prestige stamp book issued on September 17, 2009.)

Sir Matt Busby 1909–1994
Footballer and football manager

Fred Perry, tennis player (1st)
Henry Purcell, composer (1st)
Sir Matt Busby, football manager (1st)
William Gladstone, statesman (1st)
Mary Wollstonecraft, pioneering feminist (1st)
Sir Arthur Conan Doyle, author (1st)
Donald Campbell, water speed record breaker (1st)
Judy Fryd, founder of Mencap (1st)
Samuel Johnston, lexicographer (1st)
Sir Martin Ryle, radio astronomer (1st)

■ 2009, October 8. Eminent Britons

Des: Together Design. Printed in litho by Cartor. Issued in strips of five se-tenant designs, in two different sheets.

Set	11.00	11.00
Gutter pairs	28.00	–
First day cover	–	11.00
Stamp cards	6.50	26.00

Canoe slalom (1st)
Paralympic archery (1st)
Track athletics (1st)
Aquatics (1st)
Paralympic boccia (1st)
Judo (1st)
Paralympic equestrianism (1st)
Badminton (1st)
Weightlifting (1st)
Basketball (1st)

■ 2009, October 22. London 2012 Olympic and Paralympic Games (issue 1)

Des: John Royle (Canoe), George Hardie (Archery), Nathalie Guinamard (Athletics), Julian Opie (Aquatics), David Doyle (Boccia), Paul Slater (Judo), Andrew Davidson (Equestrian), David Holmes (Badminton), Guy Billout (Weightlifting), Huntley Muir (Basketball), Studio David Hillman (set). Printed in litho by Cartor. Issued in strips of five se-tenant designs in two different sheets.

Set	11.00	11.00
Gutter pairs	28.00	–
First day cover	–	11.00
Postcard and stamp set (Athletics)	9.00	–
Postcard and stamp set (Badminton)	9.00	–
Postcard and stamp set (Equestrian)	9.00	–
Postcard and stamp set (Judo)	9.00	–
Stamp cards	7.00	26.00

(* All values also appear in a commemorative sheet. The Judo, Archery, Track Athletics and Basketball designs also appear as self-adhesives in booklets; price £2.00 each mint.)

Angel by William Morris (2nd, 2nd large)
Madonna & Child by Henry Holiday (1st, 1st Large)
Joseph by Henry Holiday (56p)
Wise Man by Sir Edward Burne-Jones (90p)
Shepherd by Henry Holiday (£1.35)

■ 2009, November 3. Christmas

Des: Andrew Ross, from stained glass windows. Printed in gravure by De La Rue. Counter sheets self-adhesive, miniature sheet gummed.

Set	9.00	9.25
Gutter pairs	23.00	–
First day cover	–	10.00
Miniature sheet (one of each value)	9.50	9.25
Miniature sheet first day cover	–	10.00
Stamp cards	5.00	27.50

(* The 1st and 2nd class designs also appear in booklets, and the 2nd, 1st, 56p and 90p designs in Smilers sheets.)

'The Division Bell' by Pink Floyd, 1994 (1st)
'A Rush of Blood to the Head' by Coldplay, 2002 (1st)
'Parklife' by Blur, 1994 (1st)
'Power, Corruption and Lies' by New Order, 1983 (1st)
'Let It Bleed' by The Rolling Stones, 1969 (1st)
'London Calling' by The Clash, 1979 (1st)
'Tubular Bells' by Mike Oldfield 1973 (1st)
'IV' by Led Zepplin, 1971 (1st)
'Screamadelica' by Primal Scream, 1991 (1st)
'The Rise & Fall of Ziggy Stardust' by David Bowie, 1972 (1st)

■ 2010, January 7. Classic Album Covers

Des: Studio Dempsey. Counter sheets printed in gravure by De La Rue, self-adhesive in freeform shape, in strips of five in two different sheets. Miniature sheet printed in litho by Cartor, gummed.

Set	11.00	11.00
Gutter pairs	28.00	–
First day cover	–	12.00
Miniature sheet (one of each value)	25.00	25.00
Miniature sheet first day cover	–	30.00
Stamp cards	10.00	26.00

(* The litho-printed stamps also appear in the Classic Album Covers prestige stamp book. A souvenir sheet bearing 10 of the Division Bell designs was issued on March 6, 2010, but was not available from post offices; price £6.50)

Aircraft (1st)
Sports car (1st)
Seal with crown (1st)
Birthday cake with 'Happy birthday' message (1st)
Bird with envelope (Europe up to 20g)
Steam locomotive (1st)
Ocean liner (1st)
Poppies on barbed wire (1st)
Wrapped present (1st)
Aircraft with 'Hello' message (Worldwide up to 20g)

■ 2010, January 26. Stamps for Smilers and Business Customised Sheets

Des: Andrew Davidson (Aircraft, Sports car, Steam locomotive, Ocean liner), Hat-Trick (Seal, Poppies), Annabel Wright (Cake, Present) and Lucy Davey (Europe, Worldwide). Printed in litho by Cartor.

Miniature sheet	12.00	12.00
First day cover	–	11.00
Stamp cards	10.00	35.00

(* These designs were issued primarily for use in Smilers sheets, where they are self-adhesive. The Poppies design was also issued in self-adhesive counter sheets in 2012.)

Rainbows and activities (1st)
Brownies and activities (56p)
Guides and activities (81p)
Senior Section and activities (90p)

■ 2010, February 2. Centenary of Girlguiding

Des: Together Design. Printed in litho by Cartor.

Miniature sheet	5.50	5.50
First day cover	–	6.00
Stamp cards	3.50	22.00

Robert Boyle, chemistry (1st)
Isaac Newton, optics (1st)
Benjamin Franklin, electricity (1st)
Edward Jenner, vaccination (1st)
Charles Babbage, computing (1st)
Alfred Russel Wallace, evolution (1st)
Joseph Lister, antiseptic surgery (1st)
Ernest Rutherford, atomic structure (1st)
Dorothy Hodgkin, crystallography (1st)
Nicholas Shackleton, earth science (1st)

■ **2010, February 25. 350th Anniversary of The Royal Society**
Des: Hat-Trick Design. Printed in litho by Cartor. Issued in se-tenant blocks of ten.

Set (se-tenant block of 10)	12.00	12.00
Gutter pairs	30.00	–
First day cover	–	12.00
Stamp cards	6.25	25.00

(* All designs also appear in The Royal Society prestige stamp book.)

Pixie, mastiff cross (1st)
Button, cat (1st)
Herbie, mongrel (1st)
Mr Tumnus, cat (1st)
Tafka, border collie (1st)
Boris, bulldog cross (1st)
Casey, lurcher (1st)
Tigger, cat (1st)
Leonard, Jack Russell cross (1st)
Tia, terrior cross (1st)

■ **2010, March 11. 150th Anniversary of Battersea Dogs & Cats Home**
Des: CDT Design Ltd. Printed in litho by Cartor. Issued in se-tenant blocks of ten.

Set (se-tenant block of 10)	11.00	11.00
Gutter pairs	28.00	–
First day cover	–	12.00
Stamp cards	6.25	25.00

King James I of Scotland, 1406–37 (1st)
King James II of Scotland, 1437–60 (1st)
King James III of Scotland, 1460–88 (1st)
King James IV of Scotland, 1488–1513 (62p)
King James V of Scotland, 1513–42 (62p)
Mary Queen of Scots, 1542–67 (81p)
King James VI of Scotland, 1567–1625 (81p)

■ **2010, March 23. Kings and Queens. The House of Stewart**
Des: Atelier Works. Printed in litho by Cartor.

Set	7.50	7.50
Gutter pairs	19.00	–
Traffic light gutter pairs	35.00	–
First day cover	–	8.00
Stamp cards	7.00	35.00

St. Andrews University, 1413 (1st)
College of Surgeons, 1505 (1st)
Court of Session, 1532 (81p)
John Knox and the Reformation, 1559 (81p)

■ **2010, March 23. The Age of the Stewarts**
Des: Atelier Works. Printed in litho by Cartor.

Miniature sheet	5.50	5.50
First day cover	–	6.00
Press sheet	75.00	–

Humpback whale (1st)
Wildcat (1st)
Brown long-eared bat (1st)
Polecat (1st)
Sperm whale (1st)
Water vole (1st)
Greater horseshoe bat (1st)
Otter (1st)
Dormouse (1st)
Hedgehog (1st)

■ 2010, April 13. Endangered Species. Mammals

Des: Jason Godfrey. Printed in litho by Cartor. Issued in se-tenant blocks of ten.

Set	11.00	11.00
Gutter pairs	28.00	–
First day cover	–	12.00
Stamp cards	6.25	25.00

(* The Otter and Hedgehog designs also appear in self-adhesive form in booklets; price £3.50 each mint or used.)

Machin portrait of Queen Elizabeth II and Mackennal portrait of King George V (1st)
Mackennal and Downey portraits of King George V (£1)

■ 2010, May 6. London 2010 Festival of Stamps. Centenary of the Accession of King George V

Des: Sedley Place. Printed in litho by Cartor. 1st class design printed in sheets; 1st and £1 designs issued in miniature sheets.

1st class	2.00	2.00
Gutter pair (1st class)	5.00	–
First day cover	–	4.00
Miniature sheet	4.00	4.00
Miniature sheet first day cover	–	4.50
Press sheet	45.00	–

(* These stamps also appear in the King George V prestige stamp book. The miniature sheet was also issued on May 8, 2010, with an additional overprint in the border reading 'BUSINESS DESIGN

CENTRE, LONDON, 8–15 May 2010'; price £11.00 mint, £13.00 on first day cover. Stamp cards showing the stamps and miniature sheets of this issue were included in the issue of May 8.)

1924 British Empire Exhibition 1d stamp (1st)
1924 British Empire Exhibition 1½d stamp (1st)
1913–34 'Seahorses' £1 definitive (£1)
1913–34 'Seahorses' 10/– definitive (£1)

■ 2010, May 8. London 2010 Festival of Stamps. The King's Stamps

Des: Sedley Place. Printed in intaglio and litho by Enschedé.

Miniature sheet	6.25	6.25
First day cover	–	6.50
Press sheet	40.00	–
Stamp cards (issues of May 6 and May 8)	6.00	28.00

(* All designs also appear in the King George V prestige stamp book.)

Winston Churchill (1st)
Land girls (1st)
Home Guard (60p)
Evacuees (60p)
Air raid wardens (67p)
Women in factories (67p)
Royal broadcast, 1940 (97p)
Fire service (97p)

■ 2010, May 13. Britain Alone

Des: Why Not Associates. Printed in litho by Cartor.

Set	10.00	10.00
Gutter pairs	25.00	–
First day cover	–	9.00
Stamp cards	8.00	37.50

(* All designs also appear in the Britain Alone prestige stamp book.)

Evacuation of British soldiers from Dunkirk (1st)
Vessels involved in 'Operation Dynamo' (60p)
British soldiers on board a Royal Navy destroyer (88p)
Two boats from the Dunkirk evacuation (97p)

■ 2010, May 13. 70th Anniversary of the Evacuation of Dunkirk
Des: Why Not Associates. Printed in litho by Cartor.

Miniature sheet	6.50	6.50
First day cover	–	8.00

(* All designs also appear in the Britain Alone prestige stamp book.)

King James I, 1603–25 (1st)
King Charles I, 1625–49 (1st)
King Charles II, 1660–85 (60p)
King James II, 1685–88 (60p)
King William III, 1689–1702 (67p)
Queen Mary II, 1689–94 (67p)
Queen Anne, 1702–14 (88p)

■ 2010, June 15. Kings and Queens. The House of Stuart
Des: Atelier Works. Printed in litho by Cartor.

Set	7.25	7.50
Gutter pairs	18.00	–
Traffic light gutter pairs	35.00	–
First day cover	–	8.50
Stamp cards	7.00	35.00

William Harvey and discovery of blood circulation, 1628 (1st)
Battle of Naseby, 1645 (60p)
John Milton and 'Paradise Lost', 1667 (88p)
John Vanbrugh and Castle Howard, 1712 (97p)

■ 2010, June 15. The Age of the Stuarts
Des: Atelier Works. Printed in litho by Cartor.

Miniature sheet	5.50	5.50
First day cover	–	5.75
Press sheet	85.00	–

Paralympic rowing (1st)
Shooting (1st)
Modern pentathlon (1st)
Taekwondo (1st)
Cycling (1st)
Paralympic table tennis (1st)
Hockey (1st)
Football (1st)
Paralympic goalball (1st)
Boxing (1st)

■ 2010, July 27. London 2012 Olympic and Paralympic Games (issue 2)
Des: Marian Hill (Rowing), David Hillman (Shooting), Katherine Baxter (Modern pentathlon), James Fryer (Taekwondo), Matthew Dennis (Cycling), Michael Craig-Martin (Table tennis), Darren Hopes (Hockey), Alex Williamson (Football), Tobatron (Goalball), Stephen Ledwidge (Boxing), Studio David Hillman (set). Printed in litho by Cartor. Issued in se-tenant strips of five in two different sheets.

Set	13.00	13.00
Gutter pairs	33.00	–
First day cover	–	13.00
Postcard and stamp set (Boxing)	9.00	–
Postcard and stamp set (Rowing)	9.00	–
Stamp cards	8.00	25.00

(* All values also appear in a commemorative sheet. The Rowing, Table Tennis, Football and Cycling designs also appear in self-adhesive from in booklets; price £2.00 each mint or used.)

LMS: Coronation Class locomotive (1st)
BR: Class 9F locomotive (1st)
GWR: King Class locomotive (67p)
LNER: Class A1 locomotive (67p)
SR: King Arthur Class locomotive (97p)
LMS: NCC Class WT locomotive (97p)

■ **2010, August 19. Great British Railways**
Des: Delaney Design Consultants. Printed in gravure by De La Rue.

Set	8.50	8.50
Gutter pairs	22.00	–
First day cover	–	9.00
Stamp cards	4.50	17.50

Heart-regulating beta-blockers, 1962 (1st)
Discovery of antibiotic properties of penicillin, 1928 (58p)
Total hip replacement, 1962 (60p)
Artificial lens implant surgery, 1949 (67p)
Proof of malaria transmission by mosquitoes, 1897 (88p)
Computed tomography scanning, 1971 (97p)

■ **2010, September 16. Medical Breakthroughs**
Des: Howard Brown. Printed in litho by Cartor.

Set	8.50	8.50
Gutter pairs	22.00	–
First day cover	–	9.00
Stamp cards	4.00	17.50

(* The Beta–Blockers design also appears in self-adhesive form in booklets; price £2.00 mint or used.)

Winnie-the-Pooh and Christopher Robin

Winnie–the–Pooh, Piglet and Christopher Robin (1st)
Winnie–the–Pooh and Piglet (58p)
Winnie–the–Pooh and Rabbit (60p)
Winnie–the–Pooh and Eeyore (67p)
Winnie–the–Pooh and Friends (88p)
Winnie–the–Pooh and Tigger (97p)

■ **2010, October 12. Winnie-the-Pooh (Europa)**
Des: Magpie Studio, from the illustrations of E. H. Shepard. Printed in litho by Cartor.

Set	8.50	8.50
Gutter pairs	22.00	–
First day cover	–	9.00
Stamp cards	9.00	36.00

Winnie-the-Pooh and Christopher Robin (1st)
Christopher Robin reads to Winnie-the-Pooh (60p)
Winnie-the-Pooh and Christopher Robin set sail (88p)
Christopher Robin pulls on his wellingtons (97p)

■ **2010, October 12. Winnie-the-Pooh**
Des: Magpie Studio, from the illustrations of E. H. Shepard. Printed in litho by Cartor.

Miniature sheet	5.00	5.00
First day cover	–	5.50

Thunderbird 4 (41p)
Thunderbird 3 (60p)
Thunderbird 2 (88p)
Thunderbird 1 (97p)

Wallace and Gromit singing carols (2nd, 2nd Large)
Gromit posting Christmas cards (1st, 1st Large)
Wallace and Gromit decorating a Christmas tree (60p)
Gromit carrying a Christmas pudding (97p)
Gromit wearing a sweater (£1.46)

■ 2010, November 2. Christmas. Wallace and Gromit
Des: Aardman Animations and Nick Park. Printed in gravure by De
La Rue. Counter stamps self-adhesive; miniature sheet gummed.

Set	11.00	11.00
Gutter pairs	28.00	
First day cover	–	11.00
Miniature sheet (one of each design)	10.00	10.00
Miniature sheet first day cover	–	9.00
Stamp cards	7.00	27.00

(* The 2nd and 1st class designs also appear in booklets, and the
2nd, 1st, 60p and 97p designs in Smilers sheets.)

'Joe 90' (1st)
'Captain Scarlet' (1st)
'Thunderbirds' (1st)
'Stingray' (97p)
'Fireball XL5' (97p)
'Supercar' (97p)

■ 2011, January 11. FAB. The Genius of Gerry Anderson
Des: GBH. Printed in litho by Cartor. Issued in se-tenant strips for
each denomination.

Set (se-tenant strips of three)	8.50	8.50
Gutter pairs	22.00	–
First day cover	–	9.00
Stamp cards	11.00	35.00

(* The Thunderbirds design also exists in self-adhesive format
from a stamp booklet: price £1.75 mint or used.)

■ 2011, January 11. Thunderbirds
Des: GBH. Printed with microlenticular technology by Cartor and
Outer Aspect, New Zealand.

Miniature sheet	5.50	5.50
First day cover	–	6.00

BR Dean Goods (1st)
Peckett R2 Thor (60p)
Lancashire and Yorkshire Railway 1093 (88p)
BR WD (97p)

■ 2011, February 1. Classic Locomotives of England
Des: Delaney Design Consultants. Printed in litho by Cartor.

Miniature sheet	5.00	5.00
First day cover	–	6.00
Stamp cards	6.00	22.00

(* The 1st class design also appears in self-adhesive form in
booklets; price £2 mint.)

'Oliver' (1st)
'Blood Brothers' (1st)
'We Will Rock You' (1st)
'Spamalot' (1st)
'Rocky Horror Show' (97p)
'Me and My Girl' (97p)
'Return to the Forbidden Planet' (97p)
'Billy Elliot' (97p)

■ 2011, February 24. Musicals
Des: Webb and Webb. Printed in litho by Cartor.

Set	11.00	11.00
Gutter pairs	28.00	–
Traffic light gutter pairs	30.00	–
First day cover	–	11.50
Stamp cards	6.00	22.00

Rincewind from Terry Pratchett's Discworld series (1st)
Nanny Ogg from Terry Pratchett's Discworld series (1st)
Dumbledore from J. K. Rowling's Harry Potter series (1st)
Lord Voldemort from J. K. Rowling's Harry Potter series (1st)
Merlin from Arthurian legend (60p)
Morgan Le Fay from Arthurian legend (60p)
Aslan from C. S. Lewis's Narnia series (97p)
White Witch from C. S. Lewis's Narnia series (97p)

■ 2011, March 8. Magical Realms
Des: So Design Consultants. Printed in gravure by De La Rue.
Issued in vertical se-tenant pairs.

Set	10.00	10.00
Gutter pairs	25.00	–
First day cover	–	10.00
Stamp cards	6.00	20.00

African elephant (1st)
Mountain gorilla (1st)
Siberian tiger (1st)
Polar bear (1st)
Amur leopard (1st)
Iberian lynx (1st)
Red panda (1st)
Black rhinoceros (1st)
African wild dog (1st)
Golden lion tamarin (1st)

■ 2011, March 22. 50th Anniversary of WWF
Des: Rose Design Consultants. Printed in litho by Cartor. Issued in se-tenant strips of five, in two different sheets.

Set	10.50	11.50
Gutter pairs	26.00	–
First day cover	–	12.00
Stamp cards	9.00	35.00

(* All designs also appear in the WWF prestige stamp book.)

Spider monkey in Amazon rainforest (1st)
Hyacinth macaw in Amazon rainforest (60p)
Poison dart frog in Amazon rainforest (88p)
Jaguar in Amazon rainforest (97p)

■ 2011, March 22. Amazon Alive (Europa)
Des: Janice Nicholson and Rose Design Consultants. Printed in litho by Cartor.

Miniature sheet	6.00	6.00
First day cover	–	7.00

(* The whole sheet also appears in the WWF prestige stamp book.)

'Hamlet' (1st)
'The Tempest' (66p)
'Henry VI' (68p)
'King Lear' (76p)
'A Midsummer's Night Dream' (£1)
'Romeo and Juliet' (£1.10)

■ 2011, April 12. 50th Anniversary of the Royal Shakespeare Company
Des: Hat-Trick Design. Printed in gravure by Walsall.

Set	7.50	7.75
Gutter pairs	19.00	–
First day cover	–	8.50
Stamp cards	7.50	33.00

Royal Shakespeare Theatre, Stratford-upon-Avon (1st)
Swan Theatre, Stratford-upon-Avon (68p)
The Courtyard Theatre, Stratford-upon-Avon (76p)
The Other Place, Stratford-upon-Avon (£1)

■ 2011, April 12. 50th Anniversary of the Royal Shakespeare Company

Des: Hat-Trick Design. Printed in litho by Cartor.

Miniature sheet	5.50	5.50
First day cover	–	6.50

Prince William and Catherine Middleton, informal (1st, 1st)
Prince William and Catherine Middleton, formal (£1.10, £1.10)

■ 2011, April 21. Royal Wedding of Prince William and Catherine Middleton

Des: Atelier Works, from portraits by Mario Testino. Printed in gravure by Walsall.

Miniature sheet	6.50	6.50
First day cover	–	7.50

'Cray' by William Morris, 1884 (1st)
'Cherries' by Philip Webb, 1867 (1st)
'Seaweed' by John Henry Dearle, 1901 (76p)
'Peony' by Kate Faulkner, 1877 (76p)
'Acanthus' by William Morris and William de Morgan, 1876 (£1.10)
'The Merchant's Daughter' by Edward Burne-Jones, c1864 (£1.10)

■ 2011, May 5. Morris and Co

Des: Kate Stevens. Printed in litho by Cartor.

Set	8.00	8.00
Gutter pairs	19.00	–
First day cover	–	8.50
Stamp cards	5.00	17.50

(* All designs also appear in the Morris & Co prestige stamp book.)

Thomas (1st)
James (66p)
Percy (68p)
Daisy (76p)
Toby (£1)
Gordon (£1.10)

■ 2011, June 14. Thomas the Tank Engine

Des: Elmwood, from television stills. Printed in litho by Cartor.

Set	8.00	8.00
Gutter pairs	20.00	–
First day cover	–	8.50
Stamp cards	8.00	35.00

Thomas racing Bertie the Bus (1st)
James has a crash (68p)
Percy ends up in the sea (76p)
Henry walled up in a tunnel (£1)

■ 2011, June 14. Thomas the Tank Engine

Des: Elmwood, from book illustrations by Reginald Dalby and John Kenney. Printed in litho by Cartor.

Miniature sheet	5.00	5.00
First day cover	–	6.00

(* The 1st class design also appears in self-adhesive form in booklets; price £2.50 mint.)

Paralympic sailing (1st)
Field athletics (1st)
Volleyball (1st)
Wheelchair rugby (1st)
Wrestling (1st)
Wheelchair tennis (1st)
Fencing (1st)
Gymnastics (1st)
Triathlon (1st)
Handball (1st)

■ 2011, July 27. London 2012 Olympic and Paralympic Games (issue 3)

Des: Lara Harwood (Sailing), Anthony Pike (Field), Ben Dalling (Volleyball), Matthew Hollings (Wheelchair rugby), Daniel Stolle (Wrestling), David McConochie (Wheelchair tennis), Lyndon Hayes (Fencing), Kathy Wyatt (Gymnastics), Adam Simpson (Triathlon), David Cutter (Handball), Studio David Hillman (set). Printed in litho by Cartor. Issued in se-tenant strips of five in two different sheets.

Set (se-tenant strips of five)	10.00	10.00
Gutter pairs	25.00	–
First day cover	–	11.00
Postcard and stamp set (Sailing)	–	9.00
Postcard and stamp set (Gymnastics)	–	9.00
Composite sheet (entire series of 30)	45.00	–
Stamp cards	8.00	23.00

(* All values also appear in a commemorative sheet. The Wheelchair rugby, Paralympic sailing, Gymnastics and Fencing designs also appear as self-adhesives in booklets; price £2.50 each mint. The composite sheet comprises one of each design from parts I, II and III of the Olympic and Paralympic Games series.)

Sovereign's Sceptre with Cross (1st)
St. Edward's Crown (1st)
Rod and Sceptre with Doves (68p)
Queen Mary's Crown (68p)
The Sovereign's Orb (76p)
Jewelled Sword of Offering (76p)
Imperial State Crown (£1.10)
Coronation Spoon (£1.10)

■ 2011, August 23. The Crown Jewels

Des: Purpose. Printed in litho by Cartor.

Set	10.00	10.00
Gutter pairs	25.00	–
First day cover	–	11.00
Stamp cards	6.00	25.00

Gustav Hamel receives first mailbag (1st)
Hamel ready to leave Hendon (68p)
Greswell's Blériot at Windsor (£1)
Airmail delivered at Windsor (£1.10)

■ 2011, September 9. Centenary of the First UK Aerial Post

Des: Robert Maude and Sarah Davies, from photography by Geoff Dann. Printed in litho by Cartor.

Miniature sheet	10.00	10.00
Miniature sheet first day cover	–	8.00
Press sheet	£100	–
Stamp cards	4.75	20.00

(* The £1 and £1.10 designs also appear in the First UK Aerial Post prestige stamp book.)

King George I, 1714–27 (1st)
King George II, 1727–60 (1st)
King George III, 1760–1820 (76p)
King George IV, 1820–30 (76p)
King William IV, 1830–37 (£1.10)
Queen Victoria, 1837–1901 (£1.10)

■ 2011, September 15. Kings and Queens. The House of Hanover

Des: Ian Chilvers, Atelier Works. Printed in litho by Cartor.

Set	9.00	9.00
Gutter pairs	23.00	–
Traffic light gutter pairs	35.00	–
First day cover	–	9.00
Stamp cards	7.50	35.00

Robert Walpole, first Prime Minister, 1721 (1st)
Ceiling of Kedleston Hall by Robert Adam, 1763 (68p)
Penny Black and Uniform Penny Postage, 1840 (76p)
Queen Victoria's Diamond Jubilee, 1897 (£1)

■ 2011, September 15. The Age of the Hanoverians

Des: Ian Chilvers, Atelier Works. Printed in litho by Cartor.

Miniature sheet	5.50	6.00
First day cover	–	6.50
Press sheet	90.00	–

Angel of the North (1st)
Blackpool Tower (1st)
Carrick-a-Rede (1st)
Downing Street, London (1st)
Edinburgh Castle (1st)
Forth Railway Bridge (1st)
Glastonbury Tor (1st)
Harlech Castle (1st)
Ironbridge (1st)
Jodrell Bank (1st)
Kursaal, Southend (1st)
Lindisfarne Priory (1st)

■ 2011, October 13. UK A–Z (issue 1)

Des: Robert Maude and Sarah Davies. Printed in litho by Cartor.
Issued in se-tenant strips of six in two different sheets.

Set (se-tenant strips of six)	11.00	11.00
Gutter pairs	27.00	–
Traffic light gutter pairs	40.00	–
First day cover	–	1200
Stamp cards	9.00	27.00

The angel visits Joseph, from Matthew 1:21 (2nd, 2nd Large)
Madonna and child, from Matthew 1:23 (1st, 1st Large)
Jesus in the manger, from Luke 2:7 (68p)
The angel visits the shepherds, from Luke 2:10 (£1.10)
The wise men and the star, from Matthew 2:10 (£1.65)

■ 2011, November 8. Christmas. 400th Anniversary of the King James Bible

Des: Peter Malone, The Artworks and Together Design. Printed in gravure by De La Rue. Counter stamps self-adhesive; miniature sheet gummed.

Set	9.50	9.50
First day cover	–	10.50
Miniature sheet (one of each design)	12.00	12.00
Miniature sheet first day cover	–	10.50
Stamp cards	5.50	32.00

(* The 2nd and 1st class also appear in booklets, the 2nd, 1st, 68p, £1.10 and 1.50 in Smilers generic sheets, and the 2nd, 1st, 68p and £1.10 in customised Smilers sheets.)

Olympic Games logo (1st, Worldwide up to 20g)
Paralympic Games logo (1st, Worldwide up to 20g)

■ 2012, January 5. Olympic and Paralympic Games definitives

Des: Studio Dempsey. Printed in gravure by De La Rue. Self-adhesive. The two designs for each value are arranged in a checkerboard fashion in sheets, with the order alternating.

Set	15.00	15.00
Gutter pairs (1st class)	40.00	–
First day cover	–	15.00
Stamp cards	10.00	22.00

(* The 1st class values also appear in booklets, printed by Walsall.)

'Charlie and The Chocolate Factory' (1st)
'Fantastic Mr Fox' (66p)
'James and The Giant Peach' (68p)
'Matilda' (76p)
'The Twits' (£1)
'The Witches' (£1.10)

■ 2012, January 10. Roald Dahl
Des: Magpie Studios. Printed in litho by Cartor.

Set	7.75	8.00
Gutter pairs	18.00	–
Traffic light gutter pairs	30.00	–
First day cover	–	8.50
Stamp cards	9.00	33.00

(* All designs also appear in the Roald Dahl prestige stamp book.)

The BFG carrying Sophie (1st)
The BFG and the giants (68p)
Sophie sitting on the Queen's window-sill (76p)
The BFG and Sophie at the writing desk (£1)

■ 2012, January 10. Roald Dahl's The BFG
Des: Magpie Studios. Printed in litho by Cartor.

Miniature sheet	8.00	8.00
Miniature sheet first day cover	–	6.00

(* All designs also appear in the Roald Dahl prestige stamp book.)

King Edward VII, 1901–10 (1st)
King George V, 1910–36 (68p)
King Edward VIII, 1936 (76p)
King George VI, 1936–52 (£1)
Queen Elizabeth II, 1952– (£1.10)

■ 2012, February 2. Kings and Queens. The House of Windsor
Des: Ian Chilvers, Atelier Works. Printed in litho by Cartor.

Set	6.50	7.00
Gutter pairs	16.00	–
Traffic light gutter pairs	27.00	–
First day cover	–	7.50
Stamp cards	7.00	32.00

Scott Expedition to the South Pole, 1912 (1st)
Bomb damage in World War I, 1939–45 (68p)
England World Cup winning team, 1966 (76p)
Channel Tunnel opened, 1994 (£1)

■ 2012, February 2. The Age of the Windsors and Saxe–Coburg–Gotha
Des: Ian Chilvers, Atelier Works. Printed in litho by Cartor.

Miniature sheet	5.00	5.00
First day cover	–	6.00
Press sheet	90.00	–

Dorothy Wilding stamp portrait, 1953 (1st)
Robert Austin banknote portrait., 1960 (1st)
Harry Eccleston banknote portrait, 1971 (1st)
Mary Gillick coinage portrait, 1953 (1st)
Arnold Machin coinage portrait, 1968 (1st)
Arnold Machin stamp portrait, 1967 (1st)

■ 2012, February 6. Diamond Jubilee
Printed in gravure by Walsall. The Arnold Machin stamp portrait design has overlay text reading 'Diamond Jubilee' and source code 'MMND'.

Miniature sheet	6.00	6.00
First day cover	–	6.50
Press sheet	60.00	–
Stamp cards	5.00	20.00

(* The Arnold Machin stamp portrait design also appears in self-adhesive form in counter sheets, business sheets and booklets. The Dorothy Wilding and Arnold Machin stamp portrait designs also appear in the Diamond Jubilee prestige stamp book.)

Frederick Delius 1862–1934
Opera, choral and orchestral composer

Coventry Cathedral by Sir Basil Spence (1st)
Frederick Delius, composer (1st)
'Orange Tree' embroidery by Mary 'May' Morris (1st)
Odette Hallowes, wartime secret agent (1st)
Atmospheric steam engine by Thomas Newcomen (1st)
Kathleen Ferrier, opera singer (1st)
Interior of Palace of Westminster by Augustus Pugin (1st)
Montague Rhodes James, author (1st)
Bombe code-breaking machine by Alan Turing (1st)
Joan Mary Fry, social reformer (1st)

■ **2012, February 23. Britons of Distinction**
Des: Purpose. Printed in litho by Cartor. Issued in se-tenant strips of five in two separate sheets.

Set	11.00	11.00
Gutter pairs	27.00	–
First day cover	–	10.00
Stamp cards	7.00	22.00

(* The 1st class Bombe design also appears in the Inventive Britain prestige stamp book of 2015.)

Classic Locomotives of Scotland

BR Class D34 locomotive (1st)
BR Class D40 locomotive (68p)
Andrew Barclay No807 locomotive (£1)
BR Class 4P locomotive (£1.10)

■ **2012, March 8. Classic Locomotives of Scotland**
Des: Delaney Design Consultants. Printed in litho by Cartor.

Miniature sheet	5.50	5.50
Miniature sheet first day cover	–	6.50
Stamp cards	4.25	23.00

'The Dandy' and Desperate Dan (1st)
'The Beano' and Dennis the Menace (1st)
'Eagle' and Dan Dare (1st)
'The Topper' and Beryl the Peril (1st)
'Tiger' and Roy of the Rovers (1st)
'Bunty' and The Four Marys (1st)
'Buster' and Buster (1st)
'Valiant' and The Steel Claw (1st)
'Twinkle' and Nurse Nancy (1st)
'2000AD' and Judge Dredd (1st)

■ **2012, March 20. Comics**
Des: The Chase. Printed in litho by Cartor. Issued in se-tenant strips of five in two separate sheets.

Set	11.00	11.00
Gutter pairs	27.00	–
First day cover	–	11.00
Stamp cards	10.00	23.00

Manchester Town Hall

Manchester Town Hall (1st)
Narrow Water Castle (1st)
Old Bailey (1st)
Portmeirion (1st)
Queen's College, Oxford (1st)
Roman Baths (1st)
Stirling Castle (1st)
Tyne Bridge (1st)
Urquhart Castle (1st)
Victoria and Albert museum (1st)
White Cliffs of Dover (1st)
Station X, Bletchley Park (1st)
York Minster (1st)
ZSL London Zoo (1st)

■ **2012, April 10. UK A–Z (issue 2) (Europa)**
Des: Robert Maude and Sarah Davies. Printed in litho by Cartor. Issued in se-tenant strips of six (M–R and S–X), and in se-tenant pairs (Y–Z), in three different sheets.

Set (se-tenant strips and pairs)	18.00	18.00
Gutter pairs	45.00	–
Traffic light gutter pairs	50.00	–
First day cover	–	16.00
Stamp cards	10.00	37.00
Composite sheet (entire series of 26)	55.00	–

(* The 1st class Station X design also appears in the Inventive Britain prestige stamp book of 2015.)

Ladies' suit by Hardy Amies (1st)
Ladies' outfit by Norman Hartnell (1st)
Men's jacket by Granny Takes A Trip (1st)
Ladies' outfit by Ossie Clark (1st)
Men's suit by Tommy Nutter (1st)
Ladies' outfit by Jean Muir (1st)
Ladies' dress by Zandra Rhodes (1st)
Ladies' dress by Vivienne Westwood (1st)
Men's suit by Paul Smith (1st)
Ladies' dress by Alexander McQueen (1st)

■ **2012, May 15. Great British Fashion**
Des: Johnson Banks. Printed in litho by Cartor. Printed in se-tenant strips of five in two separate sheets.

Set (se-tenant strips of five)	11.50	11.50
Gutter pairs	30.00	–
Traffic light gutter pairs	40.00	–
First day cover	–	10.00
Stamp cards	9.00	24.00

The Queen during her Golden Jubilee, 2002 (1st)
The Queen at the Trooping of the Colour, 1967 (1st)
The Queen inspecting troops of the Royal Welsh, 2007 (77p)
The Queen making her first Christmas TV broadcast, 1957 (77p)
The Queen on a Silver Jubilee Walkabout, 1977 (87p)
The Queen at the Order of the Garter Ceremony, 1997 (87p)
The Queen addressing the United Nations, 1957 (£1.28)
The Queen at the Commonwealth Games, 1982 (£1.28)

■ **2012, May 31. Diamond Jubilee**
Des: Kate Stephens. Printed in litho by Cartor. Issued in se-tenant pairs of each denomination.

Set	12.50	12.50
Gutter pairs	30.00	–

Traffic light gutter pairs	32.00	–
First day cover	–	12.00
Stamp cards	8.00	30.00

(* All designs also appear in the Diamond Jubilee prestige stamp book. The Golden Jubilee design also appears in self-adhesive form in a booklet; price £2.25 mint or used.)

Mr Bumble from 'Oliver Twist' (2nd)
Mr Pickwick from 'The Pickwick Papers' (1st)
The Marchioness from 'The Old Curiosity Shop' (77p)
Mrs Gamp from 'Martin Chuzzlewit' (87p)
Captain Cuttle from 'Dombey & Son' (£1.28)
Mr Micawber from 'David Copperfield' (£1.90)

■ **2012, June 19. Bicentenary of the Birth of Charles Dickens**
Des: Howard Brown, from illustrations by 'Kyd' (Joseph Clayton Clarke). Printed in litho by Cartor.

Set	10.00	10.00
Gutter pairs	25.00	–
Traffic light gutter pairs	32.00	–
First day cover	–	15.00
Stamp cards	8.00	40.00

Scene from 'Nicholas Nickleby' (1st)
Scene from 'Bleak House' (1st)
Scene from 'Little Dorrit' (1st)
Scene from 'A Tale of Two Cities' (1st)

■ **2012, June 19. Bicentenary of the Birth of Charles Dickens**
Des: Howard Brown, from illustrations by 'Phiz' (Hablot Knight Brown). Printed in litho by Cartor.

Miniature sheet	5.50	5.50
Miniature sheet first day cover	–	6.00

Miniature sheet (1st, 1st, 1st, 1st, 1st, 1st): 29 different sheet designs

■ **2012, July 27–August 12. London 2012 Olympic Games Gold Medal Winners**
Des: True North. Base design printed in litho by Walsall (at Cartor), with photographic image and event-specific inscriptions added in litho by regional printers Acorn Press (Swindon), Allander Print (Edinburgh), Aquatint BSC (London), B&D (Preston), Breckland (Attleborough) and Crescent (Solihull). Miniature sheets comprising six 1st class stamps, issued the day after each gold medal win and initially available from 518 selected post offices.

	Mint	Used	FDC
Miniature sheet Rowing, women's pairs: Heather Stanning, Helen Glover (Aug 2)	9.00	9.50	10.00
Miniature sheet Cycling, men's time trial: Bradley Wiggins (Aug 2)	9.00	9.50	10.00
Miniature sheet Canoeing, men's double slalom: Etienne Stott, Tim Baillie (Aug 3)	9.00	9.50	10.00
Miniature sheet Shooting, men's double trap: Peter Wilson (Aug 3)	9.00	9.50	10.00
Miniature sheet Cycling, men's team sprint: Philip Hindes, Chris Hoy, Jason Kenny (Aug 3)	9.00	9.50	10.00
Miniature sheet Rowing, women's double sculls: Anna Watkins, Katherine Grainger (Aug 4)	9.00	9.50	10.00
Miniature sheet Cycling, men's pursuit: Ed Clancy, Geraint Thomas, Steven Burke, Peter Kennaugh (Aug 4)	9.00	9.50	10.00
Miniature sheet Cycling, women's keirin: Victoria Pendleton (Aug 4)	9.00	9.50	10.00
Miniature sheet Rowing, men's four: Alex Gregory, Tom James, Pete Reed, Andrew Triggs-Hodge (Aug 5)	9.00	9.50	10.00
Miniature sheet Rowing, women's lightweight double sculls: Kat Copeland, Sophie Hosking (Aug 5)	9.00	9.50	10.00
Miniature sheet Cycling, women's team pursuit: Danielle King, Joanna Rowsell, Laura Trott (Aug 5)	9.00	9.50	10.00
Miniature sheet Athletics, women's heptathlon: Jessica Ennis (Aug 5)	9.00	9.50	10.00
Miniature sheet Athletics, men's long jump: Greg Rutherford (Aug 5)	9.00	9.50	10.00
Miniature sheet Athletics, men's 10,000 metres: Mo Farah (Aug 5)	9.00	9.50	10.00
Miniature sheet Sailing, finn class: Ben Ainslie (Aug 6)	9.00	9.50	10.00
Miniature sheet Tennis, men's singles: Andy Murray (Aug 6)	9.00	9.50	10.00
Miniature sheet Equestrian, team show-jumping: Scott Brash, Peter Charles, Ben Maher, Nick Skelton (Aug 7)	9.00	9.50	10.00
Miniature sheet Cycling, men's sprint: Jason Kenny (Aug 7)	9.00	9.50	10.00
Miniature sheet Athletics, men's triathlon: Alistair Brownlee (Aug 8)	9.00	9.50	10.00
Miniature sheet Equestrian, team dressage: Laura Bechtolsheimer, Charlotte Dujardin, Carl Hester (Aug 8)	9.00	9.50	10.00
Miniature sheet Cycling, women's omnium: Laura Trott (Aug 8)	9.00	9.50	10.00
Miniature sheet Cycling, men's keirin: Chris Hoy (Aug 8)	9.00	9.50	10.00
Miniature sheet Equestrian, individual dressage: Charlotte Dujardin (Aug 10)	9.00	9.50	10.00
Miniature sheet Boxing, women's flyweight: Nicola Adams (Aug 10)	9.00	9.50	10.00
Miniature sheet Taekwando, women's under 57kg: Jade Jones (Aug 10)	9.00	9.50	10.00
Miniature sheet Kayaking, men's K1 sprint: Ed McKeever (Aug 12)	9.00	9.50	10.00
Miniature sheet Athletics, men's 5,000 metres: Mo Farah (Aug 12)	9.00	9.50	10.00
Miniature sheet Boxing, men's bantamweight: Luke Campbell (Aug 12)	9.00	9.50	10.00
Miniature sheet Boxing, men's super heavyweight: Anthony Joshua (Aug 13)	9.00	9.50	10.00

Miniature sheet (1st, 1st,): 34 different sheet designs

■ **2012, August 31–September 10. London 2012 Paralympic Games Gold Medal Winners**
Des: True North. Base design printed in litho by Walsall (at Cartor), with photographic image and event-specific inscriptions added in litho by regional printers Acorn Press (Swindon), Allander Print (Edinburgh), Aquatint BSC (London), B&D (Preston), Breckland (Attleborough) and Crescent (Solihull). Miniature sheets comprising two 1st class stamps, issued within four days of each gold medal win and initially available from 518 selected post offices.

	Mint	Used	FDC
Miniature sheet Cycling, women's C5 pursuit: Sarah Storey (Aug 31)	3.50	4.00	4.50
Miniature sheet Swimming, men's S7 100m backstroke: Jonathan Fox (Sep 1)	3.50	4.00	4.50
Miniature sheet Cycling, men's C1 pursuit: Mark Colbourne (Sep 3)	3.50	4.00	4.50
Miniature sheet Athletics, women's T34 100m: Hannah Cockcroft (Sep 3)	3.50	4.00	4.50
Miniature sheet Cycling, men's 1km time trial B: Neil Fachie, Barney Storey (Sep 3)	3.50	4.00	4.50
Miniature sheet Athletics, men's T42 200m: Richard Whitehead (Sep 3)	3.50	4.00	4.50
Miniature sheet Equestrian, individual championship test, grade II: Natasha Baker (Sep 3)	3.50	4.00	4.50
Miniature sheet Cycling, women's 500m time trial C4–5: Sarah Storey (Sep 3)	3.50	4.00	4.50
Miniature sheet Swimming, women's 400m freestyle S6: Ellie Simmonds (Sep 3)	3.50	4.00	4.50
Miniature sheet Rowing, coxed four: Pam Relph, Naomi Riches, David Smith, James Roe, Lily Broecke (Sep 4)	3.50	4.00	4.50
Miniature sheet Athletics, men's F42 discus: Aled Davies (Sep 4)	3.50	4.00	4.50
Miniature sheet Cycling, men's individual sprint B: Anthony Kappes, Craig MacLean (Sep 4)	3.50	4.00	4.50
Miniature sheet Swimming, women's S14 200m freestyle: Jessica-Jane Applegate (Sep 4)	3.50	4.00	4.50
Miniature sheet Equestrian, individual championship test grade Ia: Sophie Christiansen (Sep 4)	3.50	4.00	4.50
Miniature sheet Athletics, men's 5000m T54: David Weir (Sep 4)	3.50	4.00	4.50
Miniature sheet Equestrian, individual freestyle test grade II: Natasha Baker (Sep 4)	3.50	4.00	4.50
Miniature sheet Swimming, women's 200m individual medley SM6: Ellie Simmonds (Sep 4)	3.50	4.00	4.50
Miniature sheet Athletics, men's 100m T53: Mickey Bushell (Sep 5)	3.50	4.00	4.50
Miniature sheet Archery, women's individual compound open: Danielle Brown (Sep 5)	3.50	4.00	4.50
Miniature sheet Swimming, women's 100m backstroke S8: Heather Frederiksen (Sep 5)	3.50	4.00	4.50
Miniature sheet Equestrian, individual freestyle test grade Ia: Sophie Christiansen (Sep 5)	3.50	4.00	4.50
Miniature sheet Athletics, men's T54 1500m: David Weir (Sep 7)	3.50	4.00	4.50
Miniature sheet Cycling, women's time trial C5: Sarah Storey (Sep 7)	3.50	4.00	4.50
Miniature sheet Swimming, men's 200m individual medley SM8: Oliver Hynd (Sep 7)	3.50	4.00	4.50
Miniature sheet Equestrian, team: Sophie Christiansen, Deborah Criddle, Lee Pearson, Sophie Wells (Sep 7)	3.50	4.00	4.50
Miniature sheet Sailing, 2.4mR single-person keelboat: Helena Lucas (Sep 8)	3.50	4.00	4.50
Miniature sheet Cycling, women's C4–5 road race: Sarah Storey (Sep 8)	3.50	4.00	4.50
Miniature sheet Swimming, men's S7 400m freestyle: Josef Craig (Sep 8)	3.50	4.00	4.50
Miniature sheet Athletics, women's T34 200m: Hannah Cockcroft (Sep 8)	3.50	4.00	4.50
Miniature sheet Athletics, men's 800m T54: David Weir (Sep 10)	3.50	4.00	4.50
Miniature sheet Athletics, men's 100m T44: Jonnie Peacock (Sep 10)	3.50	4.00	4.50
Miniature sheet Athletics, women's discus F51/52/53: Josie Pearson (Sep 10)	3.50	4.00	4.50
Miniature sheet Cycling, mixed road race T1-2: David Stone (Sep 10)	3.50	4.00	4.50
Miniature sheet Athletics, men's marathon T54: David Weir (Sep 10)	3.50	4.00	4.50

Fencer and Tower Bridge (1st)
Track athletes and Olympic Stadium (1st)
Diver and Tate Modern (£1.28)
Track cyclist and London Eye (£1.28)

■ **2012, July 27. Welcome to the London 2012 Olympic Games**
Des: Hat–Trick. Printed in litho by Cartor.

Miniature sheet	7.50	7.50
Miniature sheet first day cover	–	7.00
Stamp cards	8.50	25.00

Amputee athlete and Olympic Stadium (1st)
Wheelchair basketball player and Houses of Parliament (1st)
Weightlifter and St. Paul's Cathedral (£1.28)
Cyclist and London Eye (£1.28)

■ **2012, August 29. Welcome to the London 2012 Paralympic Games**
Des: Hat–Trick. Printed in litho by Cartor.

Miniature sheet	7.50	7.50
Miniature sheet first day cover	–	7.00
Stamp cards	8.50	25.00

Paralympic Games: ParalympicsGB team (1st)
Olympic Games: games makers (1st)
Paralympic Games: opening ceremony (£1.28)
Olympic Games: closing ceremony (£1.28)

■ **2012, September 27. Memories of London 2012**
Des: The Chase. Printed in litho by Walsall (at Cartor).

Miniature sheet	7.50	7.50
Miniature sheet first day cover	–	7.50
Stamp cards	11.00	25.00

Sun | Particles ejected from the solar surface seen by the SOHO satellite

Sun (1st)
Venus (1st)
Mars (77p)
Lutetia (77p)
Saturn (£1.28)
Titan (£1.28)

■ **2012, October 16. Space Science.**
Des: Osborne Ross Design. Printed in litho by Cartor.

Set	8.50	8.50
Gutter pairs	21.00	–
First day cover	–	9.00
Stamp cards	6.00	25.00

Poppies (1st)

■ **2012, October 23. Lest We Forget.**
Des: Hat–Trick Design. Printed in gravure by Walsall. Design as the Poppies 1st class of January 26, 2010, but self–adhesive.

1st	1.50	1.50
Gutter pair	4.50	–

Reindeer (2nd, 2nd Large)
Father Christmas with robin (1st, 1st Large)
Snowman with penguin (87p)
Robin holding star (£1.28)
Christmas tree with cat and mouse (£1.90)

■ 2012, November 6. Christmas

Des: Brian Webb from illustrations by Axel Scheffler. Printed in gravure by De La Rue. Counter sheets self–adhesive; miniature sheet gummed.

Set	11.00	11.50
Gutter pairs	27.00	–
First day cover	–	12.00
Miniature sheet	11.00	11.50
Miniature sheet first day cover	–	12.00
Stamp cards	5.50	35.00

(* The 2nd class and 1st class also appear in retail stamp books printed by Walsall. The 2nd class, 1st class, 87p and £1.28 also appear in generic and customised Smilers sheets.)

Metropolitan Railway opens, 1863 (2nd)
Tunnelling beneath London, 1898 (2nd)
Commute from the suburbs, 1911 (1st)
Boston Manor station, 1934 (1st)
Classic rolling stock, 1938 (£1.28)
Canary Wharf station, 1999 (£1.28)

■ 2013, January 9. 150th Anniversary of the London Underground

Des: Hat-trick Design. Printed in litho by Cartor.

Set	7.50	8.00
Gutter pairs	18.00	–
First day cover	–	9.00
Stamp cards	8.00	45.00

(* The Boston Manor 1st class also appears, self–adhesive, in a booklet; price £2.00, mint or used.)

Posters: Golders Green; To Fresh Air; Summer Sales (1st)
Posters: For The Zoo; Power; The Seen (77p)
Posters: Every 90 Seconds; Thanks; Cut Travelling Time (87p)
Posters: Transport Collection; London Zoo; Tate Gallery (£1.28)

■ 2013, January 9. Art on the London Underground

Des: NB Studios. Printed in litho by Cartor.

Miniature sheet	5.75	6.00
Miniature sheet first day cover	–	7.00

'Pride & Prejudice' (1st)
'Sense & Sensibility' (1st)
'Mansfield Park' (77p)
'Emma' (77p)
'Northanger Abbey' (£1.28)
'Persuasion' (£1.28)

■ 2013, February 21. Jane Austen

Des: Angela Barrett. Printed in litho by Cartor.

Set	8.50	8.50
Gutter pairs	21.00	–
Traffic light gutter pairs	23.00	–
First day cover	–	10.00
Stamp cards	7.50	18.00

The 11th Doctor, played by Matt Smith (1st)
The 10th Doctor, played by David Tennant (1st)
The 9th Doctor, played by Christopher Eccleston (1st)
The 8th Doctor, played by Paul McGann (1st)
The 7th Doctor, played by Sylvester McCoy (1st)
The 6th Doctor, played by Colin Baker (1st)
The 5th Doctor, played by Peter Davison (1st)
The 4th Doctor, played by Tom Baker (1st)
The 3rd Doctor, played by Jon Pertwee (1st)
The 2nd Doctor, played by Patrick Troughton (1st)
The 1st Doctor, played by William Hartnell (1st)

■ 2013, March 26. 50 Years of Doctor Who

Des: GBH. Printed in litho by Cartor. Issued in se–tenant strips of three, four and four in three separate sheets.

Set	11.00	11.00
Gutter pairs	27.00	–
First day covers (set of two)	–	13.00
Stamp cards	18.00	45.00

(* All designs also appear in the 50 Years of Doctor Who prestige stamp book. The Matt Smith 1st class and William Hartnell 1st class designs also appear, self–adhesive, in a booklet; price £7 each mint or used.)

The Ood (2nd)
Cyberman (2nd)
Weeping Angel (2nd)
Dalek (2nd)
Tardis (1st)

■ 2013, March 26. 50 Years of Doctor Who
Des: GBH. Printed in litho by Cartor. Self-adhesive.

Miniature sheet	5.50	5.50
Miniature sheet first day cover	–	7.50

(* The 1st class design also appears in a booklet and in Smilers
sheets, and, with normal gum, in the 50 Years of Doctor Who
prestige stamp book; price £2.50 mint.)

Norman Parkinson (1st)
Vivien Leigh (1st)
Peter Cushing (1st)
David Lloyd George (1st)
Elizabeth David (1st)
John Archer (1st)
Benjamin Britten (1st)
Mary Leakey (1st)
Bill Shankley (1st)
Richard Dimbleby (1st)

■ 2013, April 16. Great Britons
Des: Together Design. Printed in litho by Cartor. Issued in
se-tenant strips of five in two separate sheets.

Set (se-tenant strips of five)	10.50	11.00
Gutter pairs	26.00	–
First day cover	–	11.00
Stamp cards	8.00	25.00

Jimmy Greaves (1st)
John Charles (1st)
Gordon Banks (1st)
George Best (1st)
John Barnes (1st)
Kevin Keegan (1st)
Denis Law (1st)
Bobby Moore (1st)
Bryan Robson (1st)
Dave Mackay (1st)
Bobby Charlton (1st)

■ 2013, May 9. Football Heroes
Des: Andrew Kinsman. Printed in litho by Cartor. Issued in
se-tenant strips of five and six, in two separate sheets.

Set	11.00	11.00
Gutter pairs	27.00	–
First day cover	–	12.00
Miniature sheet (all 11 designs)	11.00	11.00
Miniature sheet first day cover	–	12.00
Stamp cards	8.50	50.00

(* All 11 designs also appear in the Football Heroes prestige stamp
book. The George Best, Bobby Moore, John Charles and Dave
Mackay designs also appear, self-adhesive, in booklets; price
£2.50 each, mint or used.)

Portrait of Queen Elizabeth II by Terence Cuneo, 1953 (2nd)
Portrait of Queen Elizabeth II by Nicola Philipps, 2013 (1st)
Portrait of Queen Elizabeth II by Andrew Festing, 1999 (78p)
Portrait of Queen Elizabeth II by Pietro Annigoni, 1955 (88p)
Portrait of Queen Elizabeth II by Sergei Pavlenko, 2000 (£1.28)
Portrait of Queen Elizabeth II by Richard Stone, 1992 (£1.88)

■ **2013, May 30. 60th Anniversary of the Coronation. Royal Portraits**
Des: Atelier Works. Printed in gravure by Walsall.

Set	10.00	10.00
Gutter pairs	25.00	–
Traffic light gutter pairs	40.00	–
First day cover	–	13.00
Stamp cards	5.00	19.00

UTA W No.103 (1st)
UTA SG3 No.35 (78p)
Peckett No.2 (88p)
CDRJC Class 5 No.4 (£1.28)

■ **2013, June 18. Classic Locomotives of Northern Ireland**
Des: Delaney Design Consultants. Printed in litho by Cartor.

Miniature sheet	6.00	6.00
Miniature sheet first day cover	–	7.50
Stamp cards	4.50	25.00

(* The 1st class design also appears, self-adhesive, in a booklet; price £1.50, mint or used.)

Comma (1st)
Orange-tip (1st)
Small copper (1st)
Chalkhill blue (1st)
Swallowtail (1st)
Purple emperor (1st)
Marsh fritillary (1st)
Brimstone (1st)
Red admiral (1st)
Marbled white (1st)

■ **2013, July 11. Butterflies**
Des: Marc & Anna. Printed in litho by Cartor. Issued in se-tenant strips of five in two separate sheets.

Set (in se-tenant strips of 5)	10.00	10.00
Gutter pairs	25.00	–
First day cover	–	11.00
Stamp cards	7.75	25.00

(* The Chalkhill Blue 1st class and Comma 1st class also appear, self-adhesive, in a booklet; price £2.50 each, mint or used.)

Andy Murray kissing the championship trophy (1st)
Andy Murray serving (1st)
Andy Murray returning with a backhand (£1.28)
Andy Murray holding the championship trophy (£1.28)

■ **2013. August 8. Andy Murray, Gentlemen's Singles Champion, Wimbledon 2013**
Des: Hat-trick. Printed in litho by International Security Printers.

Miniature sheet	6.50	6.25
Miniature sheet first day cover	–	7.50

Jaguar E-Type, 1961 (1st)
Rolls-Royce Silver Shadow, 1965 (1st)
Aston Martin DB5, 1963 (1st)
MG MGB, 1962 (£1.28)
Morgan Plus 8, 1968 (£1.28)
Lotus Esprit, 1976 (£1.28)

■ **2013, August 13. British Auto Legends**
Des: Why Not Associates. Printed in litho by Cartor. Issued in se-tenant strips of three in two separate sheets.

Set	10.00	10.00
Gutter pairs	22.00	–
First day cover	–	10.00
Stamp cards	8.50	42.00

Morris Minor van operated by Royal Mail (1st)
Austin FX4 operated as a taxi (1st)
Ford Anglia 105E operated by the police (1st)
Land Rover Defender 110 operated by HM Coastguard (1st)

■ **2013, August 13. British Auto Legends: The Workhorses (Europa)**
Des: Robert Maude and Sarah Davies. Printed in litho by Cartor.

Miniature sheet	6.00	6.00
Miniature sheet first day cover	–	5.50
Press sheet	50.00	–

(* The Morris Minor 1st class design also appears, self-adhesive, in a booklet printed in gravure by Walsall; price £2.00 mint or used.)

Royal Mail Ship Britannia 1840

BARYONYX

East Indiaman 'Atlas', 1813 (1st)
Royal Mail ship 'Britannia', 1840 (1st)
Tea clipper 'Cutty Sark', 1870 (1st)
Cargo liner 'Clan Metheson', 1919 (£1.28)
Royal Mail ship 'Queen Elizabeth', 1940 (£1.28)
Bulk carrier 'Lord Hinton', 1986 (£1.28)

■ 2013, September 19. The Merchant Navy

Des: Silk Pearce. Printed in litho by International Security Printers.

Set	10.00	10.00
Gutter pairs	22.00	–
First day cover	–	10.50
Stamp cards	8.50	30.00

(* All designs also appear in the Merchant Navy prestige stamp book, printed by Enschedé. The Britannia 1st class design also appears, self–adhesive, in a booklet printed in gravure by Walsall; price £2.00 mint or used.)

THE ATLANTIC AND ARCTIC CONVOYS
The only thing that ever really frightened me during the war was the U–boat peril.
WINSTON CHURCHILL

HMS 'Vanoc' escorting Atlantic convoy (1st)
Merchant ship in the Thames Estuary (1st)
Clearing ice on HMS 'King George V' in Arctic waters (1st)
Naval convoy in the North Sea (1st)

■ 2013, September 19. The Merchant Navy: The Atlantic and Arctic Convoys

Des: Silk Pearce. Printed in litho by Enschedé.

Miniature sheet	4.50	4.50
Miniature sheet first day cover	–	5.50

(* All designs also appear in the Merchant Navy prestige stamp book.)

Polacanthus (1st)
Ichthyosaurus (1st)
Iguanodon (1st)
Ornithocheirus (1st)
Baryonyx (1st)
Dimorphodon (1st)
Hypsilophodon (1st)
Cetiosaurus (1st)
Megalosaurus (1st)
Plesiosaurus (1st)

■ 2013, October 10. Dinosaurs

Des: John Sibbick and Why Not Associates. Printed in litho by International Security Printers. Self–adhesive. Issued in strips of five in two separate sheets.

Set	10.50	10.50
Gutter pairs	25.00	–
First day cover	–	11.00
Stamp cards	8.00	25.00

'Virgin and Child with the Young St. John the Baptist', by Antoniazzo Romano (2nd, 2nd Large)
'Madonna and Child', by Francesco Granacci (1st, 1st Large)
'St. Roch Praying to the Virgin for an End to the Plague', by Jacques–Louis David (88p)
'The Virgin of the Lilies', by William–Adolphe Bouguereau (£1.28)
'Theotokos, Mother of God', by Fadi Mikhail (£1.88)

■ 2013, November 5. Christmas. Madonna and Child

Des: Robert Maude and Sarah Davies. Printed in gravure by De La Rue. Counter sheets self–adhesive; miniature sheet gummed.

Set	11.50	11.50
Gutter pairs	27.00	–
First day cover	–	12.50
Miniature sheet	11.50	11.50
Miniature sheet first day cover	–	12.50
Stamp cards	6.25	35.00

(* The 2nd class and 1st class designs also appear in booklets printed by Walsall. The 2nd, 1st, 88p, £1.28 and £1.88 also appear in Smilers sheets.)

Three Singing Angels (2nd)
A Jolly Father Christmas (1st)

■ 2013, November 5. Children's Christmas

Des: Rosie Hargreaves, aged 10 (2nd), and Molly Robson, aged 7 (1st). Printed in gravure by International Security Printers. Self-adhesive.

Set	2.50	2.50
First day cover	–	5.00

Andy Pandy (1st)
Ivor the Engine (1st)
Dougal from The Magic Roundabout (1st)
Windy Miller from Camberwick Green (1st)
Mr Benn (1st)
Great Uncle Bulgaria from The Wombles (1st)
Bagpuss (1st)
Paddington Bear (1st)
Postman Pat (1st)
Bob the Builder (1st)
Peppa Pig (1st)
Shaun the Sheep (1st)

■ 2014, January 7. Classic Children's TV

Des: Interabang. Printed in gravure by International Security Printers. Self-adhesive. Issued in strips of six in two separate sheets.

Set	12.00	12.00
Gutter pairs	30.00	–
First day cover	–	13.00
Stamp cards	10.00	30.00

Riding for the Disabled Association (1st)
The King's Troop ceremonial horses (1st)
Dray horses (88p)
Royal Mews carriage horses (88p)
Police horses (£1.28)
Forestry horse (£1.28)

■ 2014, February 4. Working Horses

Des: Michael Denny and Harold Batten. Printed in litho by International Security Printers.

Set	9.00	9.50
Gutter pairs	21.00	–
First day cover	–	10.50
Stamp cards	5.00	18.00

LMS 2F No7720 (1st)
Hunslet No589 'Blanche' (78p)
W&LLR No822 'The Earl' (88p)
BR 5600 No5652 (£1.28)

■ 2014, February 20. Classic Locomotives of Wales

Des: Delaney Design Consultants. Printed in litho by International Security Printers.

Miniature sheet	6.00	6.50
Miniature sheet first day cover	–	7.50
Stamp cards	4.00	25.00

(* All four designs also appear in the Classic Locomotives of the UK prestige stamp book, printed by Enschedé. The 1st class design also appears, self-adhesive, in a booklet printed in gravure by Walsall; price £2.50 mint or used.)

Dylan Thomas 1914–1953
Bardd ac awdur · Poet and writer

Roy Plomley (1st)
Barbara Ward (1st)
Joe Mercer (1st)
Kenneth More (1st)
Dylan Thomas (1st)
Sir Alec Guinness (1st)
Noorunissa Inayat Khan (1st)
Max Perutz (1st)
Joan Littlewood (1st)
Abram Games (1st)

■ 2014, March 25. Remarkable Lives
Des: Purpose. Printed in litho by International Security Printers.
Issued in se-tenant strips of five.

Set	10.50	10.50
Gutter pairs	25.00	–
First day cover	–	11.00
Stamp cards	7.50	25.00

Buckingham House, c1700 (1st)
Buckingham House, 1714 (1st)
Buckingham House, 1819 (1st)
Buckingham Palace, 1846 (1st)
Buckingham Palace, c1862 (1st)
Buckingham Palace, 2014 (1st)

■ 2014, April 15. Buckingham Palace
Des: Howard Brown. Printed in litho by International Security Printers. Issued in se-tenant strips of three.

Set	6.50	6.50
Gutter pairs	15.00	–
First day cover	–	7.50
Stamp cards	8.00	30.00

(* All designs also appear in the Buckingham Palace prestige stamp book.)

The Throne Room (1st)
The Grand Staircase (1st)
The Blue Drawing Room (1st)
The Green Drawing Room (1st)

■ 2014, April 15. Buckingham Palace
Des: Robert Maude and Sarah Davies. Printed in litho by Enschedé.

Miniature sheet	5.00	5.00
Miniature sheet first day cover	–	5.50

(* All designs also appear in the Buckingham Palace prestige stamp book. The Grand Staircase 1st class and Throne Room 1st class designs also appear, self-adhesive, in a booklet printed in gravure by Walsall; price £2.50 each mint or used.)

'A Matter of Life and Death' (1st)
'Lawrence of Arabia' (1st)
'2001: A Space Odyssey' (1st)
'Chariots of Fire' (£1.28)
'Secrets & Lies' (£1.28)
'Bend It Like Beckham' (£1.28)

■ 2014, May 13. Great British Film
Des: Johnson Banks. Printed in litho by International Security Printers. Issued in se-tenant strips of three.

Set	10.00	10.00
Gutter pairs	23.00	–
First day cover	–	10.50
Stamp cards	8.00	33.00

'Night Mail' (1st)
'Love on the Wing' (1st)
'The Colour Box' (1st)
'Spare Time' (1st)

■ 2014, May 13. The GPO Film Unit
Des: Magpie Studio. Printed in litho by Enschedé.

Miniature sheet	5.00	5.00
Miniature sheet first day cover	–	5.50

Herring (1st)
Red gunard (1st)
Dab (1st)
Pouting (1st)
Cornish sardine (1st)
Common skate (1st)
Spiny dogfish (1st)
Wolffish (1st)
Sturgeon (1st)
Conger eel (1st)

■ 2014, June 5. Sustainable Fish
Des: Kate Stephens. Printed in litho by International Security Printers. Issued in se-tenant strips of five.

Set	10.50	10.50
Gutter pairs	25.00	–
First day cover	–	12.00
Stamp cards	7.50	25.00

(*The Common Skate and Cornish Sardine 1st class designs also appear, self-adhesive, in a booklet printed in gravure by Walsall; price £2.50 each mint or used.)

Judo (2nd)
Swimming (1st)
Marathon (97p)
Squash (£1.28)
Netball (£1.47)
Para-sport track cycling (£2.15)

■ 2014, July 17. Commonwealth Games, Glasgow
Des: Howard Brown and Nanette Hoogslag. Printed in litho by International Security Printers.

Set	12.00	12.00
Gutter pairs	30.00	–
First day cover	–	13.00
Stamp cards	5.00	22.00

(* The Swimming 1st class design also appears, self-adhesive, in a booklet printed in gravure by Walsall; price £2.50 mint or used.)

Poppy, by Fiona Strickland (1st)
'For The Fallen', by Laurence Binyon (1st)
Private William Cecil Tickle (1st)
'A Star Shell', by C. R. W. Nevinson (£1.47)
'The Response', by William Goscombe John (£1.47)
Princess Mary's Gift Fund Box (£1.47)

■ 2014, July 28. First World War, 1914
Des: Hat-trick. Printed in litho by International Security Printers.

Set	11.00	11.00
Gutter pairs	27.00	–
First day cover	–	12.00
Stamp cards	5.00	20.00

(* All designs also appear in the Great War 1914 prestige stamp book.)

Tinside Lido, Plymouth

Harold Wilson

Eastbourne bandstand (1st)
Tinside Lido, Plymouth (1st)
Bangor Pier (97p)
Southwold Lighthouse (97p)
Blackpool Pleasure Beach (£1.28)
Bexhill-on-Sea shelter (£1.28)

Margaret Thatcher (1st)
Harold Wilson (1st)
Clement Attlee (1st)
Winston Churchill (1st)
William Gladstone (1st)
Robert Peel (1st)
Charles Grey (1st)
William Pitt the Younger (1st)

■ 2014, September 18. Seaside Architecture (Europa)
Des: Why Not Associates, after photography by Lee Mawdseley.
Printed in litho by International Security Printers.

Set	9.50	9.50
Gutter pairs	23.00	–
First day cover	–	11.00
Stamp cards	8.00	38.00

■ 2014, October 14. Prime Ministers
Des: Together. Printed in litho by International Security Printers.
Issued in se-tenant strips of four.

Set	10.50	10.50
Gutter pairs	25.00	–
First day cover	–	12.00
Stamp cards	6.00	22.00

BRITISH PIERS

Llandudno Pier (1st)
Worthing Pier (1st)
Dunoon Pier (£1.28)
Brighton Pier (£1.28)

■ 2014, September 18. Seaside Architecture. British Piers
Des: Why Not Associates, after photography by Lee Mawdseley.
Printed in litho by Enschedé.

Miniature sheet	6.00	6.50
Miniature sheet first day cover	–	8.00

Taking home the Christmas tree (2nd, 2nd Large)
Posting cards into a pillar box (1st, 1st Large)
Decorating a snowman (£1.28)
Singing carols (£1.47)
Skating (£2.15)

■ 2014, November 4. Christmas
Des: True North, after illustrations by Andrew Bannecker. Printed
in gravure by De La Rue. Counter sheets self-adhesive; miniature
sheet gummed.

Set	12.50	12.50
Gutter pairs	28.00	–
First day cover	–	14.00
Miniature sheet	12.50	12.50
Miniature sheet first day cover	–	14.00
Stamp cards	6.00	38.00

(* The 2nd class and 1st class also appear in booklets printed
by International Security Printers. The 2nd, 1st, £1.28 and £1.47
designs also appear in Smilers sheets.)

The White Rabbit (2nd)
Down the rabbit hole (2nd)
'Drink Me' (1st)
The White Rabbit's house (1st)
The Cheshire Cat (81p)
A mad tea party (81p)
The Queen of Hearts (£1.28)
The game of croquet (£1.28)
Alice's evidence (£1.47)
A pack of cards (£1.47)

■ 2015, January 6. Alice in Wonderland

Des: Godfrey Design, after illustrations by Grahame Baker-Smith. Printed in litho by International Security Printers. Issued in vertical se-tenant pairs.

Set	16.00	16.50
Gutter pairs	35.00	–
First day cover	–	16.00
Stamp cards	7.50	35.00

(* The 1st class designs also appear, self-adhesive, in booklets printed in gravure by Walsall; price £2.00 each, mint or used.)

Well done: '1st' (1st)
Mum: 'Mum Mummy Mother' (1st)
New baby: baby with envelope as nappy (1st)
Wedding: three-tiered cake (1st)
Happy birthday: three smiling candles (1st)
Dad: 'DAD' (1st)
Grandparent: child's hand in adult's hand (1st)
Love: birds in a heart shape (1st)

■ 2015, January 20. Smilers

Des: Webb & Webb (Well Done and DAD), The Chase (Mum), NB Studio (New Baby, Happy Birthday and Grandparent), Caroline Gardner (Wedding), Rebecca Sutherland (Love). Printed in litho by International Security Printers.

Miniature sheet	8.00	8.50
Miniature sheet first day cover	–	9.00
Stamp cards	6.50	30.00

(* All designs also appear, self-adhesive, in a booklet and Smilers sheets.)

Colossus (1st)
World Wide Web (1st)
Catseyes (81p)
Fibre optics (81p)
Stainless steel (£1.28)
Carbon fibre (£1.28)
DNA sequencing (£1.47)
i-Limb (£1.47)

■ 2015, February 19. Inventive Britain

Des: GBH. Printed in litho by International Security Printers. Issued in horizontal se-tenant pairs.

Set	14.00	14.50
Gutter pairs	32.00	–
First day cover	–	16.00
Stamp cards	6.00	26.00

(* All designs also appear in the Inventive Britain prestige stamp book.)

Tarr Steps, River Barle (1st)
Row Bridge, Mosedale Beck (1st)
Pulteney Bridge, River Avon (1st)
Craigellachie Bridge, River Spey (1st)
Menai Suspension Bridge, Menai Strait (1st)
High Level Bridge, River Tyne (1st)
Royal Border Bridge, River Tweed (1st)
Tees Transporter Bridge, River Tees (1st)
Humber Bridge, River Humber (1st)
Peace Bridge, River Foyle (1st)

■ 2015, March 6. Bridges

Des: GBH. Printed in litho by International Security Printers. Issued in se-tenant strips of five.

Set	10.50	10.50
Gutter pairs	21.00	–
Traffic light gutter pairs	26.00	–
First day cover	–	11.50
Stamp cards	7.50	25.00

Spike Milligan (1st)
The Two Ronnies (1st)
Billy Connolly (1st)
Morecambe & Wise (1st)
Norman Wisdom (1st)
Lenny Henry (1st)
Peter Cook & Dudley Moore (1st)
Monty Python (1st)
French & Saunders (1st)
Victoria Wood (1st)

■ 2015, April. 1 Comedy Greats
Des: The Chase. Printed in litho by International Security Printers.
Issued in se-tenant strips of five.

Set	10.50	10.50
Gutter pairs	25.00	–
First day cover	–	11.50
Stamp cards	7.00	25.00

(* The Norman Wisdom and Morecambe & Wise designs also
appear, self-adhesive, in a booklet printed in gravure by
International Security Printers; price £3.00 each, mint or used.)

Penny Black (1st, 1st)
Twopenny Blue (1st, 1st)

■ 2015, May 6. 175th Anniversary of the Penny Black
Printed in litho by International Security Printers.

Miniature sheet	3.50	3.50
Miniature sheet first day cover	–	5.50
Press sheet	55.00	–
Stamp cards	2.50	15.00

(* The Penny Black design also exists, self-adhesive, in a booklet
printed in gravure by International Security Printers; price £1.50
mint or used. Both designs also appear in Smilers sheets. The
miniature sheet also exists with the frame around the stamps
inscribed to note the London 2015 Europhilex international stamp
exhibition, and an individual serial number, sold only at the
exhibition in a special pack in a limited edition of 7,500.)

Poppy, by Howard Hodgkin (1st)
'All the Hills & Vales Along', by C. H. Sorley (1st)
Rifleman Kulbir Thapa (1st)
'The Kensingtons at Laventie', by Eric Kennington (£1.52)
Cape Helles, Gallipoli, Turkey (£1.52)
London Irish Rifles' football from Loos (£1.52)

■ 2015, May 14. First World War, 1915
Des: Hat-Trick. Printed in litho by International Security Printers.

Set	11.00	11.00
Gutter pairs	27.00	–
First day cover	–	12.00
Stamp cards	4.50	20.00

(* All designs also appear in the Great War 1915 prestige stamp
book.)

Magna Carta, 1215 (1st)
Simon de Montfort's Parliament, 1265 (1st)
Bill of Rights, 1689 (£1.33)
American Bill of Rights, 1791 (£1.33)
Universal Declaration of Human Rights, 1948 (£1.52)
Charter of the Commonwealth, 2013 (£1.52)

■ 2015, June 2. 800th Anniversary of Magna Carta
Des: Howard Brown. Printed in litho by International Security
Printers.

Set	11.50	11.50
Gutter pairs	25.00	–
First day cover	–	12.50
Stamp cards	4.50	21.00

The defence of Hougoumont (1st)
The Scots Greys during the charge of the Union Brigade (1st)
The French cavalry's assault on Allied defensive squares (£1.00)
The defence of La Haye Sainte by the King's German Legion (£1.00)
The capture of Plancenoit by the Prussians (£1.52)
The French Imperial Guard's final assault (£1.52)

■ **2015, June 18. 200th Anniversary of the Battle of Waterloo**
Des: Silk Pearce. Printed in litho by International Security Printers.

Set	10.50	10.50
Gutter pairs	25.00	–
First day cover	–	11.50
Stamp cards	7.50	40.00

(* All designs also appear in the Battle of Waterloo prestige stamp book.)

15th Infantry Regiment, IV Corps, Prussian Army (1st)
Light Infantry, King's German Legion, Anglo-Allied Army (1st)
92nd Gordon Highlanders, Anglo-Allied Army (£1.33)
Grenadiers, Imperial Guard, French Army (£1.33)

■ **2015, June 18. 200th Anniversary of the Battle of Waterloo**
Des: Webb and Webb, after illustrations by Chris Collingwood.
Printed in litho by International Security Printers.

Miniature sheet	6.50	6.50
Miniature sheet first day cover	–	8.00

(* All designs also appear in the Battle of Waterloo prestige stamp book.)

Pilots scramble to their Hawker Hurricanes (1st)
Supermarine Spitfires on patrol (1st)
Armourer replaces ammunition boxes (1st)
Spotters of the Auxiliary Territorial Service (£1.33)
Operations Room at Bentley Priory (£1.33)
Pilots of 32 Squadron await orders (£1.33)

■ **2015, July 16. 75th Anniversary of the Battle of Britain**
Des: Supple Studio. Printed in litho by International Security Printers.

Miniature sheet	9.50	9.50
Miniature sheet first day cover	–	11.00
Stamp cards	5.00	25.00

Scabious bee (2nd)
Great yellow bumblebee (1st)
Northern colletes bee (£1.00)
Bilberry bumblebee (£1.33)
Large mason bee (£1.52)
Potter flower bee (£1.28)

■ **2015, August 18. Bees**
Des: Anna Ekelund, after illustrations by Richard Lewington.
Printed in litho by International Security Printers.

Set	12.00	12.00
Gutter pairs	26.00	–
First day cover	–	13.00
Stamp cards	7.50	50.00

(* The 1st class design also appears, self-adhesive, in booklets; price £2.00, mint or used.)

Waggle dance (1st)
Pollination (1st)
Making honey (£1.33)
Tending young (£1.33)

■ **2015, August 18. The Honeybee**
Des: Interabang, after illustrations by Andy English. Printed in litho by International Security Printers.

Miniature sheet	6.50	6.50
Miniature sheet first day cover	–	7.50

William Wyon's City Medal and Machin portrait (1st)
Wilding portrait and Machin portrait (1st)
Machin definitive (1st)
Badge of the House of Windsor and Machin portrait (£1.33)
The Queen's personal flag and Machin portrait (£1.33)

■ **2015, September 9. Long To Reign Over Us**
Des: Sedley Place. Printed in intaglio and gravure by International
Security Printers.

Miniature sheet	7.50	8.00
Miniature sheet first day cover	–	9.00
Press sheet	50.00	–
Stamp cards	4.00	30.00

(* The Machin definitive in amethyst purple was also issued in
sheets and in booklets of six.)

Tackle (2nd)
Scrum (2nd)
Try (1st)
Conversion (1st)
Pass (£1.00)
Drop goal (£1.00)
Ruck (£1.52)
Line-out (£1.52)

■ **2015, September 18. Rugby World Cup**
Des: Hat-trick; illustrations by Geoff Appleton. Printed in litho by
International Security Printers. Issued in se-tenant pairs.

Set	12.00	12.00
Gutter pairs	28.00	–
First day cover	–	13.00
Stamp cards	5.50	23.00

(*The two 1st class designs also appear in self-adhesive form in a
retail booklet; price £2.00 each, mint or used.)

Darth Vader (1st)
Yoda (1st)
Obi-Wan Kenobi (1st)
Stormtrooper (1st)
Han Solo (1st)
Rey (1st)
Princess Leia (1st)
The Emperor (1st)
Luke Skywalker (1st)
Boba Fett (1st)
Finn (1st)
Kylo Renn (1st)

■ **2015, October 20. Star Wars**
Des: Interabang, from illustrations by Malcolm Tween. Printed in
litho by International Security Printers. Issued in se-tenant strips
of six in two separate sheets.

Set	12.00	14.00
Gutter pairs	28.00	–
First day cover	–	13.00
Stamp cards	15.00	65.00

(* All designs also appear in the Making of Star Wars prestige
stamp book of December 17, 2015. The Han Solo, Darth Vader,
Yoda and Stormtrooper designs also appear in Smilers sheets.)

X-Wing T-65 Starfighter (1st)
X-Wing T-70 Starfighter (1st)
Millennium Falcon (1st)
Single-seater TIE Fighter (1st)
Two-seater TIE Fighter (1st)
AT-AT Walker (1st)

■ **2015, October 20. Star Wars: The Vehicles**
Des: GBH. Printed in litho by International Security Printers. Self-
adhesive.

Miniature sheet	6.00	6.00
Miniature sheet first day cover	–	7.50

(* These design also appear in the Making of Star Wars prestige
stamp book of December 17, 2015.)

The journey to Bethlehem (2nd and 2nd Large)
The Nativity (1st and 1st Large)
The animals of the Nativity (£1.00)
The Shepherds (£1.33)
The Three Wise Men (£1.52)
The Annunciation (£2.25)

■ 2015, November 3. Christmas

Des: Studio David Hillman, from illustrations by David Holmes.
Printed in gravure by De La Rue. Counter stamps self–adhesive;
miniature sheet gummed.

Set	15.00	15.00
Gutter pairs	33.00	–
First day cover	–	16.00
Stamp cards	6.00	50.00
Miniature sheet	15.00	15.00
Miniature sheet first day cover	–	14.00

(* The 2nd and 1st class designs also appear in retail booklets
printed by International Security Printers. The 2nd, 1st, £1.00, £1.33,
£1.52 and £1.25 designs also appear in Smilers sheets.)

Entering the Antarctic ice, December 1914 (1st)
'Endurance' frozen in pack ice, January 1915 (1st)
Striving to free 'Endurance', February 1915 (£1.00)
Trapped in a pressure crack, October 1915 (£1.00)
Patience Camp, December 1915, April 1916 (£1.33)
Safe arrival at Elephant Island, April 1916 (£1.33)
Setting out for South Georgia, April 1916 (£1.52)
Rescue of 'Endurance' crew, August 1916 (£1.52)

■ 2016, January 7. Shackleton and the Endurance Expedition

Des: Robert Maude and Sarah Davies. Printed in litho by
International Security Printers. Issued in se–tenant pairs.

Set	14.00	14.00
Gutter pairs	32.00	–
First day cover	–	15.00
Stamp cards	6.00	27.00

Sir Brian Tuke: Master of the Posts in 1516 (1st)
Packet ship: 'Mail Packet off Eastbourne' by Victor Howes (1st)
Penfold pillar box: hexagonal postbox of 1866 (1st)
River post: river postwoman in World War I (£1.52)
Mail coach: London–Glasgow horse–drawn coach (£1.52)
Medway Mail Centre: sorting machines (£1.52)

■ 2016, February 17. Royal Mail 500

Des: Atelier Works. Printed in litho by International Security
Printers.

Set	11.00	11.00
Gutter pairs	25.00	–
First day cover	–	12.00
Stamp cards	7.50	37.00

(* All designs also appear in the 500 Years of Royal Mail prestige
stamp book.)

'Quickest Way by Airmail' (1st)
'Address Your Letters Plainly' (1st)
'Pack your Parcels Carefully' (£1.33)
'Stamps in Books Save Time' (£1.33)

■ 2016, February 17. Classic GPO Posters

Des: Purpose. Printed in litho by International Security Printers.

Miniature sheet	6.00	6.00
Miniature sheet first day cover	–	7.50

(* These designs also appear in the 500 Years of Royal Mail
prestige stamp book. The miniature sheet also exists with the
border inscribed 'Spring Stampex, 17–20 February 2016', sold only
within a special pack at the exhibition.)

Penny red (1st)

■ 2016, February 18. 175th Anniversary of the Penny Red
Printed in litho by International Security Printers. Self-adhesive. Issued in booklets of six.

1st	2.00	–
First day cover	–	4.00

(*This design also appears in Smilers sheets and, with normal gum, from the 500 Years of Royal Mail prestige stamp book; price £2.00)

Nicholas Winton (1st)
Sue Ryder (1st)
John Boyd Orr (1st)
Eglantyne Jebb (£1.33)
Joseph Rowntree (£1.33)
Josephine Butler (£1.33)

■ 2016, March 15. British Humanitarians
Des: Hat-Trick Design. Printed in litho by International Security Printers. Issued in se-tenant strips of three.

Set	10.00	10.00
Gutter pairs	22.00	–
First day cover	–	11.00
Stamp cards	4.50	20.00

'To thine own self be true' from Hamlet (1st)
'Cowards die many times...' from Julius Caesar (1st)
'Love is a smoke...' from Romeo and Juliet (1st)
'The fool doth think he is wise...' from As You Like It (1st)
'There was a star danced...' from Much Ado About Nothing (1st)
'But if the while I think on thee...' from Sonnet 30 (1st)
'Love comforteth like sunshine after rain' from Venus and Adonis (1st)
'We are such stuff...' from The Tempest (1st)
'Life's but a walking shadow...' from Macbeth (1st)
'I wasted time...' from Richard II (1st)

■ 2016, April 5. 400th Anniversary of the Death of William Shakespeare
Des: The Chase. Printed in litho by International Security Printers. Issued in se-tenant strips of five in two separate sheets.

Set	10.50	10.50
Gutter pairs	23.00	–
First day cover	–	12.00
Stamp cards	7.00	25.00

Princess Elizabeth II with King George VI, c.1930 (1st)
Queen Elizabeth at the State Opening of Parliament, 2012 (1st)
Queen Elizabeth with Princess Anne and Prince Charles, 1952 (1st)
Queen Elizabeth visiting New Zealand, 1977 (£1.52)
Queen Elizabeth with the Duke of Edinburgh, 1957 (£1.52)
Queen Elizabeth with Nelson Mandela, 1996 (£1.52)

■ 2016, April 21. The Queen's 90th Birthday
Des: Kate Stephens. Printed in litho by International Security Printers. Issued in se-tenant strips of three.

Set	11.00	11.00
Gutter pairs	25.00	–
First day cover	–	12.00
Stamp cards	19.00	45.00

(* All designs also appear in the Queen's 90th Birthday prestige stamp book.)

Prince Charles (1st)
Queen Elizabeth II (1st)
Prince George (1st)
Prince William (1st)

■ 2016, April 21. The Queen's 90th Birthday
Des: photograph by Ranald Mackechnie. Printed in litho by International Security Printers.

Miniature sheet	4.00	4.00
Miniature sheet first day cover	–	5.00
Press sheet	55.00	–

(* The miniature sheet also appears in the Queen's 90th Birthday prestige stamp book, and all four designs, in self-adhesive form, in retail booklets; price £2 each, mint or used.)

Woodpecker (1st)
Snake holding a stamp (1st)
Chimpanzee (£1.05)
Bat (£1.05)
Orangutan (£1.33)
Koala with baby (£1.33)

■ 2016, May 17. Animail
Des: Magpie Studio. Printed in litho by International Security Printers. Self-adhesive.

Miniature sheet	10.00	10.00
Miniature sheet first day cover	–	11.00
Stamp cards	5.00	35.00

'Battlefield Poppy', by Giles Revell (1st)
'To My Brother', by Vera Brittain (1st)
Munitions worker Lottie Meade (1st)
'Travoys Arriving With wounded', by Stanley Spencer (£1.52)
Thiepval Memorial, Somme, France (£1.52)
Captain A. C. Green's Battle of Jutland commemorative medal (£1.52)

■ 2016, June 21. First World War, 1916
Des: Hat-Trick. Printed in litho by International Security Printers.

Set	11.00	11.00
Gutter pairs	25.00	–
First day cover	–	12.00
Stamp cards	4.50	35.00

(* All designs also appear in the Great War 1916 prestige stamp book.)

The Post Office Rifles (1st)
Writing a letter from the Western Front (1st)
Home Depot at Regent's Park, London (£1.33)
Delivering the mail on the Home Front (£1.33)

■ 2016, June 21. The Post Office at War, 1914–1918
Des: Hat-Trick. Printed in litho by International Security Printers.

Miniature sheet	6.00	6.00
Miniature sheet first day cover	–	7.50

(*All designs also appear in the Great War 1916 prestige stamp book.)

'The Piper at the Gates of Dawn' album cover (1st)
'Atom Heart Mother' album cover (1st)
'The Dark Side of the Moon' album cover (1st)
'Wish You Were Here' album cover (£1.52)
'Animals' album cover (£1.52)
'The Endless River' album cover (£1.52)

■ 2016, July 7. Pink Floyd
Based on design by Studio Dempsey. Printed in gravure by International Security Printers. Self-adhesive in free-form shape.

Set	11.00	11.00
Gutter pairs	24.00	–
First day cover	–	12.00
Stamp cards	7.00	35.00

(* The Dark Side of the Moon design also appears in a souvenir sheet of 10, not available from post offices; price £12.95.)

On stage at the UFO Club, 1966 (1st)
The Dark Side of the Moon tour, 1973 (1st)
The Wall tour, 1981 (£1.52)
The Division Bell tour, 1994 (£1.52)

■ **2016, July 7. Pink Floyd Live**
Printed in litho by International Security Printers.

Miniature sheet	7.00	7.00
Miniature sheet first day cover	–	8.00

Peter Rabbit with his mother (1st)
Peter Rabbit entering Mr. McGregor's garden (1st)
Peter Rabbit feeling sick after eating too much (£1.33)
Peter Rabbit escaping from Mr. McGregor (£1.33)

■ **2016, July 28. The Tale of Peter Rabbit**
Printed in litho by International Security Printers.

Miniature sheet	6.00	6.00
Miniature sheet first day cover	–	7.50

(* All designs also appear in the Beatrix Potter prestige stamp book.)

'The Tale of Peter Rabbit' (1st)
'The Tale of Mrs Tiggy-Winkle' (1st)
'The Tale of Squirrel Nutkin' (£1.33)
'The Tale of Jemima Puddle-Duck' (£1.33)
'The Tale of Tom Kitten' (£1.52)
'The Tale of Benjamin Bunny' (£1.52)

■ **2016, July 28. 150th Anniversary of the Birth of Beatrix Potter**
Des: Charlie Smith Design. Printed in litho by International Security Printers. Issued in se-tenant pairs.

Set	11.00	11.00
Gutter pairs	24.00	–
First day cover	–	12.00
Stamp cards	7.00	35.00

(* All designs also appear in the Beatrix Potter prestige stamp book. The two 1st class designs also appear, in self-adhesive form, in a retail booklet printed in gravure; price £2.00 each, mint or used.)

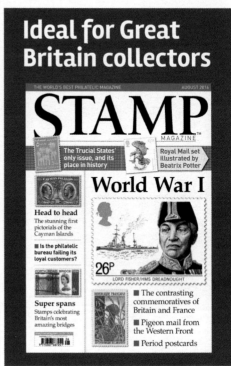

3 ISSUES OF STAMP MAGAZINE FOR JUST £1*

- Get your first 3 issues for just £1* (saving 92%)
- No obligation to continue
- Pay just £3.33 for every future issue (saving £9.84 per 12 issues)
- Delivered conveniently to your door

3 SIMPLE WAYS TO ORDER

FIRST 3 ISSUES FOR £1 FOLLOWED BY £9.99 EVERY 3 MONTHS*

BY PHONE: 0344 243 9023** quote ref. V944

ONLINE: stamp.secureorder.co.uk/STP/V944

REGIONAL ISSUES

Prices in this section are quoted in two columns: mint (left) and fine used (right).
The definitive issues for Guernsey, the Isle of Man and Jersey pre-date their postal independence in 1969, 1973 and 1969 respectively.

CHANNEL ISLANDS

Gathering seaweed (1d)

Islanders gathering seaweed (2½d)

■ **1948, May 10. Third Anniversary of Liberation**
Des: J.R.R. Stobie (1d), E. Blampied (2½d). Printed in gravure by Harrison. Wmk: Multiple Crowns and GVIR. Perf: 15x14.

Set	0.15	0.20
First day cover	–	17.50

GUERNSEY

2½d

3d, 4d, 5d

■ **1958–1969**
Des: E.A. Piprell. Printed in gravure by Harrison. Perf: 15x14.

A) Wmk: Multiple St Edward's Crown. Non phosphor (except where stated).

2½d red (June 8, 1964)	0.30	0.35
3d lilac (August 18, 1958)	0.30	0.30
one centre phos band (May 24, 1967)	0.10	0.15
4d ultramarine (February 7, 1966)	0.20	0.25
two phos bands (October 24, 1967)	0.10	0.15
First day cover (2½d)	–	25.00
First day cover (3d)	–	20.00
First day cover (4d)	–	10.00

B) No watermark. Chalky paper. Two phosphor bands (except where stated).

4d ultramarine (April 16, 1968)	0.10	0.15
4d sepia (September 4, 1968)		
one centre phosphor band	0.10	0.15
4d red (February 26, 1969)		
one centre phosphor band	0.10	0.20
5d deep blue (September 4, 1968)	0.10	0.20
First day cover (4d sepia, 5d)	–	2.00
First day cover (4d red)	–	1.50

ISLE OF MAN

2½d

3d, 4d, 5d

■ 1958–1969
Des: J. Nicholson. Printed in gravure by Harrison. Perf: 15x14.

A) Wmk: Multiple St Edward's Crown. Non phosphor (except where stated).

2½d carmine–red (June 8, 1964)	0.20	0.35
3d lilac (August 18, 1958)	0.15	0.20
chalky paper (May 17, 1964)	4.50	4.00
one centre phos band (June 27, 1968)	0.10	0.15
4d ultramarine (February 7, 1966)	0.75	0.75
a) two phosphor bands (July 5, 1967)	0.10	0.15
First day cover (2½d)	–	25.00
First day cover (3d)	–	30.00
First day cover (4d)	–	10.00

B) No watermark. Chalky paper. Two phosphor bands (except where stated).

4d ultramarine (June 24, 1968)	0.10	0.15
4d sepia (September 4, 1968)		
one centre phosphor band	0.10	0.15
4d red (February 26, 1969)		
one centre phosphor band	0.20	0.30
5d deep blue (September 4, 1968)	0.20	0.30
First day cover (4d sepia, 5d)	–	2.00
First day cover (4d red)	–	1.50

■ 1971–1973
Des: J. Matthews. Printed in gravure by Harrison. Perf: 15x14.

2½p magenta (July 7, 1971)	0.20	0.20
3p ultramarine (July 7, 1971)	0.20	0.20
5p violet (July 7, 1971)	0.60	0.60
7½p pale brown (July 7, 1971)	0.75	0.60
First day cover	–	2.50

(* The 2½p and 3p exist on either ordinary coated paper or fluorescent–coated paper.)

JERSEY

2½d

3d, 4d, 5d

■ 1958–1969
Des: E. Blampied (2½d), W.M. Gardner (others). Printed in gravure by Harrison. Perf: 15x14.

A) Wmk: Multiple St. Edward's Crown. Non phosphor (except where stated).

2½d carmine–red (June 8, 1964)	0.20	0.25
3d lilac (August 18, 1958)	0.25	0.25
one centre phos band (June 9, 1967)	0.10	0.15
4d ultramarine (February 7, 1966)	0.20	0.25
two phos bands (September 5, 1967)	0.10	0.15
First day cover (2½d)	–	25.00
First day cover (3d)	–	20.00
First day cover (4d)	–	10.00

B) No watermark. Chalky paper, PVA gum. One centre phosphor band (4d), two phosphor bands (5d).

4d sepia (September 4, 1968)	0.10	0.15
4d red (February 26, 1969)	0.10	0.20
5d deep blue (September 4, 1968)	0.10	0.20
First day cover (4d sepia, 5d)	–	2.00
First day cover (4d red)	–	1.50

NORTHERN IRELAND DEFINITIVES

Prices in this section are quoted in two columns: mint (left) and fine used (right).

PRE-DECIMAL WILDING ISSUES

3d lilac, 4d blue, 5d blue

6d purple, 9d green

1/3 green, 1/6 grey-blue

■ 1958–1969
Des: W. Hollywood (3d, 4d, 5d), L.Philton (6d, 9d), T. Collins (1/3, 1/6). Printed in gravure by Harrisons. Perf 15x14.
A) Wmk: Multiple St Edward's Crown. Non-phosphor except where stated.

3d lilac (August 18, 1958)	0.15	0.15
3d lilac, one phos band	0.15	0.20
4d blue (February 7, 1966)	0.15	0.15
4d blue, two phos bands	0.15	0.15
6d purple (September 29, 1958)	0.20	0.20
9d green (March 1, 1967). two phos bands	0.35	0.40
1/3 green (September 29, 1958)	0.35	0.40
1/6 grey-blue (March 1, 1967), two phos bands	0.40	0.40
First day cover (3d)	–	25.00
First day cover (6d, 1/3)	–	30.00
First day cover (4d)	–	7.50
First day cover (9d, 1/6)	–	4.00

B) No wmk. Two phosphor bands and PVA gum except where stated.

4d blue, gum Arabic (June 27, 1968)	0.15	0.15
4d sepia (September 4, 1968), one phos band	0.15	0.25
4d red (February 26, 1969)	0.20	0.30
5d blue (September 4, 1968)	0.20	0.20
1/6 grey-blue (May 20, 1969)	1.50	1.40
First day cover (4d sepia, 5d)	–	2.50
First day cover (4d red)	–	1.00

(* The 4d blue also exists with PVA gum, but this was not placed on sale in Northern Ireland; price £8.50 mint.)

DECIMAL MACHIN ISSUES WITHOUT ELLIPTICAL PERFORATIONS

3p blue

Des: J. Matthews. Type I has the symbol close to the top of the design; type II (1983) has the symbol redrawn and edged down.

■ 1971–1980. Printed in gravure by Harrisons
Perf 15x14. Two phosphor bands except where stated.
A) Original coated paper. PVA gum.

2½p pink (July 7, 1971), one phos band	0.40	0.40
3p blue (July 7, 1971)	0.15	0.15
5p violet (July 7, 1971)	0.50	0.50
7½p brown (July 7, 1971)	0.55	0.55

B) Fluorescent coated paper. PVA gum.

2½p pink (June 1973), one phos band	5.25	4.00
3p blue (April 1973)	7.50	7.00
3p blue, one centre band	0.35	0.30

C) Fluorescent coated paper. PVAD gum.

3p blue (January 23, 1974), one phos band	0.15	0.85
3½p green (January 23, 1974)	0.15	0.20
3½p green, one centre band	0.20	0.20
4½p grey-blue (November 6, 1974)	0.15	0.20
5½p deep violet (January 23, 1974)	0.15	0.25
5½p deep violet, one centre band	0.15	0.25
6½p green-blue (January 14, 1976), one band	0.15	0.30
7p red-brown (January 18, 1978), one band	0.20	0.30
8p red (January 23, 1974)	0.20	0.35
8½p green (January 14, 1976)	0.20	0.35
9p violet-blue (January 18, 1978)	0.20	0.30

10p orange (October 20, 1976)	0.35	0.35
10p orange, one phos band	0.35	0.30
10½p grey-blue (January 18, 1978)	0.40	0.30
11p red (October 20, 1976)	0.40	0.30

D) Phosphor coated paper. PVAD gum.

12p yellow-green (July 23, 1980)	0.35	0.35
13½p red-brown (July 23, 1980)	0.35	0.35
15p blue (July 23, 1980)	0.35	0.35

First day cover (2½p, 3p, 5p, 7½p)	–	1.70
First day cover (3½p, 5½p, 8p)	–	1.40
First day cover (4½p)	–	0.80
First day cover (6½p, 8½p)	–	0.80
First day cover (10p, 11p)	–	0.90
First day cover (7p, 9p, 10½p)	–	0.90
First day cover (12p, 13½p, 15p)	–	1.70

■ 1981–1993. Printed in litho by Questa

A) Perf: 13½x14. Phosphor coated paper, except 11½p and 12½p (left side band). PVA gum (11½p, 14p, 18p, 22p), PVAD gum (others).

11½p mushroom (April 8, 1981)	0.70	0.65
12½p light green (February 24, 1982)	0.35	0.30
14p steel-blue (April 8, 1981)	0.50	0.50
15½p pale violet (February 24, 1982)	0.60	0.60
16p light mushroom (April 27, 1983)	0.70	0.70
18p mauve (April 8, 1981)	0.70	0.70
19½p grey-green (February 24, 1982)	1.20	1.20
20½p bright blue (April 27, 1983)	1.70	1.70
22p deep blue (April 8, 1981)	0.70	0.70
26p red (February 24, 1982), type I	0.70	0.70
28p blue (April 27, 1983), type I	0.75	0.70

B) Perf: 15x14. One phosphor band (12p, 12½p, 13p, 14p, 15p), phosphor coated paper (16p, 17p, 18p, 19p, 20p, 22p, 23p, 24p, 31p, 32p, 34p, 37p, 39p), advanced coated paper (22p, 26p, 28p), or as stated. PVAD gum except where stated.

12p emerald green (January 7, 1986)	1.00	0.80
12½p light green (February 28, 1984)	3.00	3.00
12½p light green, PVA gum	4.00	–
13p red-brown (October 23, 1984), type 1	0.60	0.60
13p deep brown, type II	0.80	0.75
14p deep blue (November 8, 1988)	0.50	0.55
15p bright blue (November 28, 1989)	0.55	0.60
16p light mushroom (February 28, 1984)	5.00	4.50
17p steel blue (October 23, 1984), type 1	1.00	0.80
17p steel blue, type I, advanced coated paper	0.70	0.80
17p steel blue, type II, advanced coated paper	£125	£100
18p deep green (January 6, 1987)	0.90	0.80
18p bright green, centre phos band	0.60	0.60
18p bright green, perf 14	5.00	5.00
18p bright green, left phos band	2.00	1.80
19p orange-red (November 8, 1988)	0.40	0.40
20p brownish-black (November 28, 1989)	0.60	0.60
22p yellowish-green (October 23, 1984)	0.80	0.70
22p orange-red (December 4, 1990)	1.00	0.70
23p bright green (November 8, 1988)	0.70	0.85
24p deep red (November 28, 1989)	1.00	1.00
24p chestnut (August 10, 1993), two bands	2.00	2.00

26p red (January 27, 1987), type II	2.00	2.00
26p drab (December 4, 1990), phos paper	0.90	0.90
28p blue (January 27, 1987), type II	1.00	0.90
28p blue-grey (Dec 3, 1991), phos paper	1.10	1.10
31p purple (October 23, 1984), type I	1.00	1.00
31p purple (April 14, 1987), type II	1.80	1.50
32p greenish blue (November 8, 1988)	1.25	1.00
34p bluish grey (November 28, 1989)	0.90	0.90
37p rosine (December 4, 1990)	1.20	1.20
39p mauve (December 3, 1991)	1.50	1.30

(* The 18p with left phosphor band and 24p chestnut with two phosphor bands come from prestige stamp books. The 13p also exists printed on paper supplied by Coated Papers Ltd, with PVA gum, in 1987)

First day cover (11½p, 14p, 18p, 22p)		1.00
First day cover (12½p, 15½p, 19½p, 26p)	–	1.50
First day cover (16p, 20½p, 28p)	–	1.50
First day cover (13p, 17p, 22p, 31p)	–	1.00
First day cover (12p)	–	1.50
First day cover (18p)	–	1.50
First day cover (14p, 19p, 23p, 32p)	–	2.00
First day cover (15p, 20p, 24p, 34p)	–	2.00
First day cover (17p, 22p, 26p, 37p)	–	2.00
First day cover (18p, 24p, 28p, 39p)	–	2.00

DECIMAL MACHIN ISSUES WITH ELLIPTICAL PERFORATIONS

1st red

■ 1993–1996. Printed in litho by Questa

Perf 15x14. One phosphor band (19p and 20p), or two phosphor bands (others).

19p bistre (December 7, 1993), left band	2.00	1.00
19p bistre, right band	1.25	2.00
20p bright green (July 23, 1996)	0.70	1.50
25p red (December 7, 1993)	0.85	0.75
26p red-brown (July 23, 1996)	0.80	1.00
30p olive-grey (December 7, 1993)	1.00	1.50
37p mauve (July 23, 1996)	1.40	2.00
41p grey-brown (December 7, 1993)	1.50	1.00
63p emerald (July 23, 1996)	2.75	2.50

(* The 19p with phosphor band to right comes from the 1995 National Trust prestige stamp book.)

■ 1997–2000. Printed in gravure by Walsall

A) Perf 15x14. One phosphor band (19p and 20p), two phosphor bands (others).

19p bistre (June 8, 1999)	2.00	2.00
20p bright green (July 1, 1997)	1.25	0.90
26p chestnut (July 1, 1997)	2.00	0.90
37p mauve (July 1, 1987)	1.30	1.30
38p ultramarine (June 8, 1999)	6.50	5.50
40p azure (April 25, 2000)	3.00	3.00
63p emerald (July 1, 1997)	3.50	5.25
64p turquoise (June 8, 1999)	6.00	6.00
65p greenish blue (April 25, 2000)	3.00	3.00

(* The 20p with right phosphor band, the 26p perf 15x14 and perf 14, and the 37p also exist printed by Harrisons, from prestige stamp books.)

B) Perf 15x14 except where stated. One phosphor band.

1st orange-red (February 15, 2000), perf 14	2.25	2.20
1st orange-red (April 25, 2000)	6.50	6.50

(* The perf 14 stamp was issued only in the Special By Design prestige stamp book.)

First day cover (19p, 25p, 30p, 41p)	–	3.50
First day cover (20p, 26p, 37p, 63p)	–	5.00
First day cover (19p, 38p, 64p)	–	5.00
First day cover (1st, 40p, 65p)	–	6.00

PICTORIAL ISSUES WITHOUT WHITE BORDERS

Basalt columns (2nd)   Patchwork fields (1st)

Linen (E)   Pattern on vase (65p, 68p)

■ 2001–2002

Des: Rodney Miller Associates. Printed in litho by Walsall (2nd, 1st, E, 65p), De La Rue (E, 68p), or Enschedé (2nd, 1st). Perf 15x14. One phosphor band (2nd), two phosphor bands (others).

2nd (March 6, 2001,Walsall)	0.75	0.80
2nd (February 25, 2003, Enschedé)	1.00	1.00
1st (March 6, 2001,Walsall)	1.20	0.90
1st (February 25, 2003, Enschedé)	1.40	1.40
E (March 6, 2001,Walsall)	1.75	1.75
E (October 15, 2002, De La Rue)	1.75	1.75
65p (March 6, 2001)	2.50	2.50
68p (July 4, 2002)	2.50	2.50

(* The 2nd and 1st printed by Enschedé come from the 2003 Microcosmos prestige stamp book.)

First day cover (2nd, 1st, E, 65p)	–	4.50
First day cover (68p)	–	4.50
Stamp cards	6.00	15.00

PICTORIAL ISSUES WITH WHITE BORDERS

Basalt columns (2nd)   Patchwork fields (1st)

Linen (E, 40p, 42p, 44p, 48p, 50p, 56p, 60p, 87p, 88p, 97p, £1.00, £1.05)   Pattern on vase (68p, 72p, 78p, 81p, 90p, 97p, £1.10, £1.28, £1.33)

■ 2003 to date

Des: Rodney Miller Associates. Printed in litho by De La Rue (2nd, 1st, E, 40p, 42p, 44p, 68p, 72p, 78p, 81p), in litho by Walsall (42p), in gravure by De La Rue (2nd, 1st, 48p, 50p, 56p, 60p, 72p, 78p, 81p, 90p, 97p), in litho by Enschedé (1st, in prestige stamp books only) or in litho by Cartor (2nd, 1st, 68p, 87p, 88p, £1.00, £1.05, £1.10, £1.28, £1.33). Perf 15x14. One phosphor band (2nd) or two phosphor bands (others).

2nd (October 14, 2003, De La Rue)	0.80	0.70
2nd (January 3, 2013, Cartor)	0.80	0.70
1st (October 14, 2003, De La Rue)	1.00	0.85
1st (January 3, 2013, Cartor)	1.00	0.85
E (October 14, 2003)	2.00	2.00
40p (May 11, 2004)	1.10	0.75
42p (Walsall, April 5, 2005)	1.20	1.00
42p (De La Rue, July 26, 2005)	1.20	1.00
44p (March 25, 2006)	1.75	1.50
48p (March 27, 2007)	1.00	1.00
50p (April 1, 2008)	1.00	1.00
56p (March 31, 2009)	1.00	1.00
60p (March 30, 2010)	1.50	1.50
68p (October 14, 2003, De La Rue)	2.00	2.00
68p (March 29, 2011, Cartor)	1.20	1.00
72p (March 28, 2006)	2.00	2.00
78p (March 27, 2007)	1.75	1.75
81p (April 1, 2008)	1.75	1.75
87p (April 25, 2012)	1.90	1.90
88p (March 27, 2013)	1.90	1.90
90p (March 31, 2009)	1.70	1.70
97p (March 30, 2010)	2.00	1.90
97p (March 26, 2014)	2.00	2.00
£1.00 (March 24, 2015)	1.75	1.75
£1.05 (March 22, 2016)	1.75	1.75

£1.10 (March 29, 2011)	2.00	1.50
£1.28 (April 25, 2012)	2.50	2.50
£1.33 (March 24, 2015)	2.60	2.60

(* Various values have also appeared in miniature sheets and prestige stamp books. The 1st class also exists, self–adhesive, in Smilers sheets. Although January 3, 2013, was the official date of issue of the 1st class and 2nd class printed by Cartor, both stamps were available earlier from post offices.)

First day cover (2nd, 1st, E, 68p)	–	5.50
First day cover (40p)	–	2.50
First day cover (42p)	–	2.50
First day cover (44p, 72p)	–	2.50
First day cover (48p, 78p)	–	3.00
First day cover (50p, 81p)	–	3.50
First day cover (56p, 90p)	–	4.00
First day cover (60p, 97p)	–	4.00
First day cover (68p, £1.10)	–	5.00
First day cover (87p, £1.28)	–	5.00
First day cover (88p)	–	2.00
First day cover (97p)	–	2.25
First day cover (£1.00, £1.33)	–	4.00
First day cover (£1.05)	–	2.25
Stamp cards	5.00	12.00

SCOTLAND DEFINITIVES

Prices in this section are quoted in two columns: mint (left) and fine used (right).

PRE-DECIMAL WILDING ISSUES

3d lilac, 4d blue, 5d blue

6d purple, 9d green

1/3 green, 1/6 grey-blue

▪ 1958–1970

Des: G. F. Huntley (3d, 4d, 5d), J. B. Fleming (6d, 9d), A. B. Imrie (1/3, 1/6). Printed in gravure by Harrisons. Perf 15x14.

A) Wmk: Multiple St Edward's Crown. Non phosphor except where stated.

3d lilac (August 18, 1958)	0.15	0.15
3d lilac, two phos bands	8.00	2.00
3d lilac, one left band	0.20	0.35
3d lilac, one right band	0.20	0.35
3d lilac, one centre band	0.20	0.30
4d blue (February 7, 1966)	0.15	0.15
4d blue, two phos bands	0.15	0.15
6d purple (September 29, 1958)	0.15	0.15
6d purple, two phos bands	0.20	0.25
9d green (March 1, 1967), two phos bands	0.35	0.40
1/3 green (September 29, 1958)	0.35	0.25
1/3 green, two phos bands	0.35	0.40
1/6 grey-blue (March 1, 1967), two phos bands	0.40	0.50

First day cover (3d)	–	10.00
First day cover (6d, 1/3)	–	20.00
First day cover (3d, 6d, 1/3 phosphor)	–	£100
First day cover (4d)	–	10.00
First day cover (9d, 1/6)	–	2.75

B) No watermark. Two phosphor bands except where stated. PVA gum except where stated.

3d lilac (May 16, 1968), one band, gum Arabic	0.15	—
3d lilac, one centre band (July 11, 1968)	0.15	0.20
4d blue (November 28, 1967), gum Arabic	0.15	—
4d blue (July 25, 1968)	0.15	0.20
4d sepia (September 4, 1968), one band	0.15	0.20
4d red (February 26, 1969), one band	0.20	0.20
5d blue (September 4, 1968)	0.20	0.25
9d green (September 28, 1970)	3.25	3.25
1/6 grey-blue (December 12, 1968)	1.25	1.00

First day cover (4d sepia, 5d)	–	2.50
First day cover (4d red)	–	1.00

DECIMAL MACHIN ISSUES WITHOUT ELLIPTICAL PERFORATIONS

3½p green

Des: J. Matthews. Type I has the eye on the lion symbol appearing as a circle, while the tongue and claws are thin; type II (1983) has a solid eye and thicker tongue and claws.

▪ 1971–1980. Printed in gravure by Harrisons

Perf 15x14. Two phosphor bands except where stated.

A) Original coated paper. PVA gum.

2½p pink (July 7, 1971), one phos band	0.15	0.15
3p blue (July 7, 1971)	0.15	0.15
5p violet (July 7, 1971)	0.50	0.50
7½p brown (July 7, 1971)	0.55	0.55

B) Fluorescent coated paper. Gum Arabic.

2½p pink (Sep 22, 1972), one phos band	0.40	–
3p blue (December 14, 1972)	1.00	–

C) Fluorescent coated paper. PVA gum.

2½p pink (January 1973), one phos band	5.00	4.00
3p blue (January 23, 1974)	11.00	10.50
3p blue, one phos band	2.00	2.00
3½p green (January 23, 1974)	10.00	–
5p violet (January 23, 1974)	25.00	21.50
7½p brown (January 23, 1974)	80.00	70.00

D) Fluorescent coated paper. PVAD gum.

3p blue (November 6, 1974), one phos band	0.40	–
3½p green (November 6, 1974)	0.15	0.30
3½p green, one phos band	0.15	0.30
4½p grey–blue (November 6, 1974)	0.15	0.30
5½p deep violet (January 23, 1974)	0.15	0.25
5½p deep violet, one phos band	0.15	0.30
6½p green–blue (January 14, 1976), one band	0.20	0.30
7p red–brown (January 18, 1974), one band	0.20	0.30
8p red (January 23, 1974)	0.20	0.30
8½p green (January 14, 1976)	0.20	0.30
9p violet–blue (January 18, 1978)	0.20	0.35
10p orange (October 20, 1976)	0.20	0.40
10p orange, one phos band	0.30	0.40
10½p grey–blue (January 18, 1978)	0.30	0.35
11p red (October 20, 1976)	0.30	0.35

E) Phosphor coated paper. PVAD gum.

12p yellow–green (July 23, 1980)	0.35	0.35
13½p red–brown (July 23, 1980)	0.50	0.50
15p blue (July 23, 1980)	0.35	0.35

First day cover (2½p, 3p, 5p, 7½p)	–	1.70
First day cover (3½p, 5½p, 8p)	–	1.40
First day cover (4½p)	–	0.80
First day cover (6½p, 8½p)	–	0.80
First day cover (10p, 11p)	–	0.80
First day cover (7p, 9p, 10½p)	–	0.90
First day cover (12p, 13½p, 15p)	–	1.70

■ 1981–1986. Printed in litho by Waddingtons
Perf 13½x14. Phosphor coated paper, except 11½p, 12p, 12½p, 13p (left side phosphor band), 22p (advanced coated paper). PVAD gum except 11½p, 12½p (PVA).

11½p mushroom (April 8, 1981)	0.40	0.40
12p emerald–green (January 7, 1986)	1.80	1.80
12½p light green (February 24, 1982)	0.35	0.35
13p light brown, type 1 (Oct 23, 1984)	0.45	0.45
13p light brown, type II	8.00	8.00
14p grey–blue (April 8, 1981)	0.35	0.35
15½p pale-violet (February 24, 1982)	0.40	0.40
16p light mushroom (April 27, 1983)	0.50	0.50
17p steel blue (October 23, 1984), type I	2.50	2.50
17p steel blue, type II	1.50	1.50
17p steel blue, type II, PVA gum	1.50	1.50
18p violet (April 8, 1981)	0.50	0.50
19½p grey–green (February 24, 1982)	1.00	1.00
20½p bright blue (April 27, 1983)	2.50	2.50

22p deep blue (April 8, 1981)	0.50	0.50
22p yellowish green (Oct 23, 1984), type I	3.00	1.55
22p yellowish green, type II	20.00	20.00
26p red (February 24, 1982), type I	0.60	0.60
28p blue (April 27, 1983), type I	0.60	0.60
31p purple (October 23, 1984), type I	1.10	1.10
31p purple, type II	£110	85.00

(* The 16p also exists printed by Harrisons on advanced coated paper in 1983; price £4 mint, £3.75 used.)

First day cover (11½p, 14p, 18p, 22p)	–	1.00
First day cover (12½p, 15½p, 19½p, 26p)	–	1.50
First day cover (16p, 20½p, 28p)	–	1.50
First day cover (13p, 17p, 22p, 31p)	–	1.50
First day cover (12p)	–	1.10

■ 1986–1993. Printed in litho by Questa
Perf 15x14. One centre phosphor band (12p, 13p, 14p, 18p), phosphor coated paper (19p, 20p, 23p, 24p, 26p, 28p, 32p, 34p, 37p, 39p), or as indicated. PVAD gum.

12p emerald–green (April 29, 1986)	1.20	1.20
13p light brown (November 4, 1986)	0.60	0.60
14p deep blue (November 8, 1988)	0.40	0.40
14p deep blue, left band	0.40	0.40
15p bright blue (Nov 28, 1989), left band	0.35	0.35
17p steel blue (April 29, 1986)	2.00	2.00
18p deep green (January 6, 1987)	1.00	1.00
18p bright green (December 3, 1991)	1.00	1.00
18p bright green, perf 14	1.00	0.90
18p bright green, left band	1.80	1.80
19p orange–red (November 8, 1988)	0.50	0.50
19p orange–red, two bands	1.00	1.00
20p brownish–black (November 28, 1989)	0.50	0.50
22p green (Jan 27, 1987), advanced coated paper	0.75	0.80
22p orange–red (Dec 4, 1990), phos paper	0.60	0.60
23p bright green (November 8, 1988)	0.75	0.75
23p bright green, two bands	9.00	9.00
24p deep red (November 28, 1989)	0.45	0.65
24p chestnut (December 3, 1991)	0.70	0.70
24p chestnut, perf 14	5.00	5.00
24p chestnut, two bands	1.50	1.50
26p red (Jan 27, 1987), advanced coated paper	2.00	2.00
26p drab (December 4, 1990)	0.75	0.75
28p blue (Jan 27, 1987), advanced coated paper	0.70	0.70
28p bluish grey (December 3, 1991)	0.80	0.80
28p bluish grey, perf 14	7.00	7.00
31p purple (April 29, 1986)	1.50	1.50
32p greenish blue (November 8, 1988)	0.90	0.90
34p bluish grey (November 28, 1989)	1.00	1.00
37p rosine (December 4, 1990)	1.20	1.20
39p mauve (December 3, 1991)	1.20	1.20
39p mauve, perf 14	6.00	6.00

(* The 19p and 23p with two bands come from a prestige stamp book. The 13p also exists printed on paper supplied by Coated Papers Ltd, with PVA gum, in 1987)

First day cover (12p, 17p, 31p)	–	10.00
First day cover (13p)	–	9.00
First day cover (18p)	–	1.00
First day cover (22p, 26p, 28p)	–	1.70

First day cover (14p, 19p, 23p, 32p)	–	2.90
First day cover (15p, 20p, 24p, 34p)	–	2.90
First day cover (17p, 22p, 26p, 37p)	–	2.90
First day cover (18p, 24p, 28p, 39p)	–	2.90

DECIMAL MACHIN ISSUES WITH ELLIPTICAL PERFORATIONS

37p mauve

■ 1993–1996. Printed in litho by Questa

Perf 15x14. One phosphor band (19p and 20p), or two phosphor bands (others).

19p bistre (December 7, 1993)	0.60	0.60
19p bistre, one right band	2.50	2.50
20p bright green (July 23, 1996)	0.90	0.90
25p red (December 7, 1993)	0.80	0.85
26p red-brown (July 23, 1996)	0.90	0.90
30p olive-grey (December 7, 1993)	1.00	0.90
37p mauve (July 23, 1996)	2.00	2.00
41p grey-brown (December 7, 1993)	3.00	3.00
63p emerald (July 23, 1996)	2.00	2.00

(* The 19p with phosphor band to right comes from the 1995 National Trust prestige stamp book.)

■ 1997–2000. Printed in gravure by Walsall

A) Perf 15x14. except where stated. One phosphor band (20p), or two phosphor bands (others).

20p bright green (July 1, 1997)	1.25	1.25
26p chestnut (July 1, 1997)	1.00	1.00
37p mauve (July 1, 1997)	1.30	1.30
63p emerald (July 1, 1997)	2.00	2.00

(* The 20p with right phosphor band, the 26p perf 15x14 and perf 14, and the 37p also exist printed by Harrisons, from prestige stamp books.)

B) Perf 15x14. One phosphor band.

1st orange-red (February 15, 2000)	1.35	1.20

(* This stamp was issued only in the Special By Design prestige stamp book.)

First day cover (19p, 25p, 30p, 41p)	–	3.50
First day cover (20p, 26p, 37p, 63p)	–	3.50

PICTORIAL ISSUES WITHOUT WHITE BORDERS

Scottish flag (2nd)   Scottish lion (1st)

Thistle (E)   Tartan (64p, 65p, 68p)

■ 1999–2002

Des: A. Morris (2nd), F. Pottinger and T. Chalk (1st, E), Tayburn (64p), all adapted by Tayburn. Printed in gravure by Walsall (2nd, 1st, E, 64p, 65p), Questa (2nd, 1st, E, 65p), or De La Rue (2nd, 1st, 68p). Perf 15x14. One phosphor band (2nd), two phosphor bands (others).

2nd (June 8, 1999, Walsall)	0.70	0.75
2nd (August 4, 2000, Questa)	0.75	1.00
2nd (June 5, 2002, De La Rue)	0.75	0.75
1st (June 8, 1999, Walsall)	1.10	0.80
1st (October 22, 2001, Questa)	1.35	1.25
1st (June 5, 2002, De La Rue)	1.10	0.80
E (June 8, 1999, Walsall)	1.50	1.25
E (October 22, 2001, Questa)	1.50	1.50
64p (June 8, 1999)	5.00	5.00
65p (April 25, 2000, Walsall)	3.00	3.00
65p (August 4, 2000, Questa)	4.00	4.00
68p (July 4, 2002)	3.00	2.00

(* The 2nd, 1st, E and 65p printed by Questa come from the 2000 Queen Mother and 2001 Unseen and Unheard prestige stamp books.)

First day cover (2nd, 1st E, 64p)	6.50	6.50
First day cover (65p)	4.50	4.50
First day cover (68p)	2.50	2.50
Stamp cards	5.00	14.00

PICTORIAL ISSUES WITH WHITE BORDERS

Scottish flag (2nd)

Scottish lion (1st)

Thistle (E, 40p, 42p, 44p, 48p, 50p, 56p, 60p, 87p, 88p, 97p, £1.00, £1.05)

Tartan (68p, 72p, 78p, 81p, 90p, 97p, £1.10, £1.28, £1.33)

■ 2003 to date

Des: A. Morris (2nd), F. Pottinger and T. Chalk (1st, E), Tayburn (68p), all adapted by Tayburn. Printed in gravure by De La Rue (2nd, 1st, E, 40p, 42p, 44p, 48p, 50p, 56p, 60p, 68p, 72p, 78p, 81p, 90p, 97p), in gravure by Walsall (42p), in gravure by Enschedé (2nd, 1st, 50p, 81p), in litho by De La Rue (1st, 78p, 81p), in litho by Enschedé (1st, in prestige stamp books only) or in litho by Cartor (2nd, 1st, 68p, 87p, 88p, £1.00, £1.05, £1.10, £1.28, £1.33). Perf 15x14. One phosphor band (2nd) or two phosphor bands (others).

2nd (October 14, 2003, De La Rue)	0.80	0.70
2nd (January 3, 2013, Cartor), silver head	0.80	0.70
2nd (2016, Cartor), grey head	0.80	0.70
1st (October 14, 2003, De La Rue)	1.00	0.85
1st (January 3, 2013, Cartor)	1.00	0.85
E (October 14, 2003)	1.60	1.60
40p (May 11, 2004)	1.50	1.50
42p (April 5, 2005, Walsall)	1.20	1.20
42p (May 10, 2005, De La Rue)	1.25	1.20
44p (March 28, 2006)	1.25	1.20
48p (March 27, 2007)	1.25	1.20
50p (April 1, 2008)	1.25	1.20
56p (March 31, 2009)	1.25	1.20
60p (March 30, 2010)	1.50	1.50
68p (October 14, 2003, De La Rue)	2.00	2.00
68p (March 29, 2011, Cartor)	1.20	1.00
72p (March 28, 2006)	2.00	2.00

78p (March 27, 2007)	1.70	1.70
81p (April 1, 2008)	1.70	1.70
87p (April 25, 2012)	2.00	2.00
88p (March 27, 2013)	2.00	2.00
90p (March 31, 2009)	2.00	2.00
97p (March 30, 2010)	2.00	2.00
97p (March 26, 2014)	2.00	2.00
£1.00 (March 24, 2015)	1.75	1.75
£1.05 (March 22, 2016)	1.75	1.75
£1.10 (March 29, 2011)	2.00	1.50
£1.28 (April 25, 2012)	2.50	2.50
£1.33 (March 24, 2015)	2.60	2.60

(* Various values have also appeared in miniature sheets and prestige stamp books. The 1st class also exists, self-adhesive, in Smilers sheets. Although January 3, 2013, was the official date of issue of the 1st class and 2nd class printed by Cartor, both stamps were available earlier from post offices.)

First day cover (2nd, 1st, E, 68p)	–	5.00
First day cover (40p)	–	2.50
First day cover (42p)	–	2.50
First day cover (44p, 72p)	–	2.50
First day cover (48p, 78p)	–	2.50
First day cover (50p, 81p)	–	3.50
First day cover (56p, 90p)	–	4.00
First day cover (60p, 97p)	–	4.00
First day cover (68p, £1.10)	–	5.00
First day cover (87p, £1.28)	–	5.00
First day cover (88p)	–	2.00
First day cover (97p)		2.25
First day cover (£1.00, £1.33)	–	4.00
First day cover (£1.05)	–	2.25
Stamp cards	5.00	11.00

The ideal magazine for Great Britain collectors

WALES DEFINITIVES

Prices in this section are quoted in two columns: mint (left) and fine used (right).

PRE-DECIMAL WILDING ISSUES

3d lilac, 4d blue, 5d blue   6d purple, 9d green

1/3 green, 1/6 grey-blue

■ 1958–1969
Des: Reynolds Stone. Printed in gravure by Harrisons. Perf 15x14.

A) Wmk: Multiple St Edward's Crown. Non-phosphor except where stated.

3d lilac (August 18, 1958)	0.15	0.15
3d lilac, one phos band	0.15	0.20
4d blue (February 7, 1966)	0.20	0.15
4d blue, two phos bands	0.15	0.15
6d purple (September 29, 1958)	0.30	0.25
9d green (March 1, 1967), two phos bands	0.35	0.30
1/3 green (September 29, 1958)	0.45	0.40
1/6 grey-blue (March 1, 1967), two bands	0.40	0.30
First day cover (3d)	–	10.00
First day cover (6d, 1/3)	–	20.00
First day cover (4d)	–	7.50
First day cover (9d, 1/6)	–	2.75

B) No watermark. Two phosphor bands except where stated. PVA gum except where stated.

3d lilac (June 6, 1967), one band, gum Arabic	0.20	0.20
4d blue (June 21, 1968)	0.20	0.30

4d sepia (September 4, 1968), one band	0.15	0.15
4d red (February 26, 1969), one band	0.40	0.15
5d blue (September 4, 1968)	0.30	0.25
1/6 grey-blue (December 12, 1968)	2.00	2.00
First day cover (4d sepia, 5d)	–	2.50
First day cover (4d red)	–	1.00

DECIMAL MACHIN ISSUES WITHOUT ELLIPTICAL PERFORATIONS

3p blue

Des: J. Matthews. Type I has the eye on the dragon symbol appearing as a circle, while the tongue, claws and tail are thin; type II (1983) has a solid eye, and thicker tongue, claws and tail.

■ 1971–1980. Printed in gravure by Harrisons
Perf 15x14. Two phosphor bands except where stated.

A) Original coated paper. PVA gum.

2¹⁄₂p pink (July 7, 1971), one phos band	0.15	0.15
3p blue (July 7, 1971)	0.15	0.15
5p violet (July 7, 1971)	0.50	0.50
7¹⁄₂p brown (July 7, 1971)	0.55	0.55

B) Fluorescent coated paper. Gum Arabic.

2¹⁄₂p pink (September 22, 1972), one band	0.35	–
3p blue (June 6, 1973)	0.75	–

C) Fluorescent coated paper. PVA gum.

2¹⁄₂p pink (1973), one phos band	2.25	2.00
3p blue (February 1973)	9.00	7.00
3p blue (January 1, 1974), one phos band	0.35	0.30
5p violet (June 1973)	18.00	18.00

D) Fluorescent coated paper. PVAD gum.

3¹⁄₂p green (January 23, 1974)	0.15	0.25
3¹⁄₂p green, one phos band	0.15	0.25
4¹⁄₂p grey-blue (November 6, 1974)	0.15	0.30
5¹⁄₂p deep violet (January 23, 1974)	0.15	0.25
5¹⁄₂p deep violet, one phos band	0.20	0.30
6¹⁄₂p green-blue (January 14, 1976), one band	0.20	0.35
7p red-brown (January 18, 1978), one band	0.20	0.30
8p red (January 23, 1974)	0.20	0.35
8¹⁄₂p green (January 14, 1976)	0.20	0.35

9p violet–blue (January 18, 1978)	0.40	0.35
10p orange (October 20, 1976)	0.40	0.35
10p orange, one phos band	0.40	0.35
10¹/₂p grey–blue (January 18, 1978)	0.45	0.40
11p red (October 20, 1976)	0.45	0.40

E) Phosphor coated paper. PVAD gum.

12p yellow–green (July 23, 1980)	0.45	0.45
13¹/₂p red–brown (July 23, 1980)	0.50	0.50
15p blue (July 23, 1980)	0.45	0.45

First day cover (2¹/₂p, 3p, 5p, 7¹/₂p)	–	1.70
First day cover (3¹/₂p, 5¹/₂p, 8p)	–	1.40
First day cover (4¹/₂p)	–	0.80
First day cover (6¹/₂p, 8¹/₂p)	–	0.80
First day cover (10p, 11p)	–	0.90
First day cover (7p, 9p, 10¹/₂p)	–	0.90
First day cover (12p 13¹/₂p, 15p)	–	1.70

■ **1981–1991. Printed in litho by Questa**
A) Perf 13¹/₂x14. Phosphor coated paper, except 11¹/₂p and 12¹/₂p (left side band). PVA gum (11¹/₂p, 14p, 18p, 22p), PVAD gum (others).

11¹/₂p mushroom (April 8, 1981)	0.40	0.40
12¹/₂p light green (February 24, 1982)	0.25	0.35
14p steel–blue (April 8, 1981)	0.35	0.35
15¹/₂p pale–violet (February 24, 1982)	0.40	0.40
16p light mushroom (April 27, 1983)	0.75	0.75
18p mauve (April 8, 1981)	0.70	0.75
19¹/₂p grey–green (February 24, 1982)	0.70	0.70
20¹/₂p bright blue (April 27, 1983)	1.50	1.50
22p deep blue (April 8, 1981)	0.50	0.50
26p red (February 24, 1982), type I	1.00	0.60
28p blue (April 27, 1983), type I	0.60	0.60

B) Perf 15x14. One side phosphor band (12p, 12¹/₂p, 13p), phosphor coated paper (16p, 17p, 19p, 20p, 22p, 23p, 24p, 26p, 28p, 31p, 32p, 34p, 37p, 39p), or as indicated. PVAD gum.

12p emerald–green (January 7, 1986)	1.20	1.20
12¹/₂p light green (January 10, 1984)	5.00	5.00
13p reddish–brown (Oct 23, 1984), type I	0.65	0.60
13p deep brown, type II	2.75	2.75
14p deep blue (November 8, 1988)	0.50	0.50
15p bright blue (November 28, 1989)	0.65	0.65
16p light mushroom (January 10, 1984)	1.20	1.20
17p steel–blue (October 23, 1984), type I	2.00	2.00
17p steel–blue, type I, advanced coated paper	1.25	1.25
17p steel–blue, type II	40.00	40.00
17p deep blue (December 4, 1990), one band	0.60	0.90
18p deep green (January 6, 1987)	0.95	0.60
18p bright green (December 3, 1991)	1.00	1.00
18p bright green, centre band	0.90	0.45
18p bright green, left band	1.80	1.80
18p bright green, right band	1.50	1.50
18p bright green, perf 14	2.00	4.00
19p orange–red (November 8, 1988)	0.50	0.75
20p brownish–black (November 28, 1989)	0.50	0.60
22p green (Oct 23, 1984), advanced paper	1.00	1.00
22p orange–red (December 4, 1990)	0.60	0.65
23p bright green (November 8, 1988)	1.00	1.00

24p deep red (November 28, 1989)	0.65	0.90
24p chestnut (December 3, 1991)	0.70	0.80
24p chestnut, two bands	1.80	1.10
24p chestnut, perf 14	3.00	2.00
26p red (Jan 27, 1987), type II, advanced paper	2.00	2.00
26p drab (December 4, 1990)	0.75	0.95
28p blue (Jan 27, 1987), type II, advanced paper	0.70	1.05
28p bluish grey (December 3, 1991)	0.80	0.95
31p purple (October 23, 1984)	1.00	0.95
31p purple, advanced coated paper	1.00	1.00
32p greenish blue (November 8, 1988)	1.00	1.20
34p bluish grey (November 28, 1989)	1.20	1.20
37p rosine (December 4, 1990)	1.20	1.35
39p mauve (December 3, 1991)	1.20	1.35

(* The 18p with one band at left or right comes from prestige stamp books. The 13p also exists printed on paper supplied by Coated Papers Ltd, with PVA gum, in 1987)

First day cover (11¹/₂p, 14p, 18p, 22p)	–	1.00
First day cover (12¹/₂p, 15¹/₂p. 19¹/₂p, 26p)	–	1.50
First day cover (16p, 20¹/₂p, 28p)	–	1.50
First day cover (12p, 17p, 22p, 31p)	–	1.50
First day cover (12p)	–	1.50
First day cover (18p)	–	1.50
First day cover (14p, 19p, 23p, 32p)	–	2.00
First day cover (15p, 20p, 24p, 34p)	–	2.00
First day cover (17p, 22p, 26p, 37p)	–	2.00
First day cover (18p, 24p, 28p, 39p)	–	2.00

DECIMAL MACHIN ISSUES WITH ELLIPTICAL PERFORATIONS

30p olive–grey

■ **1993–1996. Printed in litho by Questa**
Perf 15x14. One phosphor band (19p and 20p), two phosphor bands (others).

19p bistre (December 7, 1993)	0.60	0.70
19p bistre, right band	2.25	2.25
20p bright green (July 23, 1996)	1.25	1.25
25p red (December 7, 1993)	0.85	0.80
26p red–brown (July 23, 1996)	0.90	1.25
30p olive–grey (December 7, 1993)	1.00	0.95
37p mauve (July 23, 1996)	1.30	2.50
41p grey–brown (December 7, 1993)	1.30	1.80
63p emerald (July 23, 1996)	2.75	2.75

(* The 19p with phosphor band to right comes from the 1995 National Trust prestige stamp book.)

26p chestnut

■ 1997–2000. Printed in gravure by Walsall

A) Perf 15x14. One phosphor band (19p and 20p), two phosphor bands (others).

20p bright green (July 1, 1997)	1.00	1.00
26p chestnut (July 1, 1997)	0.90	0.90
37p mauve (July 1, 1997)	2.00	2.00
63p emerald (July 1, 1997)	2.50	2.50

(* The 20p with right phosphor band, the 26p perf 15x14 and perf 14, and the 37p also exist printed by Harrisons, from prestige stamp books.)

B) Perf 15x14. One phosphor band.

1st orange-red (February 15, 2000)	2.00	2.00

(* This stamp was issued only in the Special By Design prestige stamp book.)

First day cover (19p, 25p, 30p, 41p)	–	2.50
First day cover (20p, 26p, 37p, 63p)	–	2.50

PICTORIAL ISSUES WITHOUT WHITE BORDERS

Leek (2nd)

Welsh dragon (1st)

Daffodil (E)

Prince of Wales' feathers (64p, 65p, 68p)

■ 1999–2002

Des: D. Petersen (2nd), T. and G. Petersen (1st), I. Rees (E), R. Evans (64p), all adapted by Tutssels. Printed in gravure by Walsall (2nd, 1st, E, 64p, 65p) or De La Rue (2nd, 1st, 68p). Perf 15x14. One phosphor band (2nd), two phosphor bands (others).

2nd (June 8, 1999, Walsall)	0.75	0.80
2nd (September 18, 2000, Walsall), right band	3.35	3.00
2nd (May 28, 2003, De La Rue)	0.75	0.80
1st (June 8, 1999, Walsall)	1.20	0.95
1st (March 4, 2003, De La Rue)	1.20	0.95
E (June 8, 1999)	1.50	1.20
64p (June 8, 1999)	5.00	5.00
65p (April 25, 2000)	2.00	2.00
68p (July 4, 2002)	2.25	2.25

(* The 2nd class with band at right comes from the 2000 Treasury of Trees prestige stamp book.)

First day cover (2nd, 1st, E, 64p)	–	6.50
First day cover (65p)	–	4.50
First day cover (68p)	–	2.50
Stamp cards	5.00	15.00

PICTORIAL ISSUES WITH WHITE BORDERS

Leek (2nd)

Welsh dragon (1st)

Daffodil (E, 40p, 42p, 44p, 48p, 50p, 56p, 60p, 87p, 88p, 97p, £1.00, £1.05)

Prince of Wales' feathers (68p, 72p, 78p, 81p, 90p, 97p, £1.10, £1.28, £1.33)

■ 2003 to date

Des: D. Petersen (2nd), T. and G. Petersen (1st), I. Rees (E), R. Evans (68p), all adapted by Tutssels. Printed in gravure by De La Rue (2nd, 1st, E, 40p, 42p, 44p, 48p, 50p, 56p, 60p, 68p, 72p, 78p,

81p, 90p, 97p), in gravure by Walsall (42p), in litho by De La Rue (1st, 78p, 81p), in litho by Enschedé (1st, in prestige stamp books only) or in litho by Cartor (2nd, 1st, 68p, 87p, 88p, £1.00, £1.05, £1.10, £1.28, £1.33). Perf 15x14. One phosphor band (2nd) or two phosphor bands (others).

2nd (October 14, 2003, De La Rue)	0.80	0.70
2nd (January 3, 2013, Cartor)	0.80	0.70
1st (October 14, 2003, De La Rue)	1.00	0.85
1st (January 3, 2013, Cartor)	1.00	0.85
E (October 14, 2003)	1.60	1.70
40p (May 11, 2004)	1.70	1.90
42p (April 5, 2005, Walsall)	1.25	1.25
42p (May 10, 2005, De La Rue)	1.25	1.25
44p (March 28, 2006)	1.30	1.30
48p (March 27, 2007)	1.30	1.30
50p (April 1, 2008)	1.30	1.30
56p (March 31, 2009)	1.30	1.30
60p (March 30, 2010)	1.50	1.50
68p (October 14, 2003, De La Rue)	2.00	2.00
68p (March 29, 2011, Cartor)	1.30	1.10
72p (March 28, 2006)	2.00	2.00
78p (March 27, 2007)	1.75	1.75
81p (April 1, 2008)	1.75	1.75
87p (April 25, 2012)	2.00	2.00
88p (March 27, 2013)	2.00	2.00
90p (March 31, 2009)	1.75	1.75
97p (March 30, 2010)	2.00	1.75
97p (March 26, 2014)	2.00	2.00
£1.00 (March 24, 2015)	1.75	1.75
£1.05 (March 22, 2016)	1.75	1.75
£1.10 (March 29, 2011)	2.00	1.50
£1.28 (April 25, 2012)	2.50	2.50
£1.33 (March 24, 2015)	2.60	2.60

(* Various values have also appeared in miniature sheets and prestige stamp books. The 1st class also exists, self-adhesive, in Smilers sheets. Although January 3, 2013, was the official date of issue of the 1st class and 2nd class printed by Cartor, both stamps were available earlier from post offices.)

First day cover (2nd, 1st, E, 68p)	–	3.50
First day cover (40p)	–	2.50
First day cover (42p)	–	2.50
First day cover (44p, 72p)	–	2.50
First day cover (48p, 78p)	–	3.25
First day cover (50p, 81p)	–	3.50
First day cover (56p, 90p)	–	4.00
First day cover (60p, 97p)	–	4.00
First day cover (68p, £1.10)	–	5.00
First day cover (87p, £1.28)	–	5.00
First day cover (88p)	–	2.00
First day cover (97p)	–	2.25
First day cover (£1.00, £1.33)	–	4.00
First day cover (£1.05)	–	2.25
Stamp cards	5.00	11.00

ENGLAND DEFINITIVES

Prices in this section are quoted in two columns: mint (left) and fine used (right).

PICTORIAL ISSUES

Three lions (2nd)

Crowned lion and shield (1st)

Oak tree (E)

Tudor rose (65p, 68p)

■ 2001–2002

Des: Sedley Place, after sculptures by D. Dathan. Printed in gravure by De La Rue. Perf 15x14. One phosphor band (2nd), two phosphor bands (others).

2nd (April 23, 2001)	0.90	0.70
1st (April 23, 2001)	1.20	0.90
E (April 23, 2001)	1.70	1.70
65p (April 23, 2001)	1.75	1.50
68p (July 4, 2002)	1.75	1.60

(* The 2nd and 1st class also exist printed in gravure by Questa, in the 2002 Across The Universe prestige stamp book.)

First day cover (2nd, 1st, E, 65p)	–	3.00
First day cover (68p)	–	3.00
Stamp cards	6.00	14.00

Three lions (2nd)

Crowned lion and shield (1st)

Oak tree (E, 40p, 42p, 44p, 48p, 50p, 56p, 60p, 87p, 88p, 97p,

£1.00, £1.05)

Tudor rose (68p, 72p, 78p, 81p, 90p, 97p, £1.10, £1.28, £1.33)

■ 2003 to date

Des: Sedley Place, after sculptures by D. Dathan. Printed in gravure by De La Rue (2nd, 1st, E, 40p, 42p, 44p, 48p, 50p, 56p, 60p, 68p, 72p, 78p, 81p, 90p, 97p), in gravure by Walsall (2nd, 42p), in litho by De La Rue (1st, 78p, 81p), in litho by Enschedé (1st, in prestige stamp books only) or in litho by Cartor (2nd, 1st, 68p, 87p, 88p, £1.00, £1.05, £1.10, £1.28, £1.33). Perf 15x14. One phosphor band (2nd) or two phosphor bands (others).

2nd (October 14, 2003, De La Rue)	0.80	0.70
2nd (January 3, 2013, Cartor)	0.80	0.70
1st (October 14, 2003, De La Rue)	1.00	0.85
1st (January 3, 2013, Cartor)	1.00	0.85
E (October 14, 2003)	1.90	1.90
40p (May 11, 2004)	1.10	1.25
42p (April 5, 2005, Walsall)	1.25	1.25
42p (May 10, 2005, De La Rue)	1.20	1.20
44p (May 28, 2006)	1.25	1.25
48p (Mar 27, 2007)	1.00	1.00
50p (April 1, 2008)	1.00	1.00
56p (March 31, 2009)	1.10	1.10
60p (March 30, 2010)	1.25	1.00
68p (October 14, 2003, De La Rue)	1.70	1.70
68p (March 29, 2011, Cartor)	1.30	1.00
72p (March 28, 2006)	1.50	1.50
78p (March 27, 2007)	1.60	1.60
81p (April 1, 2008)	1.70	1.70
87p (April 25, 2012)	1.90	1.90
88p (March 27, 2013)	1.90	1.90
90p (March 31, 2009)	1.80	1.80
97p (March 30, 2010)	1.80	1.80
97p (March 26, 2014)	1.80	1.80
£1.00 (March 24, 2015)	1.80	1.80
£1.05 (March 22, 2016)	1.75	1.75
£1.10 (March 29, 2011)	2.00	1.50
£1.28 (April 25, 2012)	2.50	2.50
£1.33 (March 24, 2015)	2.60	2.60

(* Various values have also appeared in miniature sheets and prestige stamp books. The 1st class also exists, self-adhesive, from Smilers sheets. Although January 3, 2013, was the official date of issue of the 1st class and 2nd class printed by Cartor, both stamps were available earlier from post offices.)

First day cover (2nd, 1st, E, 68p)	–	5.00
First day cover (40p)	–	2.50
First day cover (42p)	–	2.50
First day cover (44p, 72p)	–	2.50
First day cover (48p, 78p)	–	2.50
First day cover (50p, 81p)	–	3.50
First day cover (56p, 90p)	–	4.00
First day cover (60p, 97p)	–	4.00
First day cover (68p, £1.10)	–	5.00
First day cover (87p, £1.28)	–	5.00
First day cover (88p)	–	2.00
First day cover (97p)	–	2.25
First day cover (£1.00, £1.33)	–	4.00
First day cover (£1.05)	–	2.25
Stamp cards	5.00	11.00

STITCHED OR STAPLED BOOKLETS

In this section, items are priced in very fine mint condition only.

EDWARD VII, 1904–10

■ **2/– booklets**

24 x 1d (sold at 2s ½d). Printed by De La Rue, 1904	£270
12 x 1d, 23 x ½d. Printed by De La Rue, 1906	£1,200
18 x 1d, 11 x ½d. Printed by De La Rue, 1907–09	£1,250
18 x 1d, 11 x ½d. Printed by Harrison, 1911	£1,450

GEORGE V, 1910–35

■ **2/– booklets, Downey head**

18 x 1d, 12 x ½d. Wmk: Imperial Crown printed by Harrison, 1911	£1,000
18 x 1d, 12 x ½d. Wmk: Simple Royal Cypher printed by Harrison, 1912	£800

■ **2/– booklets, Mackennal head**

18 x 1d, 12 x ½d. Wmk: Simple Royal Cypher printed by Harrison, 1913; stamps of 1911–1913	£750
10 x 1½d, 6 x 1d, 6 x ½d. Wmk: Simple Royal Cypher printed by Harrison, 1924	£1,700
10 x 1½d, 6 x 1d, 6 x ½d. Wmk: Block GVR printed by Waterlow, 1924	£600
10 x 1½d, 6 x 1d, 6 x ½d. printed by Waterlow, 1929; PUC stamps	£450
10 x 1½d, 6 x 1d, 6 x ½d. Wmk: Block GVR printed by Harrison, 1934	£800
10 x 1½d, 6 x 1d, 6 x ½d. Wmk: Block GVR printed by Harrison, 1935; photogravure, intermediate	£1,800
10 x 1½d, 6 x 1d, 6 x ½d. Wmk: Block GVR	

printed by Harrison, 1935; photogravure, small format	£475
12 x 1½d, 4 x 1d, 4 x ½d printed by Harrison, 1935; Silver Jubilee stamps	80.00

■ **3/– booklets**

12 x 1½d, 12 x 1d, 12 x ½d. Wmk: Simple Royal Cypher printed by Harrison, 1918	£1,100
18 x 1½d, 6 x 1d, 6 x ½d. Wmk: Simple Royal Cypher printed by Harrison, 1919	£1,100
18 x 2d printed by Harrison, 1921	£1,600
24 x 1½d printed by Harrison, 1922	£1,600
18 x 1½d, 6 x 1d, 6 x ½d. Wmk: Block GVR printed by Waterlow, 1924	£450
18 x 1½d, 6 x 1d, 6 x ½d printed by Waterlow, 1929; PUC stamps	£375
18 x 1½d, 6 x 1d, 6 x ½d. Wmk: Block GVR printed by Harrison, 1934	£600
18 x 1½d, 6 x 1d, 6 x ½d. Wmk: Block GVR printed by Harrison, 1935; photogravure, intermediate	£1,550
18 x 1½d, 6 x 1d, 6 x ½d. Wmk: Block GVR printed by Harrison, 1935; photogravure, small format	£425
20 x 1½d, 4 x 1d, 4 x ½d printed by Harrison, 1935; Silver Jubilee stamps	65.00

■ **3/6 booklets**

18 x 2d, 6 x 1d printed by Harrison, 1920	£1,350
12 x 2d, 6 x 1½d, 6 x 1d, 6 x ½d printed by Harrison, 1921	£1,350

■ **5/– booklets**

34 x 1½d, 6 x 1d, 6 x ½d. Green cover printed by Waterlow, 1931	£4,000
34 x 1½d, 6 x 1d, 6 x ½d. Buff cover printed by Waterlow, 1932	£3,600
34 x 1½d, 6 x 1d, 6 x ½d printed by Harrison, 1934	£1,500
34 x 1½d, 6 x 1d, 6 x ½d printed by Harrison, 1935; photogravure, intermediate	£4,500
34 x 1½d, 6 x 1d, 6 x ½d printed by Harrison, 1935; photogravure, small format	£450

EDWARD VIII, 1936

6d booklets
4 x 1½d (plain cover). Printed by Harrison, 1937 — 30.00

2/- booklets
10 x 1½d, 6 x 1d, 6 x ½d. Printed by Harrison, 1936 — 95.00

3/- booklets
18 x 1½d, 6 x 1d, 6 x ½d. Printed by Harrison, 1936 — 95.00

5/- booklets
34 x 1½d, 6 x 1d, 6 x ½d. Printed by Harrison, 1937 — £200

GEORGE VI, 1937–52

6d booklets
4 x 1½d (plain buff cover)
printed by Harrison, 1938 — 60.00
2 x 1½d, 2 x 1d, 2 x ½d (plain pink cover)
printed by Harrison, 1938 — £240
4 x 1d, 4 x ½d (plain green cover)
printed by Harrison, 1940 — £100

1/- booklets
4 x 1½d, 4 x 1d, 4 x ½d (in panes of two)
printed by Harrison, 1947; stamps in pale shades — 11.00
4 x 1½d, 4 x 1d, 4 x ½d (in panes of four)
printed by Harrison, 1948; stamps in pale shades — £5,000
4 x 1½d, 4 x 1d, 4 x ½d (in panes of two)
printed by Harrison, 1951; stamps in changed colours — 15.00
4 x 1½d, 4 x 1d, 4 x ½d (in panes of four)
printed by Harrison, 1951; stamps in changed colours — 12.00

2/- booklets
10 x 1½d, 6 x 1d, 6 x ½d (royal cypher on cover)
printed by Harrison, 1937 — £600
10 x 1½d, 6 x 1d, 6 x ½d (GPO cypher on cover)
printed by Harrison, 1938 — £600

2/6 booklets
6 x 2½d, 6 x 2d, 6 x ½d (red cover)
printed by Harrison, 1940 — £900
6 x 2½d, 6 x 2d, 6 x ½d (blue cover)
printed by Harrison, 1940 — £900
6 x 2½d, 6 x 2d, 6 x ½d (green cover)
printed by Harrison, 1940 — £700
6 x 2½d, 6 x 2d, 6 x ½d (green cover)
printed by Harrison, 1942; stamps in pale shades — £700

6 x 2½d, 6 x 2d, 6 x ½d (green cover, no advertising)
printed by Harrison, 1943; stamps in pale shades — 85.00
6 x 2½d, 6 x 2d, 6 x ½d (green cover, no advertising)
printed by Harrison, 1951; stamps in changed colours — 40.00
6 x 2½d, 6 x 1½d, 3 x 1d, 6 x ½d
printed by Harrison, 1952 — 30.00

3/- booklets
18 x 1½d, 6 x 1d, 6 x ½d (royal cypher on cover)
printed by Harrison, 1937 — £1,050
18 x 1½d, 6 x 1d, 6 x ½d (GPO cypher on cover)
printed by Harrison, 1938 — £1,050

5/- booklets
34 x 1½d, 6 x 1d, 6 x ½d (royal cypher on cover)
printed by Harrison, 1937 — £1,250
34 x 1½d, 6 x 1d, 6 x ½d (GPO cypher on cover)
printed by Harrison, 1938 — £1,250
18 x 2½d, 6 x 2d, 6 x ½d (GPO cypher on cover)
printed by Harrison, 1940 — £1,250
18 x 2½d, 6 x 2d, 6 x ½d (GPO cypher on cover)
printed by Harrison, 1942; stamps in pale shades — £1,250
18 x 2½d, 6 x 2d, 6 x ½d (GPO cypher, no advertising)
printed by Harrison, 1944; stamps in pale shades — £120
18 x 2½d, 6 x 2d, 6 x ½d (GPO cypher, no advertising)
printed by Harrison, 1951; stamps in changed colours — 55.00
18 x 2½d, 6 x 1½d, 3 x 1d, 6 x ½d
printed by Harrison, 1952 — 35.00
12 x 2½d, 6 x 2d, 6 x 1½d, 6 x 1d, 6 x ½d
printed by Harrison, 1953 — 50.00

ELIZABETH II WILDINGS, 1953–68

1/- booklets
4 x 1½d, 4 x 1d, 4 x ½d (panes of 2). Wmk: Tudor Crown
printed by Harrison, 1953 — 3.00
4 x 1½d, 4 x 1d, 4 x ½d (panes of 4). Wmk: Tudor Crown
printed by Harrison, 1954 — 6.00
4 x 1½d, 4 x 1d, 4 x ½d (panes of 2). Wmk: St. Edward's Crown
printed by Harrison, 1957 — 40.00
4 x 1½d, 4 x 1d, 4 x ½d (panes of 4). Wmk: St. Edward's Crown
printed by Harrison, 1956 — 4.00
4 x 1½d, 4 x 1d, 4 x ½d (panes of 4). Wmk: Multiple Crowns
printed by Harrison, 1959 — 3.00

2/- booklets
4 x 3d, 4 x 1½d, 4 x 1d, 4 x ½d. Wmk: St. Edward's Crown
printed by Harrison, 1959; pink cover — 5.00
4 x 3d, 4 x 1½d, 4 x 1d, 4 x ½d. Wmk: Multiple Crowns (upright)
printed by Harrison, 1960; pink cover — 6.00

4 x 3d, 4 x 1½d, 4 x 1d, 4 x ½d. Wmk: Multiple Crowns (upright)
printed by Harrison, 1961; yellow cover   4.00

4 x 3d, 4 x 1½d, 4 x 1d, 4 x ½d. Wmk: Multiple Crowns (sideways)
printed by Harrison, 1961–62; yellow cover   30.00

4 x 3d, 4 x 1½d, 4 x 1d, 4 x ½d. Wmk: Multiple Crowns (sideways)
printed by Harrison, 1961–65; yellow cover; phos bands   50.00

4 x 4d, 2 x 1d se-tenant with 2 x 3d. Wmk: Multiple Crowns
printed by Harrison, 1965–67; 3d with no phos bands   3.00

4 x 4d, 2 x 1d se-tenant with 2 x 3d. Wmk: Multiple Crowns
printed by Harrison, 1965–67; 3d with one phos band   8.00

4 x 4d, 2 x 1d se-tenant with 2 x 3d. Wmk: Multiple Crowns
printed by Harrison, 1965–67; 3d with two phos bands   2.00

8 x 2½d, 3 x ½d se-tenant with 1 x 2½d. Wmk: Multiple Crowns
printed by Harrison, 1963   3.00

8 x ½d, 8 x 2½d (se-tenant in panes). Wmk: Multiple Crowns
printed by Harrison, 1964   3.00

8 x 3d. Wmk: Multiple Crowns (sideways)
printed by Harrison, 1965   1.00

■ 2/6 booklets

6 x 2½d, 6 x 1½d (QEII), 3 x 1d, 6 x ½d (KGVI)
printed by Harrison, 1953–54   30.00

6 x 2½d, 6 x 1½d, 6 x ½d (QEII), 3 x 1d (KGVI)
printed by Harrison, 1954   £400

6 x 2½d, 6 x 1½d, 3x 1d, 6 x ½d. Wmk: Tudor Crown
printed by Harrison, 1954–55   40.00

6 x 2½d, 6 x 1½d, 3x 1d, 6 x ½d. Wmk: St Edward's Crown
printed by Harrison, 1955–57   25.00

6 x 2½d, 6 x 2d, 6 x ½d, Wmk: St Edward's Crown
printed by Harrison, 1957   22.00

■ 3/– booklets

6 x 3d, 6 x 1½d, 6 x 1d, 6 x ½d. Wmk: St Edward's Crown
printed by Harrison, 1958   18.00

6 x 3d, 6 x 1½d, 6 x 1d, 6 x ½d. Wmk: Multiple Crowns
printed by Harrison, 1958–59   24.00

6 x 3d, 6 x 1½d, 6 x 1d, 6 x ½d. Wmk: Multiple Crowns
printed by Harrison, 1959–60; stamps with graphite lines   £180

6 x 3d, 6 x 1½d, 6 x 1d, 6 x ½d. Wmk: Multiple Crowns
printed by Harrison, 1960–65; stamps with phos bands   55.00

■ 3/9 booklets

18 x 2½d. Wmk: Tudor Crown
printed by Harrison, 1953–55   22.00

18 x 2½d. Wmk: St Edward's Crown
printed by Harrison, 1956–57   20.00

■ 4/6 booklets

18 x 3d. Wmk: St Edward's Crown
printed by Harrison, 1957–58   20.00

18 x 3d. Wmk: Multiple Crowns
printed by Harrison, 1959   20.00

18 x 3d. Wmk: Multiple Crowns
printed by Harrison, 1959–60; stamps with graphite lines   15.00

18 x 3d. Wmk: Multiple Crowns
printed by Harrison, 1960–65; stamps with phos bands   35.00

12 x 4d, 6 x 1d.Wmk: Multiple Crowns
printed by Harrison, 1965–67   18.00

12 x 4d, 6 x 1d.Wmk: Multiple Crowns
printed by Harrison, 1965–68; stamps with phos bands   7.00

■ 5/– booklets

12 x 2½d, 6 x 1½d (QEII), 6 x 2d, 6 x 1d, 6 x ½d (KGVI)
printed by Harrison, 1953–54   30.00

12 x 2½d, 6 x 1½d, 6 x ½d (QEII), 6 x 2d, 6 x 1d (KGVI)
printed by Harrison, 1954   £350

12 x 2½d, 6 x 1½d, 6 x ½d, 6 x 1d (QEII), 6 x 2d (KGVI)
printed by Harrison, 1954   £200

12 x 2½d, 6 x 1½d, 6 x ½d, 6 x 1d, 6 x 2d. Wmk: Tudor Crown
printed by Harrison, 1954–55   70.00

12 x 2½d, 6 x 1½d, 6 x ½d, 6 x 1d, 6 x 2d. Wmk: St Edward's
printed by Harrison, 1955–57   25.00

12 x 3d, 6 x 2½d, 6 x 1½d, 6 x ½d.Wmk: St Edward's Crown
printed by Harrison, 1958   18.00

12 x 3d, 6 x 2½d, 6 x 1½d, 6 x ½d. Wmk: Multiple Crowns
printed by Harrison, 1959–65   30.00

12 x 3d, 6 x 2½d, 6 x 1½d, 6 x ½d. Wmk: Multiple Crowns
printed by Harrison, 1959–60; stamps with graphite lines   £100

12 x 3d, 6 x 2½d, 6 x 1½d, 6 x ½d. Wmk: Multiple Crowns
printed by Harrison, 1960–62; 2½d with two phos bands   £150

12 x 3d, 6 x 2½d, 6 x 1½d, 6 x ½d. Wmk: Multiple Crowns
printed by Harrison, 1962–65; 2½d with one phos band   £100

■ 6/– booklets

18 x 4d.Wmk: Multiple Crowns
printed by Harrison, 1965–67   30.00

18 x 4d.Wmk: Multiple Crowns
printed by Harrison, 1965–67; stamps with phos bands   35.00

■ 10/– booklets

30 x 3d, 6 x 2d, 6 x 1½d, 6 x 1d, 6 x ½d
printed by Harrison, 1961   £100

30 x 3d, 6 x 2½d, 6 x 1½d, 6 x 1d
printed by Harrison, 1962–64   £100

24 x 4d, 6 x 3d, 6 x 1d
printed by Harrison, 1965–66   25.00

24 x 4d, 6 x 3d, 6 x 1d
printed by Harrison, 1967; 3d with side phos band   8.00

24 x 4d, 6 x 3d, 6 x 1d
printed by Harrison, 1967–68; 3d with centre phos band   5.00

ELIZABETH II PRE-DECIMAL MACHINS, 1968–70

■ 2/– booklets

4 x 4d sepia (two phos bands), 2 x 1d se-tenant with 2 x 3d
(two phos bands)
printed by Harrison, 1968; yellow cover   0.80

4 x 4d sepia (two phos bands), plus 2 x 4d sepia (centre

phos band) se-tenant with two labels
printed by Harrison, 1968–70; grey cover · · · · · · · 0.65
4 x 4d sepia (centre phos band), plus 2 x 4d sepia (centre
phos band) se-tenant with two labels
printed by Harrison, 1968–69; grey cover · · · · · · · 1.00
4 x 4d red (centre phos band) plus 2 x 4d red (centre
phos band) se-tenant with two labels
printed by Harrison, 1969–70; grey cover · · · · · · · 1.50

■ 4/6 booklets. Ships series
6 x 4d sepia, 6 x 4d sepia (two phos bands), 6 x 1d
printed by Harrison, 1968; blue plain cover · · · · · · 4.00
6 x 4d sepia, 6 x 4d sepia (two phos bands), 6 x 1d
printed by Harrison, 1968; Cutty Sark cover · · · · · · 1.00
6 x 4d sepia, 6 x 4d sepia (centre phos band), 6 x 1d
printed by Harrison, 1968; Golden Hind cover · · · · · 1.00
6 x 4d sepia, 6 x 4d sepia (centre phos band), 6 x 1d
printed by Harrison, 1968; Discovery cover · · · · · · 1.00
6 x 4d red, 6 x 4d red (centre phos band), 6 x 1d
printed by Harrison, 1969; Queen Elizabeth 2 cover · 1.50
6 x 4d red, 6 x 4d red (centre phos band), 6 x 1d
printed by Harrison, 1969; Sirius cover · · · · · · · · 2.50
6 x 4d red, 6 x 4d red (centre phos band), 6 x 1d
printed by Harrison, 1969; Dreadnought cover · · · · · 2.00
6 x 4d red, 6 x 4d red (centre phos band), 6 x 1d
printed by Harrison, 1969–70; Mauretania cover · · · · 4.00
6 x 4d red, 6 x 4d red (centre phos band), 6 x 1d
printed by Harrison, 1970; Victory cover · · · · · · · 4.00
6 x 4d red, 6 x 4d red (centre phos band), 6 x 1d
printed by Harrison, 1970; Sovereign on the Seas cover · 4.00

■ 5/– booklets. English Homes series
6 x 5d, 6 x 5d
printed by Harrison, 1968; Ightham Mote cover · · · · 2.00
6 x 5d, 6 x 5d
printed by Harrison, 1969; Little Moreton Hall cover · · 2.00
6 x 5d, 6 x 5d
printed by Harrison, 1969; Long Melford Hall cover 2.50
6 x 5d, 6 x 5d
printed by Harrison, 1969; Mompesson House cover · · 2.00
6 x 5d, 6 x 5d
printed by Harrison, 1970; Cumberland Terrace cover · 2.00
6 x 5d, 6 x 5d
printed by Harrison, 1970; Vineyard, Saffron Walden cover · 2.50
6 x 5d, 6 x 5d
printed by Harrison, 1970; Mereworth Castle cover · · 3.00
6 x 5d, 6 x 5d
printed by Harrison, 1970; Philympia 1970 cover · · · 2.00

■ 6/– booklets. Birds series
6 x 4d sepia, 6 x 4d sepia, 6 x 4d sepia (phos bands), gum arabic
printed by Harrison, 1967–68; plain purple cover · · · 40.00
6 x 4d sepia, 6 x 4d sepia, 6 x 4d sepia (phos bands), PVA gum
printed by Harrison, 1970; plain purple cover · · · · £475
6 x 4d sepia, 6 x 4d sepia, 6 x 4d sepia (two phos bands)
printed by Harrison, 1968; Kingfisher cover · · · · · · 2.00
6 x 4d sepia, 6 x 4d sepia, 6 x 4d sepia (two phos bands)
printed by Harrison, 1968; Peregrine Falcon cover · · · 1.80
6 x 4d sepia, 6 x 4d sepia, 6 x 4d sepia (centre phos band)
printed by Harrison, 1968; Peregrine Falcon cover · · · 2.00

6 x 4d sepia, 6 x 4d sepia, 6 x 4d sepia (centre phos band)
printed by Harrison, 1968; Pied Woodpecker cover · · · 2.00
6 x 4d sepia, 6 x 4d sepia, 6 x 4d sepia (centre phos band)
printed by Harrison, 1968; Great Crested Grebe cover · 2.00
6 x 4d sepia, 6 x 4d sepia, 6 x 4d sepia (centre phos band)
printed by Harrison, 1969; Barn Owl cover · · · · · · · 3.00
6 x 4d red, 6 x 4d red, 6 x 4d red (centre phos band)
printed by Harrison, 1969; Barn Owl cover · · · · · · · 3.50
6 x 4d red, 6 x 4d red, 6 x 4d red (centre phos band)
printed by Harrison, 1969; Jay cover · · · · · · · · · 3.00
6 x 4d red, 6 x 4d red, 6 x 4d red (centre phos band)
printed by Harrison, 1969; Puffin cover · · · · · · · · 3.00
6 x 4d red, 6 x 4d red, 6 x 4d red (centre phos band)
printed by Harrison, 1969–70; Cormorant cover · · · · 3.50
6 x 4d red, 6 x 4d red, 6 x 4d red (centre phos band)
printed by Harrison, 1970; Wren cover · · · · 3.50
6 x 4d red, 6 x 4d red, 6 x 4d red (centre phos band)
printed by Harrison, 1970; Golden Eagle cover · · · · · 3.50

■ 10/– booklets. Explorers series
6 x 4d sepia, 6 x 4d sepia, 6 x 4d sepia, 6 x 4d sepia (two
phos bands), 6 x 3d, 6 x 1d
printed by Harrison, 1968; Livingstone cover · · · · · 4.50
6 x 5d, 6 x 5d, 6 x 4d sepia, 6 x 4d sepia (centre phos band),
4 x 1d se-tenant with 2 x 4d sepia (one phos band)
printed by Harrison, 1968; Scott cover · · · · · · · · 4.50
6 x 5d, 6 x 5d, 6 x 4d red, 6 x 4d red (centre phos band),
4 x 1d se-tenant with 2 x 4d red (one phos band)
printed by Harrison, 1969; Kingsley cover · · · · · · · 3.50
6 x 5d, 6 x 5d, 6 x 4d red, 6 x 4d red (centre phos band),
4 x 1d se-tenant with 2 x 4d red (one phos band)
printed by Harrison, 1969; Shackleton cover · · · · · · 4.00
6 x 5d, 6 x 5d, 6 x 4d red, 6 x 4d red (centre phos band),
4 x 1d se-tenant with 2 x 4d red (one phos band)
printed by Harrison, 1970; Frobisher cover · · · · · · 5.50
6 x 5d, 6 x 5d, 6 x 4d red, 6 x 4d red (centre phos band),
4 x 1d se-tenant with 2 x 4d red (one phos band)
printed by Harrison, 1970; Cook cover · · · · · · · · 6.00

ELIZABETH II DECIMAL MACHINS, 1971–76

■ 10p booklets. Pillar box series
2 x ½p, 2 x 1p, 2 x 1½p, 2 x 2p
printed by Harrison, 1971; London's first box 1855 cover · 1.50
2 x ½p, 2 x 1p, 2 x 1½p, 2 x 2p
printed by Harrison, 1971; Pillar box 1856 cover · · · 1.50
2 x ½p, 2 x 1p, 2 x 1½p, 2 x 2p
printed by Harrison, 1971; Urban pillar box 1857 cover · 3.00

2 x ½p, 2 x 1p, 2 x 1½p, 2 x 2p
printed by Harrison, 1971–72; Penfold box 1866 cover   2.50
2 x ½p, 2 x 1p, 2 x 1½p, 2 x 2p
printed by Harrison, 1972; Double-aperture 1899 cover   2.00
2 x ½p, 2 x 1p, 2 x 1½p, 2 x 2p
printed by Harrison, 1972; Mellor type 1968 cover   2.00
2 x ½p, 2 x 1p, 2 x 1½p, 2 x 2p
printed by Harrison, 1973; KEVIII type 1936 cover   2.50
2 x ½p, 2 x 1p, 2 x 1½p, 2 x 2p
printed by Harrison, 1973; QEII type 1952 cover   3.00
2 x ½p, 2 x 1p, 2 x 1½p, 2 x 2p
printed by Harrison, 1973; Double-aperture 1973 cover   2.50
2 x ½p, 2 x 1p, 2 x 1½p, 2 x 2p
printed by Harrison, 1974; Philatelic box 1974 cover   2.00

■ 10p booklets. Postal Uniforms series
2 x ½p, 2 x 1p, 2 x 1½p, 2 x 2p
printed by Harrison, 1974; Letter carrier 1793 cover   1.00
2 x ½p, 2 x 1p, 2 x 1½p, 2 x 2p
printed by Harrison, 1974; Letter carrier 1837 cover   1.00
2 x ½p, 2 x 1p, 2 x 1½p, 2 x 2p
printed by Harrison, 1975–76; Letter carrier 1855 cover   0.75

■ 25p booklets. Veteran Transport series
5 x ½p, 9 x 2½p
printed by Harrison, 1971; Knifeboard omnibus cover   2.75
5 x ½p, 9 x 2½p
printed by Harrison, 1971; B–type Omnibus cover   4.00
5 x ½p, 9 x 2½p
printed by Harrison, 1971; Showman's Engine cover   7.00
5 x ½p, 9 x 2½p
printed by Harrison, 1972; Royal Mail Van 1913 cover   5.00
5 x ½p, 9 x 2½p
printed by Harrison, 1972; Motor Wagonette 1901 cover   4.50
5 x ½p, 9 x 2½p
printed by Harrison, 1972; London Taxi Cab 1931 cover   5.00
5 x ½p, 9 x 2½p
printed by Harrison, 1973; Electric Tramcar cover   5.50

■ 25p booklets. 80 Years of British Stamp Books
5 x ½p, 9 x 2½p
printed by Harrison, 1971; 80 Years of Stamp Books cover   3.50

■ 25p booklets. Save The Children Fund
5 x ½p, 9 x 2½p
printed by Harrison, 1973; Help Children cover   5.50

■ 30p booklets. British Birds series
10 x 3p
printed by Harrison, 1971; Curlew cover   4.00
10 x 3p
printed by Harrison, 1971; Lapwing cover   4.00
10 x 3p
printed by Harrison, 1971; Robin cover   4.50
10 x 3p
printed by Harrison, 1971–72; Pied Wagtail cover   4.00
10 x 3p
printed by Harrison, 1972; Kestrel cover   4.50
10 x 3p
printed by Harrison, 1972; Black Grouse cover   4.50

10 x 3p
printed by Harrison, 1973; Skylark cover   4.50
10 x 3p
printed by Harrison, 1973; Oystercatcher cover (purple)   6.00
10 x 3p
printed by Harrison, 1973; Oystercatcher cover (bistre)   5.50

■ 30p booklets. 80 Years of British Stamp Books
10 x 3p
printed by Harrison, 1971; 80 Years of Stamp Books cover   4.00

■ 30p booklets. Save The Children Fund
10 x 3p
printed by Harrison, 1974; Help Children cover   4.00

■ 30p booklets. Canada Life Assurance
10 x 3p
printed by Harrison, 1974; Canada Life cover   4.00

■ 35p booklets. British Coins series
10 x 3½p
printed by Harrison, 1973–74; Cuthred Penny cover   3.00
10 x 3½p
printed by Harrison, 1974; Edward I Silver Groat cover   3.00

■ 35p booklets. Canada Life Assurance
10 x 3½p
printed by Harrison, 1974; Canada Life cover   4.00

■ 45p booklets. British Coins series
10 x 4½p
printed by Harrison, 1974; Elizabeth Gold Crown cover   3.50

■ 50p booklets. British Flowers series
5 x ½p, 7 x 2½p, 10 x 3p
printed by Harrison, 1971; Large Bindweed cover   6.00
5 x ½p, 7 x 2½p, 10 x 3p
printed by Harrison, 1971; Primrose cover   6.00
5 x ½p, 7 x 2½p, 10 x 3p
printed by Harrison, 1971; Honeysuckle cover   6.00
5 x ½p, 7 x 2½p, 10 x 3p
printed by Harrison, 1971; Hop cover   6.50
5 x ½p, 7 x 2½p, 10 x 3p
printed by Harrison, 1971; Common Violet cover   6.50
5 x ½p, 7 x 2½p, 10 x 3p
printed by Harrison, 1972; Lords-and-Ladies cover   6.50
5 x ½p, 7 x 2½p, 10 x 3p
printed by Harrison, 1972; Wood Anemone cover   6.50
5 x ½p, 7 x 2½p, 10 x 3p
printed by Harrison, 1972; Deadly Nightshade cover   6.00

■ 50p booklets. Canada Life Assurance
5 x ½p, 7 x 2½p, 10 x 3p
printed by Harrison, 1973; Canada Life cover (blue-green)   6.00
5 x 3p, 10 x 3½p
printed by Harrison, 1973; Canada Life cover (deep green)   7.25

■ 85p booklets. Canada Life Assurance
5 x 3½p, 15 x 4½p
printed by Harrison, 1973; Canada Life cover   7.00

FOLDED BOOKLETS

In this section, items are priced in mint condition only.

MACHINE–VENDED BOOKLETS OF MACHIN DEFINITIVES, 1976–2000

These booklets were sold from vending machines. They contain panes attached to covers by their top selvedge, so the Queen's portrait is face–down. In most cases, panes are folded along their perforations.

■ **10p booklet**
2 x ½p, 3 x 1p, 1 x 6p
printed by Harrison, 1976–77; dotted '10p' cover   0.70

■ **10p booklets. Farm Buildings series**
2 x ½p, 2 x 1p, 1x 7p
printed by Harrison, 1978; Kent buildings cover   0.70
2 x ½p, 2 x 1p, 1x 7p
printed by Harrison, 1978; N Ireland buildings cover   0.70
2 x ½p, 2 x 1p, 1x 7p
printed by Harrison, 1978; Yorkshire buildings cover   0.60
2 x ½p, 2 x 1p, 1x 7p
printed by Harrison, 1978; Wales buildings cover   0.60
2 x ½p, 2 x 1p, 1x 7p
printed by Harrison, 1979; Scotland buildings cover   0.50
2 x ½p, 2 x 1p, 1x 7p
printed by Harrison, 1979; Sussex buildings cover   0.50

■ **10p booklet. London 1980 Exhibition**
2 x 1p, 1 x 8p
printed by Harrison, 1979–80; London 1980 cover   0.45
(* This booklet exists with differing postal rates on its inner covers.)

■ **50p booklets**
2 x ½p, 2 x 1p, 2 x 6½p (phos band at left), 4 x 8½p
printed by Harrison, 1977; bold '50p' cover   1.40
2 x ½p, 2 x 1p, 2 x 6½p (phos band at right), 4 x 8½p
printed by Harrison, 1977; bold '50p' cover   1.40
2 x 1p, 3 x 7p (phos band at left), 3 x 9p
printed by Harrison, 1977; bold '50p' cover   2.00
2 x 1p, 3 x 7p (phos band at right), 3 x 9p
printed by Harrison, 1977; bold '50p' cover   3.00

■ **50p booklets. Commercial Vehicles series**
2 x 1p, 3 x 7p (phos band at left), 3 x 9p
printed by Harrison, 1978; Clement Talbot Van cover   2.00
2 x 1p, 3 x 7p (phos band at right), 3 x 9p
printed by Harrison, 1978; Clement Talbot Van cover   3.00
2 x 1p, 3 x 7p (phos band at left), 3 x 9p
printed by Harrison, 1978; Austin Cape Taxi cover   2.00
2 x 1p, 3 x 7p (phos band at right), 3 x 9p
printed by Harrison, 1978; Austin Cape Taxi cover   3.00
2 x 1p, 3 x 7p (phos band at left), 3 x 9p
printed by Harrison, 1978; Morris Royal Mail Van cover   2.00
2 x 1p, 3 x 7p (phos band at right), 3 x 9p
printed by Harrison, 1978; Morris Royal Mail Van cover   3.50
2 x 1p, 3 x 7p (phos band at left), 3 x 9p
printed by Harrison, 1978; Guy Electric Dustcart cover   2.00
2 x 1p, 3 x 7p (phos band at right), 3 x 9p
printed by Harrison, 1978; Guy Electric Dustcart cover   3.50
2 x 1p, 3 x 7p (phos band at left), 3 x 9p
printed by Harrison, 1979; Albion Van cover   5.50
2 x 1p, 3 x 7p (phos band at right), 3 x 9p
printed by Harrison, 1979; Albion Van cover   5.00
2 x 1p, 3 x 7p (phos band at left), 3 x 9p
printed by Harrison, 1979; Leyland Fire Engine cover   3.00
2 x 1p, 3 x 7p (phos band at right), 3 x 9p

printed by Harrison, 1979; Leyland Fire Engine cover   4.00
2 x 2p, 2 x 8p (phos band at left or right), 3 x 10p
printed by Harrison, 1979; Leyland Fire Engine   2.00

■ 50p booklets. Veteran Cars series
2 x 2p, 2 x 8p (phos band left or right), 3 x 10p
printed by Harrison, 1979; Rolls Royce Silver Ghost cover   1.50
3 x 2p, 2 x 10p (phos band left or right), 2 x 12p
printed by Harrison, 1980; Grand Prix Austin cover   1.75
3 x 2p, 2 x 10p (phos band left or right), 2 x 12p
printed by Harrison, 1980; Vauxhall cover   1.50
3 x 2p, 2 x 10p (phos band left or right), 2 x 12p
printed by Harrison, 1980; Daimler cover   1.50
1 x ½p, 1 x 1p, 1 x 14p, 3 x 11½p (phos band left or right)
printed by Harrison, 1981; Lanchester cover   1.50
1 x ½p, 1 x 1p, 1 x 14p, 3 x 11½p (phos band left or right)
printed by Harrison, 1981; Bullnose Morris cover   1.75

■ 50p booklets. Follies series
1 x ½p, 1 x 1p, 1 x 14p, 3 x 11½p (phos band left or right)
printed by Harrison, 1981; Mugdock Castle cover   1.50
3 x 2½p, 2 x 4p, 3 x 11½p (phos band at left)
printed by Harrison, 1981; Mugdock Castle cover   1.50
3 x 2½p, 2 x 4p, 3 x 11½p (phos band at right)
printed by Harrison, 1981; Mugdock Castle cover   5.50
3 x 2½p, 2 x 4p, 3 x 11½p (phos band at left)
printed by Harrison, 1981; Mow Cop Castle cover   4.50
3 x 2½p, 2 x 4p, 3 x 11½p (phos band at right)
printed by Harrison, 1981; Mow Cop Castle cover   3.50
1 x ½p, 4 x 3p pink, 3 x 12½p (phos band left or right)
printed by Harrison, 1982; Paxton's Tower cover   1.50
1 x ½p, 4 x 3p pink, 3 x 12½p (phos band left or right)
printed by Harrison, 1982; Temple of the Winds cover   1.50
1 x ½p, 4 x 3p pink, 3 x 12½p (phos band left or right)
printed by Harrison, 1982; Temple of the Sun cover   1.50
1 x ½p, 4 x 3p pink, 3 x 12½p (phos band left or right)
printed by Harrison, 1982; Water Garden cover   1.60

■ 50p booklets. Rare Farm Animals series
1 x ½p, 4 x 3p pink, 3 x 12½p (phos band left or right)
printed by Harrison, 1983; Bagot Goat cover   2.00
2 x 1p, 3 x 3½p, 3 x 12½p (all with centre phos band)
printed by Harrison, 1983; Gloucester Old Spot Pig cover   3.00
2 x 1p, 3 x 3½p, 3 x 12½p (all with centre phos band)
printed by Harrison, 1983; Gloucester Old Spot Pig cover
with postal rate information corrected   10.00
2 x 1p, 3 x 3½p, 3 x 12½p (all with centre phos band)
printed by Harrison, 1983; Toulouse Goose cover   3.00
2 x 1p, 3 x 3½p, 3 x 12½p (all with centre phos band)
printed by Harrison, 1983; Orkney Sheep cover   3.00

■ 50p booklets. Orchids series
3 x 1p, 2 x 4p, 3 x 13p (all with centre phos band)
printed by Harrison, 1984; Dendrobium Nobile cover   2.00
3 x 1p, 2 x 4p, 3 x 13p (all with centre phos band)
printed by Harrison, 1985; Cyripedium and Ophrys cover   2.00
3 x 1p, 2 x 4p, 3 x 13p (all with centre phos band)
printed by Harrison, 1985; Bifienasia and Vandatricolour   2.00
3 x 1p, 2 x 4p, 3 x 13p (all with centre phos band)
printed by Harrison, 1985; Cymbidium and Arpophyllum   2.00

■ 50p booklet
3 x 17p (two phos bands, stars printed on gummed side)
printed by Harrison, 1985; Pillar box cover   2.50

■ 50p booklets. Pond Life series
3 x 17p (two phos bands, stars printed on gummed side)
printed by Harrison, 1986; Emperor Dragonfly cover   2.00
3 x 17p (two phos bands, stars printed on gummed side)
printed by Harrison, 1986; Common Frog cover   2.50
3 x 17p (two phos bands, without stars on gummed side)
printed by Harrison, 1986; Common Frog cover   2.30
1 x 1p, 2 x 5p, 3 x 13p (all with centre phos band)
printed by Harrison, 1986; Moorhen and Dabchicks cover   5.00
1 x 1p, 2 x 5p, 3 x 13p (all with centre phos band)
printed by Harrison, 1987; Giant Pond Snail cover   3.00

■ 50p booklets. Roman Britain series
2 x 1p, 4 x 12p emerald-green (all with centre phos band)
printed by Harrison, 1986; Hadrian's Wall cover   5.50
1 x 1p (right band), 1 x 13p (left band), 2 x 18p (two bands)
printed by Harrison, 1986; Roman Theatre cover   2.00
1 x 1p (right band), 1 x 13p (left band), 2 x 18p (two bands)
printed by Harrison, 1987; Portchester Castle cover   2.00

■ 50p booklets. Marylebone Cricket Club series
1 x 1p (right band), 1 x 13p (left band), 2 x 18p (two bands)
printed by Harrison, 1987; Weather Vane at Lord's cover   2.25
1 x 1p (right band), 1 x 13p (left band), 2 x 18p (two bands)
printed by Harrison, 1987; Ashes Urn cover   1.75
1 x 1p (right band), 1 x 13p (left band), 2 x 18p (two bands)
printed by Harrison, 1987; Lord's pavilion cover   1.75
1 x 1p (right band), 1 x 13p (left band), 2 x 18p (two bands)
printed by Harrison, 1988; Lord's New Stand cover   1.75

■ 50p booklets. Botanical Gardens series
1 x 1p, 2 x 5p, 3 x 13p (all with centre phos band)
printed by Harrison, 1987; Bodnant Gardens cover   3.00
1 x 1p, 2 x 5p, 3 x 13p (all with centre phos band)
printed by Harrison, 1987; Edinburgh Gardens cover   3.00
1 x 1p, 2 x 5p, 3 x 13p (centre phos bands, side edges imperf)
printed by Harrison, 1987; Mount Stuart cover   2.00
1 x 1p, 2 x 5p, 3 x 13p (all with centre phos band)
printed by Harrison, 1987; Mount Stewart (corrected)   2.00
1 x 1p, 2 x 5p, 3 x 13p (all with centre phos band)
printed by Harrison, 1988; Kew Gardens cover   2.00

■ 50p booklets. London Zoo series
1 x 1p, 1 x 13p, 2 x 18p
printed by Harrison, 1988; Pigs cover   2.00
1 x 1p, 1 x 13p, 2 x 18p
printed by Harrison, 1988; Birds cover   2.00
1 x 1p, 1 x 13p, 2 x 18p
printed by Harrison, 1988; Elephants cover   2.00

■ 50p booklets. Marine Life series
1 x 1p, 2 x 5p, 3 x 13p (all with centre phos band)
printed by Harrison, 1988; Anenome, Whelk, Jellyfish cover   2.00
1 x 14p, 2 x 19p
printed by Harrison, 1989; Crab, Bladderwrack cover   4.00

■ 50p booklets. Gilbert & Sullivan Operas series

1 x 14p, 2 x 19p
printed by Harrison, 1988; Yeomen of the Guard cover — 4.00
1 x 14p, 2 x 19p
printed by Harrison, 1989; Pirates of Penzance cover — 4.00
1 x 14p, 2 x 19p
printed by Harrison, 1989; Mikado cover — 4.00

■ 50p booklets. Aircraft series

2 x 15p, 1 x 20p
printed by Harrison, 1989; AW Atalanta & DH Dragon — 7.00
2 x 15p, 1 x 20p (Penny Black Anniversary stamps)
printed by Harrison, 1990; AW Atalanta & DH Dragon — 5.50
2 x 15p, 1 x 20p
printed by Harrison, 1990; BAC 1–11 & VC10 — 3.50
2 x 15p, 1 x 20p
printed by Harrison, 1991; BAe ATP, 146 & Concorde — 3.50

■ 50p booklets. Archaeology series

2 x 1p, 2 x 24p
printed by Harrison, 1991; Sir Arthur Evans at Crete — 2.00
2 x 1p, 2 x 24p
printed by Harrison, 1992; Howard Carter, Tutankhamun — 2.00
2 x 1p, 2 x 24p
printed by Harrison, 1992; Sir Austen Layard in Assyria — 1.50
2 x 1p, 2 x 24p
printed by Harrison, 1992; Sir Flinders Petrie at Giza — 1.60

■ 50p booklet. Sheriff's Millennium

2 x 1p, 2 x 24p
printed by Harrison, 1992; Sheriff's millennium cover — 1.50

■ 50p booklets. Postal History series

2 x 1p, 2 x 24p
printed by Harrison, 1993; Airmail markings cover — 1.50
2 x 1p, 2 x 24p
printed by Harrison, 1993; Ship mail markings cover — 1.50
2 x 1p, 2 x 24p
printed by Harrison, 1993; Registered mail cover — 1.50
2 x 25p
printed by Harrison, 1993; 'Paid' marking cover — 1.50

■ 50p booklets. Coaching Inns series

2 x 25p
printed by Harrison, 1994; Swan With Two Necks cover — 1.50
2 x 25p
printed by Harrison, 1994; Bull & Mouth cover — 1.50
2 x 25p
printed by Harrison, 1994; Golden Cross cover — 1.50
2 x 25p
printed by Harrison, 1994; Pheasant Inn cover — 1.50

■ 50p booklets. Sea Charts series

2 x 25p
printed by Harrison, 1995; John O'Groats cover — 1.50
2 x 25p
printed by Harrison, 1995; Land's End cover — 1.50
2 x 25p
printed by Harrison, 1995; St. David's Head cover — 2.00
2 x 25p
printed by Harrison, 1995; Giant's Causeway cover — 2.00

■ £1 booklets. Musical Instruments series

6 x 17p (advanced coated paper)
printed by Harrison, 1986; Violin cover — 2.50
1 x 13p (phos band at right), 5 x 18p (two phos bands)
printed by Harrison, 1986; French Horn cover — 4.00
1 x 13p (phos band at right), 5 x 18p (two phos bands)
printed by Harrison, 1987; Bass Clarinet cover — 2.75

■ £1 booklets. Sherlock Holmes series

1 x 13p (phos band at right), 5 x 18p (two phos bands)
printed by Harrison, 1987; A Study in Scarlet cover — 3.00
1 x 13p (phos band at right), 5 x 18p (two phos bands)
printed by Harrison, 1987; Hound of the Baskervilles cover — 3.00
1 x 13p (band at right), 5 x 18p (two bands), edges imperf
printed by Harrison, 1987; Adventure of the Speckled Band — 3.00
1 x 13p (band at right), 5 x 18p (two bands), edges imperf
printed by Harrison, 1988; The Final Problem cover — 3.00

■ £1 booklet. London Zoo series

1 x 13p (phos band at right), 5 x 18p (two phos bands)
printed by Harrison, 1988; Bears — 3.00

■ £1 booklets. Charles Dickens series

1 x 13p (phos band at right), 5 x 18p (two phos bands)
printed by Harrison, 1988; Oliver Twist cover — 3.25
2 x 14p (phos band at right), 4 x 19p (two phos bands)
printed by Harrison, 1988; Nicholas Nickleby cover — 3.25
2 x 14p (phos band at right), 4 x 19p (two phos bands)
printed by Harrison, 1989; David Copperfield cover — 3.25
2 x 14p (phos band at right), 4 x 19p (two phos bands)
printed by Walsall, 1989; Great Expectations cover — 7.50

■ £1 booklet. Marine Life series

2 x 14p (phos band at right), 4 x 19p (two phos bands)
printed by Harrison, 1989; Sea urchin, starfish, crab — 3.00

■ £1 booklets. Mills series

5 x 20p
printed by Harrison, 1989; Wicken Fen cover (matt) — 3.50
5 x 20p (Penny Black Anniversary stamps)
printed by Walsall, 1990; Wicken Fen cover (glossy) — 9.00
5 x 20p (Penny Black Anniversary stamps)
printed by Harrison, 1990; Click Mill cover — 4.50

2 x 17p, 3 x 22p
printed by Harrison, 1990; Jack & Jill Mills cover   2.50
2 x 17p, 3 x 22p
printed by Harrison, 1991 Howell Mill cover   2.75

■ £1 booklets. Punch Magazine series
2 x 2p, 4 x 24p
printed by Harrison, 1991; illustrations by Doyle, Hoffnung   2.00
2 x 2p, 4 x 24p
printed by Harrison, 1992; illustrations by Tenniel, Burgin   2.00
2 x 2p, 4 x 24p
printed by Harrison, 1992; illustrations by Tenniel, Anton   2.00
2 x 2p, 4 x 24p
printed by Harrison, 1992; illustrations by Tenniel, Hewison   2.00

■ £1 booklet. Sheriff's Millennium
2 x 2p, 4 x 24p
printed by Harrison, 1992; Sheriff's Millennium cover   2.00

■ £1 booklets. Educational Institutions series
2 x 2p, 4 x 24p
printed by Walsall, 1993; University of Wales cover   3.00
2 x 2p, 4 x 24p
printed by Walsall, 1993; St. Hilda's College, Oxford   3.00
2 x 2p, 4 x 24p
printed by Walsall, 1993; Marlborough College cover   3.00
4 x 25p
printed by Walsall, 1993; Free Church of Scotland College   3.00

■ £1 booklets. Prime Ministers series
4 x 25p
printed by Walsall, 1994; Herbert Asquith cover   2.00
4 x 25p
printed by Harrison, 1994; David Lloyd–George cover   2.00
4 x 25p
printed by Harrison, 1994; Winston Churchill cover   2.00
4 x 25p
printed by Harrison, 1994; Clement Attlee cover   2.00

■ £1 booklets. Second World War series
4 x 25p
printed by Harrison, 1995; Violette Szabo cover   2.00
4 x 25p
printed by Harrison, 1995; Dame Vera Lynn cover   2.00
4 x 25p
printed by Harrison, 1995; R. J. Mitchell cover   2.00
4 x 25p
printed by Harrison, 1995; Archibald McIndoe cover   2.00

■ £1 booklets. Red cover series
4 x 25p (litho)
printed by Questa, 1996; Royal Mail cruciform cover   3.00
2 x 1p, 1 x 20p, 3 x 26p (litho)
printed by Questa, 1996–97; Royal Mail cruciform cover   3.00
2 x 1p, 1 x 20p, 3 x 26p (gravure)
printed by Questa, 1998; Royal Mail cruciform cover   18.00
1 x 1p, 1 x 2p, 1 x 19p, 3 x 26p (gravure)
printed by Questa, 1999; Royal Mail cruciform cover   6.00
1 x 2nd, 3 x 1st (gravure)
printed by Questa, 2000–01; Royal Mail cruciform cover   7.00

■ £2 booklets. Postal Vehicles series
8 x 25p
printed by Harrison, 1993; Motorised Cycle cover   3.50
8 x 25p
printed by Harrison, 1994; Motor Mail Van cover   4.00
8 x 25p
printed by Harrison, 1994; Electric Mail Van cover   4.00

■ £2 booklets. Sir Rowland Hill series
8 x 25p
printed by Harrison, 1995; London & Brighton Railway   4.00
8 x 25p
printed by Harrison, 1995; Hazlewood School   4.00
8 x 25p
printed by Harrison, 1995; Secretary to the Post Office   4.00
8 x 25p
printed by Harrison, 1995; Uniform Penny Postage   4.00

■ £2 booklets. Red cover series
8 x 25p
printed by Questa, 1996; Royal Mail cruciform cover   4.00
1 x 20p, 7 x 26p (litho)
printed by Questa, 1996; Royal Mail cruciform cover   4.50
1 x 20p, 7 x 26p (gravure)
printed by Questa, 1998; Royal Mail cruciform cover   19.50
1 x 19p, 7 x 26p
printed by Questa, 1999; Royal Mail cruciform cover   5.50
2 x 2nd, 6 x 1st
printed by Questa, 2000; Royal Mail cruciform cover   6.50

COUNTER BOOKLETS OF MACHIN DEFINITIVES, 1976–89

These booklets were sold over post office counters. They contain panes attached to covers by their side selvedge, so the Queen's portrait appears upright. Panes can have a margin to the left or right; prices are the same for both, except where stated.

65p booklets
10 x 6½p (right margin)
printed by Harrison, 1976; bold '65p' cover ... 5.50
10 x 6½p (left margin)
printed by Harrison, 1976; bold '65p' cover ... 9.00

70p booklets
10 x 7p
printed by Harrison, 1977; bold '70p' cover ... 3.50

70p booklets. Country Crafts series
10 x 7p (right margin)
printed by Harrison, 1978; Horse-Shoeing cover ... 3.00
10 x 7p (left margin)
printed by Harrison, 1978; Horse-Shoeing cover ... 33.00
10 x 7p (right margin)
printed by Harrison, 1978; Thatching cover ... 3.00
10 x 7p (left margin)
printed by Harrison, 1978; Thatching cover ... £180
10 x 7p (right margin)
printed by Harrison, 1978; Dry-Stone Walling cover ... 3.00
10 x 7p (left margin)
printed by Harrison, 1978; Dry-Stone Walling cover ... £150
10 x 7p (right margin)
printed by Harrison, 1978; Wheel-Making cover ... 4.50
10 x 7p (left margin)
printed by Harrison, 1978; Wheel-Making cover ... 4.00
10 x 7p (right margin)
printed by Harrison, 1979; Wattle Fence-Making cover ... 3.50
10 x 7p (left margin)
printed by Harrison, 1979; Wattle Fence-Making cover ... 11.00
10 x 7p (right margin)
printed by Harrison, 1979; Basket-Making cover ... 3.00
10 x 7p (left margin)
printed by Harrison, 1979; Basket-Making cover ... 6.00

70p booklet. Derby Letter Office series
10 x 7p
printed by Harrison, 1979; Keddlestone Hall cover ... 5.00

80p booklets. Military Aircraft series
10 x 8p
printed by Harrison, 1979; Vickers Gun Bus cover ... 2.00

85p booklets
10 x 8½p (right margin)
printed by Harrison, 1976; bold '85p' cover ... 6.00
10 x 8½p (left margin)
printed by Harrison, 1976; bold '85p' cover ... 6.00

90p booklets
10 x 9p (left margin)
printed by Harrison, 1977; bold '90p' cover ... 3.00
10 x 9p (right margin)
printed by Harrison, 1977; bold '90p' cover ... 5.00

90p booklets. British Canals series
10 x 9p (right margin)
printed by Harrison, 1978; Grand Union Canal cover ... 4.00
10 x 9p (left margin)

printed by Harrison, 1978; Grand Union Canal cover ... 20.00
10 x 9p (right margin)
printed by Harrison, 1978; Llangollen Canal cover ... £300
10 x 9p (left margin)
printed by Harrison, 1978; Llangollen Canal cover ... 3.00
10 x 9p (right margin)
printed by Harrison, 1978; Kennet & Avon Canal cover ... 6.00
10 x 9p (left margin)
printed by Harrison, 1978; Kennet & Avon Canal cover ... 9.00
10 x 9p (right margin)
printed by Harrison, 1978; Caledonian Canal cover ... 5.00
10 x 9p (left margin)
printed by Harrison, 1978; Caledonian Canal cover ... 6.00
10 x 9p (right margin)
printed by Harrison, 1979; Regent's Canal cover ... 6.00
10 x 9p (left margin)
printed by Harrison, 1979; Regent's Canal cover ... 5.00
10 x 9p
printed by Harrison, 1979; Leeds & Liverpool Canal cover ... 3.00

90p booklets. Derby Letter Office series
10 x 9p
printed by Harrison, 1979; Tramway Museum, Crich, cover ... 6.50

£1 booklets. Industrial Archaeology series
10 x 10p (all-over phosphor)
printed by Harrison, 1979; Ironbridge, Telford, cover ... 3.00

£1 booklets. Military Aircraft series
10 x 10p (one centre phos band)
printed by Harrison, 1980; Sopwith Camel, Vickers Vimy ... 2.50
10 x 10p (one centre phos band)
printed by Harrison, 1980; Hawker Fury, HP Heyford ... 3.50
10 x 10p (one centre phos band)
printed by Harrison, 1980; Wellington, Hurricane ... 2.50

£1.15 booklets. Military Aircraft series
10 x 11½p (one centre phos band)
printed by Harrison, 1981; Spitfire, Lancaster ... 3.50
10 x 11½p (one centre phos band)
printed by Harrison, 1981; Lightning, Vulcan ... 3.50

£1.15 booklets. Museums series
10 x 11½p (one centre phos band)
printed by Harrison, 1981; Natural History Museum ... 3.50
10 x 11½p (one centre phos band)
printed by Harrison, 1981; National Museum of Antiquities ... 3.50

◼ £1.20 booklets. Industrial Archaeology series
10 x 12p yellow–green
printed by Harrison, 1980; Beetle Mill cover — 3.50
10 x 12p yellow–green
printed by Harrison, 1980; Tin Mines cover — 3.50
10 x 12p yellow–green
printed by Harrison, 1980; Bottle Kilns cover — 3.50

◼ £1.20 booklets
10 x 12p emerald–green (one centre phos band)
printed by Harrison, 1986; Pillar Box — 4.50
10 x 12p emerald–green (one centre phos band)
printed by Harrison, 1986; National Gallery cover — 4.25
10 x 12p emerald–green (one centre phos band)
printed by Harrison, 1986; 'Maybe' cover — 4.25

◼ £1.25 booklets. Museums series
10 x 12½p (one centre phos band)
printed by Harrison, 1982; Ashmolean Museum cover — 3.50
10 x 12½p (one centre phos band)
printed by Harrison, 1982; National Museum of Wales — 3.50
10 x 12½p (one centre phos band)
printed by Harrison, 1982; Ulster Museum, Belfast — 3.50
10 x 12½p (one centre phos band)
printed by Harrison, 1982; Castle Museum, York — 3.50

◼ £1.25 booklets. Railway Engines series
10 x 12½p (one centre phos band)
printed by Harrison, 1983; GWR IK Brunel cover — 4.00
10 x 12½p (one centre phos band)
printed by Harrison, 1983; LMS Class 4P cover — 4.50
10 x 12½p (one centre phos band)
printed by Harrison, 1983; LNER Mallard cover — 4.00
10 x 12½p (one centre phos band)
printed by Harrison, 1983; SR/BR Clan Line cover — 4.00

◼ £1.30 booklets. Postal History series
6 x 14p (two phos bands), 2 x 11½p (left phos band),
2 x 11½p (right phos band) (right margin)
printed by Harrison, 1981; Penny Black cover — 3.50
6 x 14p (two phos bands), 2 x 11½p (left phos band),
2 x 11½p (right phos band) (left margin)
printed by Harrison, 1981; Penny Black cover — 4.00
6 x 14p (two phos bands), 2 x 11½p (left phos band),
2 x 11½p (right phos band) (right margin)
printed by Harrison, 1981; Downey Head cover — 4.50
6 x 14p (two phos bands), 2 x 11½p (left phos band),
2 x 11½p (right phos band) (right margin)
printed by Harrison, 1981; Downey Head cover — 14.00

◼ £1.30 booklets. Trams series
10 x 13p (one centre band)
printed by Harrison, 1984; Swansea Car cover — 3.25
10 x 13p (one centre band)
printed by Harrison, 1985; Glasgow Car cover — 3.25
10 x 13p (one centre band)
printed by Harrison, 1985; Blackpool Car cover — 3.25
10 x 13p (one centre band)
printed by Harrison, 1985; London Car cover — 3.25

◼ £1.30 booklets. Special Offers series
10 x 13p (one centre band)
printed by Harrison, 1986; Books For Children offer — 3.25
10 x 13p (one centre band)
printed by Harrison, 1987; 'Keep In Touch' Pack offer — 3.25
10 x 13p (one centre band)
printed by Harrison, 1987; 'Ideas For Your Garden' offer — 3.25
10 x 13p (one centre band)
printed by Harrison, 1987; 'Brighter Writer' Pack offer — 3.25
10 x 13p (one centre band)
printed by Harrison, 1987; 'Jolly Postman' Pack offer — 3.50
10 x 13p (one centre band)
printed by Harrison, 1988; Natural History Postcards offer — 3.50
10 x 13p (one centre band)
printed by Harrison, 1988; Recipe Cards offer — 3.25
10 x 13p (one centre band)
printed by Harrison, 1988; Children's Party Pack offer — 3.25

◼ £1.40 booklets. Industrial Archaeology series
10 x 14p (phos–coated paper)
printed by Harrison, 1981; Preston Mill cover — 3.50
10 x 14p (phos–coated paper)
printed by Harrison, 1981; Talyllyn Railway cover — 3.50

◼ £1.40 booklets. Women's Costumes series
10 x 14p (phos–coated paper)
printed by Harrison, 1981; Costumes of 1800–1815 — 3.50
10 x 14p (phos–coated paper)
printed by Harrison, 1981; Costumes of 1815–1830 — 3.50

◼ £1.40 booklet. Special Offers series
10 x 14p (phos–coated paper)
printed by Harrison, 1988; Pocket Planner offer — 3.50

◼ £1.40 booklet. Fox Talbot Photography
10 x 14p (phos–coated paper)
printed by Harrison, 1989; photography equipment cover — 3.50

◼ £1.43 booklets. Postal History series
6 x 15½p (two bands), 2 x 12½p (left band), 2 x 12½p (right band)
printed by Harrison, 1982; James Chalmers cover — 3.75
6 x 15½p (two bands), 2 x 12½p (left band), 2 x 12½p (right band)
printed by Harrison, 1982; Edmund Dulac cover — 3.75
6 x 15½p (two bands), 2 x 12½p (left band), 2 x 12½p (right band)
printed by Harrison, 1982; Forces Postal Service cover — 3.75
6 x 15½p (two bands), 2 x 12½p (left band), 2 x 12½p (right band)
printed by Harrison, 1982; £5 Orange cover — 3.75
6 x 15½p (two bands), 2 x 12½p (left band), 2 x 12½p (right band)
printed by Harrison, 1983; Postmark History cover — 3.75

◼ £1.43 booklets. Holiday Postcard Stamp Book
6 x 15½p (two bands), 2 x 12½p (left band),
2 x 12½p (right band)
printed by Harrison, 1982; Golden Hinde cover — 3.75

◼ £1.45 booklet. Britain's Countryside
10 x 16p (phos–coated paper, 'D' printed on the gummed
side) printed by Harrison, 1983; Lyme Regis cover — 3.75
(* Sold at a discount of 15p off face value.)

■ **£1.46 booklets. Postal History series**
6 x 16p (two bands), 2 x 12½p (left band), 2 x 12½p (right band)
printed by Harrison, 1983; Seahorses cover   6.25
6 x 16p (two bands), 2 x 12½p (left band), 2 x 12½p (right band)
printed by Harrison, 1983; Parcel Post cover   6.25
6 x 16p (two bands), 2 x 12½p (left band), 2 x 12½p (right band)
printed by Harrison, 1983; Regional Stamps cover   6.25
(* Panes have either the four 12½p followed by one 16p on the
bottom row, or one 16p followed by four 12½p.)

■ **£1.50 booklets. Special Offer series**
6 x 17p (two bands), 2 x 12p (left band), 2 x 12p (right band)
printed by Harrison, 1986; 'Write Now' letter pack offer   4.20
6 x 17p (two bands), 2 x 12p (left band), 2 x 12p (right band)
printed by Harrison, 1986; National Gallery offer   4.20
6 x 17p (two bands), 2 x 12p (left band), 2 x 12p (right band)
printed by Harrison, 1986; 'No' Graphology offer   4.20
(* Panes have either the four 12p followed by one 17p on the
bottom row, or one 17p followed by four 12p.)

■ **£1.54 booklets. Postal History series**
6 x 17p (two bands), 2 x 13p (left band), 2 x 13p (right band)
printed by Harrison, 1984; To Pay Labels cover   3.75
6 x 17p (two bands), 2 x 13p (left band), 2 x 13p (right band)
printed by Harrison, 1985; Embossed Stamps cover   3.75
6 x 17p (two bands), 2 x 13p (left band), 2 x 13p (right band)
printed by Harrison, 1985; Surface-Printed Stamps cover   3.75
6 x 17p (two bands), 2 x 13p (left band), 2 x 13p (right band)
printed by Harrison, 1985; 350 Years of Service cover   3.75
(* Panes have either the four 13p followed by one 17p on the
bottom row, or one 17p followed by four 13p.)

■ **£1.55 booklets. Women's Costumes series**
10 x 15½p (phos-coated paper)
printed by Harrison, 1982; Costumes of 1830–1850   3.50
10 x 15½p (phos-coated paper)
printed by Harrison, 1982; Costumes of 1850–1860   3.50
10 x 15½p (phos-coated paper)
printed by Harrison, 1982; Costumes of 1860–1880   3.50
10 x 15½p (phos-coated paper)
printed by Harrison, 1982; Costumes of 1880–1900   3.50

■ **£1.55 booklet. Social Letter Writing series**
10 x 17p (phos-coated paper, 'D' printed on gummed side)
printed by Harrison, 1985; Paper Boat and Plane cover   6.00
(* Sold at a discount of 15p off face value.)

■ **£1.60 booklets. Special Offers series**
10 x 16p (phos-coated paper)
printed by Harrison, 1983; Birthday Box offer   4.25
10 x 16p (phos-coated paper)
printed by Harrison, 1984; 'Write It' wallet offer   4.00

■ **£1.60 booklet. Britain's Countryside series**
10 x 16p (phos-coated paper)
printed by Harrison, 1983; Weavers' Cottages cover   4.00

■ **£1.70 booklets. Social Letter Writing series**
10 x 17p (phos-coated paper)
printed by Harrison, 1984; Love Letters cover   4.50

10 x 17p (phos-coated paper)
printed by Harrison, 1984; Fan Letters cover   4.50

■ **£1.70 booklets. Special Offers series**
10 x 17p (phos-coated paper)
printed by Harrison, 1985; 'Write Now' pack offer   4.25
10 x 17p (phos-coated paper)
printed by Harrison, 1986; National Gallery offer   4.25
10 x 17p (phos-coated paper)
printed by Harrison, 1986; 'Yes' Graphology offer   4.25

■ **£1.80 booklets. Special Offers series**
10 x 18p (phos-coated paper)
printed by Harrison, 1986; Books For Children offer   4.25
10 x 18p (phos-coated paper)
printed by Harrison, 1987; 'Keep In Touch' Pack offer   4.25
10 x 18p (phos-coated paper)
printed by Harrison, 1987; 'Ideas For Your Garden' offer   4.25
10 x 18p (phos-coated paper)
printed by Harrison, 1987; 'Brighter Writer' Pack offer   4.25
10 x 18p (phos-coated paper)
printed by Harrison, 1987; 'Jolly Postman' Pack offer   4.25
10 x 18p (phos-coated paper)
printed by Harrison, 1988; Natural History Postcards offer   4.25
10 x 18p (phos-coated paper)
printed by Harrison, 1988; Recipe Cards offer   4.25
10 x 18p (phos-coated paper)
printed by Harrison, 1988; Children's Party Pack offer   4.25

■ **£1.90 booklet. Special Offer series**
10 x 19p
printed by Harrison, 1988; Pocket Planner offer   5.25

■ **£1.90 booklet. Fox Talbot Photography**
10 x 19p
printed by Harrison, 1989; Fox Talbot with camera cover   5.25

COUNTER BOOKLETS OF ROYAL MAIL COMMEMORATIVES, 1985

£1.53
Royal Mail
Stamps
Ten at 17p
Free
Stamp
10 for the
price of 9

■ **£1.53 booklet. 350th Anniversary of Royal Mail Service to the Public**
10 x 17p 350th Anniversary stamp ('D' pattern on gummed side)
printed by Harrison, 1985; van, plane, Concorde cover   4.00
(* Sold at a discount of 17p off face value.)

RETAIL STAMP BOOKS

In this section, items are priced in mint condition only. These booklets were intended to be sold not only over post office counters, but also through alternative retail outlets. All have a barcode on the outside back cover.

BOOKLETS OF DEFINITIVES WITHOUT ELLIPTICAL PERFORATIONS, 1987–93

Booklets with a 'window' in the cover, through which one of the stamps can be seen, and with the panes surrounded by a white margin.

■ **4 x 13p**
August 4, 1987. Printed by Harrison   2.75

■ **10 x 13p**
August 4, 1987. Printed by Harrison   3.75

■ **4 x 14p**
August 23, 1988. Printed by Harrison   4.50
October 11, 1988. Stamps by Harrison; cover by Walsall   4.50

■ **10 x 14p**
August 23, 1988. Printed by Harrison   6.25
October 11, 1988. Printed by Questa   11.00

■ **4 x 18p**
August 4, 1987. Printed by Harrison   3.00

■ **10 x 18p**
August 4, 1987. Printed by Harrison   5.00

■ **4 x 19p**
August 23, 1988. Printed by Harrison   4.25
October 11, 1988. Stamps by Harrison; cover by Walsall   4.50

■ **10 x 19p**
August 23, 1988. Printed by Harrison   8.00

October 11, 1988. Printed by Questa   12.50

■ **4 x 26p**
August 4, 1987. Printed by Harrison   8.50

■ **4 x 27p**
August 23, 1988. Printed by Harrison   8.50

Booklets with an illustration of the contents in place of the 'window' on the cover, containing panes with no margin, and with either the top and bottom or all three edges imperforate.

■ **4 x 14p**
October 11, 1988. Printed by Harrison   4.50
January 24, 1989. Stamps by printed Harrison,
cover printed by Walsall   15.00

■ **10 x 14p**
October 11, 1988. Printed by Harrison   8.00
October 11, 1988. Printed by Questa   11.00

■ **4 x 19p**
October 11, 1988. Printed by Harrison   5.00
January 24, 1989. Stamps by printed Harrison,
cover printed by Walsalll   6.00

■ **10 x 19p**
October 11, 1988. Printed by Harrison   7.00
October 11, 1988. Printed by Questa   12.50

■ **4 x 27p**
October 11, 1988. Printed by Harrison   15.00

■ **4 x 29p**
October 2, 1989. Printed by Walsall (two phos bands)   8.50
April 17, 1990. Printed by Walsall (phos paper)   9.00

■ **4 x 31p**
September 17, 1990. Printed by Walsall   4.75

■ **4 x 33p**
September 16, 1991. Printed by Walsall   4.75
September 8, 1992. Printed by Walsall (yellow strip at
right is inscribed 'For Worldwide Postcards')   5.00

■ **2 x 39p**
July 28, 1992. Printed by Harrison   3.95

■ **4 x 39p**
September 16, 1991. Printed by Walsall   4.50

Booklets with an illustration of the contents on the cover, containing non-value indicator stamps in panes with no margin, and with either the top and bottom edges or all three edges imperforate.

■ **4 x 2nd bright blue**
August 22, 1989. Printed by Walsall   4.00
November 28, 1989. Stamps printed by Harrison;
cover by Walsall   12.00
August 6, 1991. Printed by Walsall
Cover features Royal Mail cruciform   3.50
January 21, 1992. Printed by Walsall
Cover features logos of Olympic and Paralympic Games 3.50

■ **10 x 2nd bright blue**
August 22, 1989. Printed by Harrison   7.00
September 19, 1989. Printed by Questa   6.50
August 6, 1991. Printed by Walsall
Cover features Royal Mail cruciform   7.00
August 6, 1991. Printed by Questa
Cover features Royal Mail cruciform   8.00
January 21, 1992. Printed by Walsall
Cover features logos of Olympic and Paralympic Games 5.00
March 31, 1992. Printed by Questa
Cover features logos of Olympic and Paralympic Games 7.00
September 22, 1992. Printed by Harrison
Cover features Royal Mail cruciform   7.00

■ **4 x 2nd deep blue**
August 7, 1990. Printed by Walsall   3.75

■ **10 x 2nd deep blue**
August 7, 1990. Printed by Harrison   8.00
August 7, 1990. Printed by Questa   8.00
August 7, 1990. Printed by Walsall   7.00

■ **4 x 1st brownish-black**
August 22, 1989. Printed by Walsall   5.00
December 5, 1989. Stamps by Harrison; cover by Walsall 25.00

■ **10 x 1st brownish-black**
August 22, 1989. Printed by Harrison   9.00
September 19, 1989. Printed by Questa   9.50

■ **4 x 1st orange-red**
August 7, 1990. Printed by Walsall   4.25
August 7, 1990. Printed by Walsall. Perf: 13   7.00
January 21, 1992. Printed by Walsall
Cover features logos of Olympic and Paralympic Games 4.25

■ **10 x 1st orange-red**
August 7, 1990. Printed by Harrison   8.00
August 7, 1990. Printed by Questa   8.00
August 7, 1990. Printed by Walsall   8.00
January 21, 1992. Printed by Harrison
Cover features logos of Olympic and Paralympic Games 8.00
January 21, 1992. Printed by Walsall
Cover features logos of Olympic and Paralympic Games 8.00
February 9, 1993. Printed by Walsall
Cover features Royal Mail cruciform; back cover has
advertisement for Greetings stamps   8.00

BOOKLETS OF PENNY BLACK ANNIVERSARY DEFINITIVES, 1990

Booklets with an illustration of the contents on the cover, containing denominated stamps in panes with all four edges perforated, or with either two or three edges imperforate.

■ **4 x 15p**
January 30, 1990. Printed by Walsall   4.50

■ **10 x 15p**
January 30, 1990. Printed by Harrison   5.50
April 17, 1990. Printed by Questa   11.00
June 12, 1990. Printed by Walsall   6.00

■ **4 x 20p**
January 30, 1990. Printed by Walsall   5.00
April 17, 1990. Stamps by Harrison; cover by Walsall 5.00

■ **5 x 20p**
January 30, 1990.
Cover shows Wicken Fen, printed on glossy card   10.00
January 30, 1990.
Cover shows Click Mill   4.00

■ **10 x 20p**

January 30, 1990. Printed by Harrison	6.00
April 17, 1990. Printed by Questa	11.00
June 12, 1990. Printed by Walsall	7.50

■ **2 x 15p, 1 x 20p se–tenant**

January 30, 1990.

Cover showing Vickers Viscount and De Havilland Comet	3.50

BOOKLETS OF DEFINITIVES WITH ELLIPTICAL PERFORATIONS, 1993–2000

Booklets of denominated stamps in panes with all four edges perforated.

■ **4 x 30p**

May 5, 1998. Printed by Walsall	3.50
August 3, 1998. Printed by Walsall	
Cover inscribed 'Make their post memorable'	4.00

■ **4 x 35p**

November 1, 1993. Printed by Walsall	
Cover illustrates a single stamp	4.25
May 16, 1995. Printed by Walsall	
Cover shows a block of stamps	4.00
March 19, 1996. Printed by Walsall	
Back cover features Olympic symbols	7.00

■ **4 x 37p**

July 8, 1996. Printed by Walsall.	
Back cover features Olympic symbols	4.50
February 4, 1997. Printed by Walsall.	
No Olympic symbols	5.00
August 26, 1997. Printed by Walsall.	
Cover shows street names in London	5.00
August 3, 1998. Printed by Walsall	
Cover inscribed 'Make their post memorable'	5.00

■ **4 x 38p**

April 26, 1999. Printed by Walsall	4.50

■ **4 x 40p**

April 27, 2000. Printed by Walsall	5.00

■ **4 x 41p**

November 1, 1993. Printed by Walsall	
Cover illustrates a single stamp	4.25

May 16, 1995. Printed by Walsall	
Cover shows a block of stamps	4.25
March 19, 1996. Printed by Walsall	
Back cover features Olympic symbols	7.00

■ **4 x 60p**

August 9, 1994. Printed by Walsall	
Cover illustrates a single stamp	5.50
October 4, 1994. Printed by Walsall	
Cover illustrates a single stamp but 'Worldwide Airmail Stamps' in a scroll design	5.00
May 16, 1995. Printed by Walsall	
Cover shows a block of stamps	5.00
March 19, 1996. Printed by Walsall	
Back cover features Olympic symbols	5.50

■ **4 x 63p**

July 8, 1996. Printed by Walsall	
Back cover features Olympic symbols	8.50
February 4, 1997. Printed by Walsall	
No Olympic symbols. Stamps printed in litho	7.50
August 26, 1997. Printed by Walsall	
Stamps printed in gravure	5.50
May 5, 1998. Printed by Walsall	
Cover shows air mail label below block of stamps	5.50

■ **4 x 64p**

April 26, 1999. Printed by Walsall	5.50

■ **4 x 65p**

April 27, 2000. Printed by Walsall	5.50

Booklets of non–value indicator stamps in panes with all four edges perforated.

■ **4 x 2nd bright blue**

April 6, 1993. Printed by Walsall	4.25
September 7, 1993. Printed by Harrison	4.75
January 10, 1995. Printed by Harrison.	
Cover has white lines through block of stamps	4.50
December 12, 1995. Printed by Walsall.	
Cover shows block of stamps	4.50
February 6, 1996. Printed by Walsall.	
Back cover features Olympic symbols	4.50
February 4, 1997. Printed by Walsall.	
Cover has no line through block of stamps	6.00
August 26, 1997. Printed by Walsall	

Stamps printed in gravure 4.75

■ 10 x 2nd bright blue

April 6, 1993. Printed by Questa	7.00
November 1, 1993. Printed by Walsall	5.25
January 10, 1995. Printed by Questa	
Cover has white lines through block of stamps	7.00
December 12, 1995. Printed by Harrison	
Cover shows block of stamps	7.00
February 6, 1996. Printed by Harrison.	
Back cover features Olympic symbols	7.00
February 6, 1996. Printed by Questa	
Back cover features Olympic symbols	7.00
August 6, 1996. Printed by Harrison	
Cover has no white line through block of stamps	
Back cover features Olympic symbols	7.00
August 6, 1996. Printed by Questa	
Cover has no white line through block of stamps	
Back cover features Olympic symbols	7.00
February 4, 1997. Printed by Harrison	
Cover has no white line through block of stamps	7.00
February 4, 1997. Printed by Questa	
Cover has no white line through block of stamps	7.00
May 5, 1998. Printed by De La Rue	
Cover has no white line through block of stamps	7.00
December 1, 1998. Printed by Questa	
Stamps printed in gravure	7.00

■ 4 x 1st orange–red

April 6, 1993. Printed by Harrison	4.50
August 17, 1993. Printed by Walsall	4.50
January 10, 1995. Printed by Walsall	
Cover has white lines through block of stamps	4.50
February 6, 1996. Printed by Walsall	
Back cover features Olympic symbols	4.50
February 4, 1997. Printed by Walsall	
Cover has no white line through block of stamps	4.50
August 26, 1997. Printed by Walsall	
Stamps printed in gravure	5.50

■ 4 x 1st orange–red with commemorative label

July 27, 1994. Printed by Questa.	
Label marks 300th anniversary of Bank of England	5.00
May 16, 1995. Printed by Walsall	
Label marks the centenary of birth of R. J. Mitchell	5.00
April 16, 1996. Printed by Walsall	
Label marks 70th birthday of Queen Elizabeth II	5.00
February 12, 1997. Printed by Walsall	
Label marks Hong Kong '97 stamp exhibition	5.00
October 21, 1997. Printed by Walsall	
Label marks Commonwealth Heads of Govt Meeting	5.00
November 14, 1998. Printed by Walsall	
Label marks 50th birthday of the Prince of Wales	4.50
May 12, 1999. Printed by Walsall	
Label marks 50th anniversary of the Berlin Airlift	5.00
October 1, 1999. Printed by Walsall.	
Label marks the Rugby World Cup	5.00

(*Stamp cards were produced illustrating the Bank of England, R. J. Mitchell, Elizabeth II, Berlin Airlift and Rugby World Cup labels; price £10–£16 each mint, £35 postally used.)

■ 4 x 1st olive–brown with commemorative label

March 21, 2000. Printed by Walsall	
Label shows Postman Pat	5.00
April 4, 2000. Printed by Walsall	
Label shows the National Botanic Garden of Wales	5.00

(*Stamp cards were produced illustrating the Postman Pat and Botanic Garden labels; price £13–£16 mint, £30–£35 postally used.)

■ 8 x 1st orange–red, 2 x Millennium 26p

May 12, 1999. Printed by Walsall	
Containing the Settlers' Tale 26p	8.00
September 21, 1999. Printed by Walsall	
Containing the Farmers' Tale 26p	8.00

■ 8 x 1st olive–brown, 2 x Millennium 26p

May 26, 2000. Printed by Walsall	
Containing the Above and Beyond 26p	8.75
September 5, 2000. Printed by Walsall	
Containing the Stone and Soil 26p	8.75

■ 10 x 1st orange–red

April 6, 1993. Printed by Harrison	8.00
April 6, 1993. Printed by Walsall	8.00
November 1, 1993. Printed by Questa	8.00
November 1, 1993. Printed by Walsall	
Back cover has advertisement for Greetings stamps	8.00
February 22, 1994. Printed by Walsall	
With 'FREE POSTCARDS' on yellow edge at right	8.00
July 1, 1994. Printed by Walsall	
With 'OPEN NOW Chance to win a kite' on yellow strip, and 'Better luck next time' on inside back cover	8.00
July 1, 1994. Printed by Walsall	
With 'OPEN NOW Chance to win a kite' on yellow strip, and 'You've won' on inside back cover	8.00
September 20, 1994. Printed by Walsall	
With 'STAMPERS' and 'DO NOT OPEN UNTIL' on cover	8.00
September 20, 1994. Printed by Walsall	
With 'STAMPERS' and 'KEEP IN TOUCH' on cover	8.00
September 20, 1994. Printed by Walsall	
With 'STAMPERS' and 'HAPPY BIRTHDAY' on cover	8.00
September 20, 1994. Printed by Walsall	
With 'STAMPERS' and 'What's happenin' on cover	8.00
January 10, 1995. Printed by Harrison	
Cover has white lines through block of stamps	8.00
January 10, 1995. Printed by Questa	
Cover has white lines through block of stamps	8.00
January 10, 1995. Printed by Walsall	
Cover has white lines through block of stamps	8.00
February 14, 1995. Printed by Walsall.	
Cover shows Thornton's chocolates	8.00
April 4, 1995. Printed by Harrison	
Stamps have two phosphor bands	8.00
April 24, 1995. Printed by Walsall	
With 'W.H. Smith Special Offer' on yellow strip	8.00
June 26, 1995. Printed by Questa	
With 'Sainsbury's Promotion' on yellow strip	10.00
September 4, 1995. Printed by Harrison	
Cover shows Benjy Bear and Harry Hedgehog	8.00
February 6, 1996. Printed by Walsall	
Back cover features Olympic symbols	8.00

February 19, 1996. Printed by Harrison
Cover showing Walt Disney World | 8.00
March 19, 1996. Printed by Harrison
Back cover features Olympic symbols | 8.00
May 13, 1996. Printed by Harrison
Cover shows lighting the Olympic flame
Back cover shows Shot Put | 8.00
May 13, 1996. Printed by Harrison
Cover shows lighting of Olympic flame,
Back cover shows Hurdles | 8.00
May 13, 1996. Printed by Harrison
Cover shows lighting of Olympic flame
Back cover shows Archery | 8.00
July 15, 1996. Printed by Walsall
With 'W. H. Smith Offer Inside' on yellow strip | 8.00
August 16, 1996. Printed by Harrison
Cover has no white line through block of stamps
Back cover features Olympic symbols | 8.00
August 16, 1996. Printed by Walsall
Cover has no white line through block of stamps
Back cover features Olympic symbols | 8.00
September 9, 1996. Printed by Walsall
Cover shows iced cakes | 8.00
October 7, 1996. Printed by Walsall.
With 'Offer Inside' on yellow strip | 8.00
February 4, 1997. Printed by Harrison
Cover has no white line through block of stamps | 8.00
February 4, 1997. Printed by Walsall
Cover has no white line through block of stamps | 8.00
November 8, 1997. Printed by Walsall
Stamps printed in gravure | 8.00
February 2, 1998. Printed by De La Rue
With 'Win an Adventure holiday to Disney
Animal Kingdom' | 8.00
April 27, 1998. Printed by De La Rue
Cover shows Peugeot 106. 'Stick one of these on
your drive' | 8.00
May 5, 1998. Printed by De La Rue | 8.00
July 1, 1998. Printed by De La Rue
Cover shows JVC Camcorder | 8.00
August 3, 1998. Printed by De La Rue
Cover inscribed 'Make their post memorable' | 8.00
September 7, 1998. Printed by Questa
Stamps printed in litho | 8.00
December 1, 1998. Printed by Questa
Stamps printed in gravure | 8.00

■ 10 x 1st gold
April 21, 1997. Printed by Harrison | 8.00
April 21, 1997. Printed by Walsall | 8.00
September 15, 1997. Printed by Harrison
Cover shows a beach, inscribed 'FIRST CLASS TRAVEL' | 8.00

■ 10 x 1st olive–brown
January 6, 2000. Printed by Questa | 8.00
January 6, 2000. Printed by Walsall | 8.00

■ 4 x E dark blue
January 19, 1999. Printed by Walsall
Cover shows a block of stamps and 'By Air Mail' label | 6.25

BOOKLETS OF SELF–ADHESIVE DEFINITIVES, 1993–2010

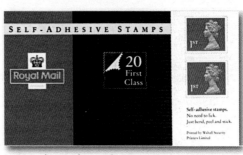

Booklets with experimental format.

■ 20 x 1st orange–red
October 19, 1993. Printed by Walsall | 14.00

Booklets with a mainly red cover, and an illustration of the contents.

■ 6 x 2nd bright blue
January 29, 2001. Printed by Walsall | 5.00

■ 10 x 2nd bright blue
January 29, 2001. Printed by Questa | 7.50

■ 12 x 2nd bright blue
January 29, 2001. Printed by Questa | 8.00

■ 6 x 1st orange–red and commemorative label
January 29, 2001. Printed by Walsall
Label marks centenary of the death of Queen Victoria | 10.00

■ 6 x 1st orange–red
January 29, 2001. Printed by Walsall | 6.75
July 4, 2002. Printed by Questa | 6.75

■ 10 x 1st orange–red
January 29, 2001. Printed by Questa | 8.50

■ 12 x 1st orange–red
January 29, 2001. Printed by Questa   9.50
January 29, 2001. Printed by Walsall   9.50

Booklets in the colour of the stamps, and with one (1st class), two (2nd class) or no notches (other values) along the right hand edge.

■ 12 x 2nd bright blue
July 4, 2002. Printed by Questa   8.75
March 27, 2003. Printed by Walsall
Inscription 'The Real Network' under Royal Mail cruciform   8.75
June 15, 2004. Printed by Walsall
No 'The Real Network' inscription   8.75
June 5, 2007. Printed by Walsall
Includes PiP information   8.75

■ 6 x 1st gold
June 5, 2002. Printed by Questa   5.25
June 5, 2002. Printed by Walsall   5.25
March 27, 2003. Printed by Walsall
Inscription 'The Real Network' under Royal Mail cruciform   5.25
June 15, 2004. Printed by Walsall
Inscription 'Supporting London 2012'   5.25
March 22, 2005. Printed by Walsall
Advertisement for Smilers on inside front cover   5.25
June 5, 2007. Printed by Walsall
Includes PiP information   5.25
June 5, 2007. Printed by Walsall
Includes facsimile of Arnold Machin's signature   5.25
August 28, 2007. Printed by Walsall
Advertisement for Harry Potter stamps   5.25
September 29, 2007. Printed by Walsall
Improved postcode information   5.25
June 10, 2008. Printed by Walsall
Advertisement for Classic Carry On & Hammer stamps   5.25

■ 12 x 1st gold
June 5, 2002. Printed by Walsall   10.50
March 27, 2003. Printed by Walsall
Inscription 'The Real Network' under Royal Mail cruciform   10.50
June 5, 2007. Printed by Walsall
Includes PiP information   10.50

■ 6 x E
July 4, 2002. Printed by Walsall   10.00
May 28, 2003. Printed by Walsall
Inscription 'The Real Network' under Royal Mail cruciform   10.00

■ 6 x 42p
July 4, 2002. Printed by Walsall   19.50
May 28, 2003. Printed by Walsall
Inscription 'The Real Network' under Royal Mail cruciform   19.50

■ 6 x 68p
July 4, 2002. Printed by Walsall   19.50
May 28, 2003. Printed by Walsall
Inscription 'The Real Network' under Royal Mail cruciform   19.50

■ 4 x Europe up to 20g
March 30, 2010. Printed by Walsall   6.00

■ 4 x Europe up to 40g
March 27, 2003. Printed by Walsall
Inscription 'The Real Network' under Royal Mail cruciform   10.00
June 15, 2004. Printed by Walsall
No 'The Real Network' inscription   8.00

■ 4 x Worldwide up to 20g
April 1, 2004. Printed by Walsall   10.00
March 30, 2010. Printed by Walsall   8.00

■ 4 x Worldwide up to 40g
March 27, 2003. Printed by Walsall
Inscription 'The Real Network' under Royal Mail cruciform   11.50
June 15, 2004. Printed by Walsall
No 'The Real Network' inscription   10.00

BOOKLETS OF SELF–ADHESIVE DEFINITIVES & COMMEMORATIVES, 2001–2008

Booklets with a cover illustrating the special stamps inside (except Cats & Dogs).

■ 2 x 1st orange–red, 10 x 1st Cats & Dogs
February 13, 2001. Printed by Walsall   22.00

■ **4 x 1st orange–red, 2 x 1st Submarines**
April 17, 2001. Printed by Questa 60.00

■ **4 x 1st orange–red, 2 x 1st Punch & Judy**
September 4, 2001. Printed by Questa 20.00

■ **4 x 1st orange–red, 2 x 1st Flags & Ensigns**
October 22, 2001. Printed by Questa 20.00

■ **4 x 1st orange–red, 2 x 1st Airliners**
May 2, 2002. Printed by Questa 7.50

■ **4 x 1st orange–red, 2 x 1st World Cup**
May 21, 2002. Printed by Questa 7.50

■ **4 x 1st gold, 2 x 1st Bridges of London**
September 10, 2002. Printed by Questa 7.50

■ **4 x 1st gold, 2 x 1st Hello!**
March 4, 2003. Printed by Questa 7.50

■ **4 x 1st gold, 2 x 1st Extreme Endeavours**
April 29, 2003. Printed by De La Rue 7.50

■ **4 x 1st gold, 2 x 1st British Journey: Scotland**
July 15, 2003. Printed by De La Rue 7.50

■ **4 x 1st gold, 2 x 1st Toys**
September 18, 2003. Printed by De La Rue 7.50

■ **4 x 1st gold, 2 x 1st British Journey: Northern Ireland**
March 16, 2004. Printed by De La Rue 7.50

■ **4 x 1st gold, 2 x 1st Ocean Liners**
April 13, 2004. Printed by De La Rue 8.00

■ **4 x 1st gold, 2 x 1st British Journey: Wales**
June 15, 2004. Printed by De La Rue 7.50

■ **4 x 1st gold, 2 x 1st Beside The Seaside**
March 13, 2008. Printed by Walsall 7.50

BOOKLETS OF SELF–ADHESIVE SMILERS STAMPS, 2005 to date

■ **6 x 1st Smilers stamps of October 4, 2005**
October 4, 2005. Printed by Walsall 10.00
July 17, 2006. Printed by Walsall. With PiP information. 9.00

■ **6 x 1st Smilers stamps of October 17, 2006**
October 17, 2006. Printed by Walsall 8.00

■ **1 x 1st 'Love', 5 x 1st gold**
January 16, 2007. Printed by Walsall 15.00

■ **2 x 1st 'Love', 4 x 1st gold**
January 15, 2008. Printed by Walsall 8.00

■ **6 x 1st Smilers stamps of 2005 and 2006**
February 28, 2008. Printed by Walsall 25.00

■ **12 x 1st Smilers stamps of 2015**
January 6, 2015. Printed by ISP 11.00

BOOKLETS OF SELF–ADHESIVE PRICING–IN–PROPORTION DEFINITIVES, 2006–07

■ **12 x 2nd bright blue**
September 12, 2006. Printed by Walsall 9.00

■ **4 x 2nd Large bright blue**
August 15, 2006. Printed by Walsall 6.00

■ **6 x 1st gold**
September 12, 2006. Printed by Walsall 7.00
February 1, 2007. Printed by Walsall
With postcode advertisement inside front cover 7.00

■ **12 x 1st gold**
September 12, 2006. Printed by Walsall 11.00

■ **4 x 1st Large gold**
August 15, 2006. Printed by Walsall 6.00

BOOKLETS OF SELF-ADHESIVE SECURITY DEFINITIVES, 2009 to date

12 x 2nd blue
March 31, 2009. Printed by Walsall
Printer's name on outside back cover   10.00
August 19, 2010. Printed by Walsall
Printer's name removed from outside back cover   10.00
October 25, 2011. Printed by Walsall
FSC logo added to outside back cover   10.00

4 x 2nd Large blue
March 31, 2009. Printed by Walsall
Printer's name on outside back cover   6.00
March 22, 2011. Printed by Walsall
Printer's name removed from outside back cover   6.50
October 25, 2011. Printed by Walsall
FSC logo added to outside back cover   6.50

6 x 1st gold
March 31, 2009. Printed by Walsall
Web address on inside front cover reads 'Postcodes4free'   6.00
December 15, 2009. Printed by Walsall
Printer's name removed from outside back cover   7.00
January 26, 2010. Printed by Walsall
Web address on inside front cover reads 'postcodes4free'   7.00
March 30, 2010. Printed by Walsall
Publicity for Festival of Stamps on inside front cover   7.50
October 25, 2011. Printed by Walsall
FSC logo added to outside back cover   6.25

12 x 1st gold
March 31, 2009. Printed by Walsall
Printer's name on outside back cover   11.50
December 15, 2009. Printed by Walsall
Printer's name removed from outside back cover   10.50
October 25, 2011. Printed by Walsall
FSC logo added to outside back cover   11.00

4 x 1st Large gold
March 31, 2009. Printed by Walsall
Printer's name on outside back cover   6.50
March 22, 2011. Printed by Walsall
Printer's name removed from outside back cover   7.00

October 25, 2011. Printed by Walsall
FSC logo added to outside back cover   7.00

6 x 1st diamond blue
October 1, 2012. Printed by Walsall   6.25
(* This booklet was available from some post offices before its official release date.)

12 x 1st diamond blue
February 6, 2012. Printed by Walsall   11.50

4 x 1st Large diamond blue
April 25, 2012. Printed by Walsall   7.00

6 x 1st red
January 3, 2013. Printed by Walsall   6.25
July 28, 2016. Printed by ISP
Padlock motif added to front cover   6.00

12 x 1st red
January 3, 2013. Printed by Walsall   11.00

4 x 1st Large red
January 3, 2013. Printed by Walsall   7.00

6 x 1st amethyst purple
September 9, 2015. Printed by ISP   6.00
2015. Printed by ISP
Security overlay extended over backing paper   6.00
(* These booklets include a label portraying the Queen and inscribed 'Happy and glorious'.)

BOOKLETS OF SELF-ADHESIVE SECURITY DEFINITIVES & COMMEMORATIVES, 2009 to date

6 x 1st. British Design Classics
4 x 1st gold, 1 x 1st Telephone Kiosk, 1 x 1st Routemaster
March 10, 2009. Printed by Walsall   7.00
4 x 1st gold, 2 x 1st Mini
April 21, 2009. Printed by Walsall   7.00
4 x 1st gold, 2 x 1st Concorde
August 18, 2009. Printed by Walsall   7.00

4 x 1st gold, 2 x 1st Mini Skirt
September 17, 2009. Printed by Walsall   7.00
4 x 1st gold, 2 x 1st Spitfire
September 15, 2010. Printed by Walsall   7.00

■ **6 x 1st. National Association of Flower Arrangement Societies**
4 x 1st, gold 1 x 1st Iris latifolia, 1 x 1st Tulipa
May 21, 2009. Printed by Walsall   7.50

■ **6 x 1st. Olympic and Paralympic Games**
4 x 1st gold, 1 x 1st Paralympic Archery, 1 x 1st Judo
January 7, 2010. Printed by Walsall   7.00
4 x 1st gold, 1 x 1st Track Athletics, 1 x 1st Basketball
February 25, 2010. Printed by Walsall   7.00
4 x 1st gold, 1 x 1st Paralympic Rowing,
1 x 1st Table Tennis
July 27, 2010. Printed by Walsall   7.00
4 x 1st gold, 1 x 1st Football, 1 x 1st Cycling
October 12, 2010. Printed by Walsall   7.00
4 x 1st gold, 1 x 1st Wheelchair Rugby,
1 x 1st Paralympic Sailing
July 27, 2011. Printed by Walsall   7.00
4 x 1st gold, 1 x 1st Gymnastics, 1 x 1st Fencing
September 15, 2011. Printed by Walsall   7.00

■ **6 x 1st. Mammals**
4 x 1st gold, 1 x 1st Otter, 1 x 1st Hedgehog
June 15, 2010. Printed by Walsall   12.00

■ **6 x 1st. Thunderbirds**
4 x 1st gold, 2 x 1st Thunderbirds
January 11, 2011. Printed by Walsall   7.00

■ **6 x 1st. Medical Breakthroughs**
4 x 1st gold, 2 x 1st Beta–Blockers
February 24, 2011. Printed by Walsall   7.50

■ **6 x 1st. Thomas the Tank Engine**
4 x 1st gold, 2 x 1st Goodbye Bertie
June 14, 2011. Printed by Walsall   7.50

■ **6 x 1st. Classic Locomotives of England**
4 x 1st gold, 2 x 1st BR Dean Goods locomotive
August 23, 2011. Printed by Walsall   7.50

■ **6 x 1st. Diamond Jubilee**
4 x 1st diamond blue, 2 x 1st Golden Jubilee 2002
May 31, 2012. Printed by Walsall   8.75

■ **6 x 1st. Classic Locomotives of Scotland**
4 x 1st diamond blue, 2 x 1st Class D34 locomotive
September 27, 2012. Printed by Walsall   7.00

■ **6 x 1st. London Underground**
4 x 1st red, 2 x 1st Boston Manor Station
January 9, 2013. Printed by Walsall   7.00

■ **6 x 1st. Football Heroes (first issue)**
4 x 1st red, 1 x 1st George Best, 1 x 1st Bobby Moore
May 9, 2013. Printed by Walsall   7.00

■ **6 x 1st. Classic Locomotives of Northern Ireland**
4 x 1st red, 2 x 1st UTA W No.103 locomotive
June 18, 2013. Printed by Walsall   6.50

■ **6 x 1st. Butterflies**
4 x 1st red, 1 x 1st Chalkhill Blue, 1 x 1st Comma
July 11, 2013. Printed by Walsall   7.00

■ **6 x 1st. Royal Mail Transport**
4 x 1st red, 1 x 1st Morris Minor van, 1 x 1st RMS 'Britannia'
September 19, 2013. Printed by Walsall   7.50

■ **6 x 1st. Football Heroes (second issue)**
4 x 1st red, 1 x 1st John Charles, 1 x 1st Dave Mackay
February 20, 2014. Printed by Walsall   7.50

■ **6 x 1st. Buckingham Palace**
4 x 1st red, 1 x 1st Grand Staircase, 1 x 1st Throne Room
April 15, 2014. Printed by Walsall   6.00

■ **6 x 1st. Glasgow 2014 Commonwealth Games**
4 x 1st red, 2 x 1st Swimming
July 17, 2014. Printed by Walsall   8.00

■ **6 x 1st. Sustainable Fish**
4 x 1st red, 1 x 1st Common Skate, 1 x 1st Cornish Herring
August 18, 2014. Printed by Walsall   8.00

■ **6 x 1st. Classic Locomotives of Wales**
4 x 1st red, 2 x 1st LMS 2F No.7720 locomotive
September 18, 2014. Printed by Walsall   8.00

■ **6 x 1st. Alice in Wonderland**
4 x 1st red, 1 x 1st Drink Me, 1 x 1st White Rabbit's House
January 6, 2015. Printed by ISP   8.00

■ **6 x 1st. Comedy Greats**
4 x 1st red, 1 x 1st Norman Wisdom, 1 x 1st Morecambe & Wise
April 1, 2015. Printed by ISP   8.00

■ **6 x 1st. Bees**
4 x 1st red, 2 x 1st Great Yellow Bumblebee
August 18, 2015. Printed by ISP   8.00

■ **6 x 1st. Rugby World Cup**
4 x 1st amethyst, 1 x 1st Try, 1 x 1st Conversion
September 18, 2015. Printed by ISP   6.00

■ **6 x 1st. The Queen's 90th Birthday (issue 1)**
4 x 1st amethyst, 1 x 1st Prince Charles, 1 x 1st Queen
Elizabeth II
April 21, 2016. Printed by ISP   6.00

■ **6 x 1st. The Queen's 90th Birthday (issue 2)**
4 x 1st amethyst, 1 x 1st Prince George, 1 x 1st Prince William
June 9, 2016. Printed by ISP   6.00

■ **6 x 1st. Beatrix Potter**
4 x 1st amethyst, 1 x 1st Peter Rabbit, 1 x 1st Mrs Tiggy–Winkle
July 28, 2016. Printed by ISP   6.00

BOOKLETS OF SELF–ADHESIVE OLYMPIC GAMES DEFINITIVES, 2012

■ **6 x 1st. Olympic and Paralympic Games**
3 x 1st Olympic Games logo, 3 x 1st Paralympic Games logo
Cover: Union flag. Inside front cover: quote from Lord Coe
January 5, 2012. Printed by Walsall   6.50

■ **6 x 1st. Olympic and Paralympic Games**
3 x 1st Olympic Games logo, 3 x 1st Paralympic Games logo
Cover: Union flag. Inside front cover: timetable of events
January 5, 2012. Printed by Walsall   6.50
(* The cover design and the arrangement of the stamps varies between these two booklets.)

BOOKLETS OF SELF–ADHESIVE COMMEMORATIVES, 2013–15

■ **6 x 1st. Doctor Who**
4 x 1st Tardis, 1 x 1st Matt Smith, 1 x 1st William Hartnell
March 26, 2013. Printed by Walsall   6.50

■ **6 x 1st. 175th Anniversary of the Penny Black**
6 x 1st Penny Black
May 6, 2015. Printed by ISP   6.00

■ **6 x 1st. 175th Anniversary of the Penny Red**
6 x 1st Penny Red
February 18, 2016. Printed by ISP   6.00

CHRISTMAS BOOKLETS

In this section, prices are quoted for mint condition only.
These booklets contain definitive stamps and Christmas
special issues.

COUNTER BOOKLETS

■ **1978, November 15**
£1.60 (10 x 7p, 10 x 9p definitives).
Decoration of holly cover, 'Greetings Christmas 1978'   3.50

■ **1979, November 14**
£1.80 (10 x 8p, 10 x 10p definitives).
Christmas cracker cover, 'Greetings Christmas 1979'   3.75

■ **1980, November 12**
£2.20 (10 x 10p, 10 x 12p definitives).
Nativity scene, cover 'Greetings Christmas 1980'   4.00

■ **1981, November 11**
£2.55 (10 x 14p, 10 x 11½p definitives).
Skating scene cover, 'Christmas Greetings 1981'   5.00

■ **1982, November 10**
£2.50 (10 x 15½p, 10 x 12½p definitives).
Christmas mummers cover   6.00
(* Sold at a discount of 30p off face value; stamps
have a blue star printed on the gummed side)

■ **1983, November 9**
£2.20 (20 x 12½p definitives).
Pantomime scene cover   5.50
(* Sold at a discount of 30p off face value; stamps
have a blue star printed on the gummed side.)

■ **1984, November 20**
£2.30 (20 x 13p Christmas stamps).
Manger scene cover   5.00
(* Sold at a discount of 30p off face value; stamps
have a blue star printed on the gummed side)

■ **1985, November 19**
£2.40 (20 x 12p Christmas stamps).
Cinderella's slipper cover   5.00

■ **1986, December 2**
£1.20 (10 x 13p definitives).
Cooking Shetland yule cakes cover   5.50
(* Sold at a discount of 10p off face value; stamps
have a blue star printed on the gummed side.)

RETAIL BOOKLETS

■ **1990, November 13**
20 x 17p Christmas stamps   6.00

■ **1991, November 12**
20 x 18p Christmas stamps   6.00

■ **1992, November 10**
20 x 18p Christmas stamps   7.00

■ **1993, November 9**
20 x 19p Christmas stamps   6.00
10 x 25p Christmas stamps   5.50

■ **1994, November 1**
20 x 19p Christmas stamps   6.75
10 x 25p Christmas stamps   5.00

■ 1995, October 30
20 x 19p Christmas stamps	7.00
10 x 25p Christmas stamps	4.50
4 x 60p Christmas stamps	4.50

■ 1996, October 28
20 x 2nd Christmas stamps	14.00
10 x 1st Christmas stamps	9.00

■ 1997, October 27
20 x 2nd Christmas stamps	12.00
10 x 1st Christmas stamps	9.00

■ 1998, November 2
20 x 20p Christmas stamps	7.50
10 x 26p Christmas stamps	5.50

■ 1999, November 2
20 x 19p The Christians' Tale stamps	7.00
10 x 26p The Christians' Tale stamps	5.00

■ 2000, November 7
20 x 2nd Spirit and Faith stamps	9.00
10 x 1st Spirit and Faith stamps	9.00

SELF–ADHESIVE FOLDERS

■ 2001, November 6
24 x 2nd Christmas stamps	12.00
12 x 1st Christmas stamps	10.00

■ 2002, November 5
24 x 2nd Christmas stamps	12.00
12 x 1st Christmas stamps	10.00

■ 2003, November 4
24 x 2nd Christmas stamps	17.00
12 x 1st Christmas stamps	10.00

■ 2004, November 2
24 x 2nd Christmas stamps	15.00
12 x 1st Christmas stamps	10.00

■ 2005, November 1
24 x 2nd Christmas stamps	17.00
12 x 1st Christmas stamps	10.00

SELF–ADHESIVE BOOKLETS

■ 2006, November 7
12 x 2nd Christmas stamps	9.00
12 x 1st Christmas stamps	11.00

■ 2007, November 6
12 x 2nd Christmas stamps	9.00
12 x 1st Christmas stamps	11.00

■ 2008, November 4
12 x 2nd Christmas stamps. Pane inscribed 'Oh yes it is'	9.00
12 x 2nd Christmas stamps. Pane inscribed 'Oh no it isn't'	9.00
12 x 1st Christmas stamps. Pane inscribed 'It's behind you'	10.00
12 x 2nd Christmas stamps. Pane inscribed 'Abracadabra'	10.00

■ 2009, November 3
12 x 2nd Christmas stamps	9.00
12 x 1st Christmas stamps	10.00

■ 2010, November 2
12 x 2nd Christmas stamps	10.00
12 x 1st Christmas stamps	11.00

■ 2011, November 8
12 x 2nd Christmas stamps	9.00
12 x 1st Christmas stamps	11.00

■ 2012, November 6
12 x 2nd Christmas stamps	9.00
12 x 1st Christmas stamps	11.00

■ 2013, November 5
12 x 2nd Christmas stamps	10.00
12 x 1st Christmas stamps	11.00

■ 2014, November 4
12 x 2nd Christmas stamps	10.00
12 x 1st Christmas stamps	11.00

■ 2015, November 3
12 x 2nd Christmas stamps	10.00
12 x 1st Christmas stamps	11.00

JERWOOD PHILATELICS

(Established 2010)

Great Britain dealer specialising in:

* Stitched Booklets
* Folded Booklets
* Window Booklets
* Prestige Booklets
* Greetings & Christmas Booklets
* Machins, including Cylinder, Date Blocks etc.
* Smilers™ Sheets, inc. Business Customised Sheets
* Post & Go™ stamps
* Modern commemoratives, inc. errors & varieties
* Royal Mail Year Books & Year Packs
* Accessories, including stockcards, mounts etc.
* Range of newly published catalogues
* Selected material from earlier reigns

Collections & quality single items bought

Detailed booklet listings using both the Stanley Gibbons and Modern British Philatelic Circle catalogues.

Website: www.jerwoodphilatelics.co.uk
Email: dave@jerwoodphilatelics.co.uk
Telephone: (0121) 663 0415

Insert bsmv17 at checkout to receive a 10% discount on any order over £25. Free P&P on all UK orders.

MBPC catalogue numbers are used with kind permission.
For more information on the Circle's activities and
benefits of membership, please visit
www.mbp-circle.co.uk

Member of the Philatelic Traders Society
(Membership Number: 6026)

GREETINGS BOOKLETS

In this section, prices are quoted for mint condition only. These booklets contain Greetings stamps, which are listed individually in the Queen Elizabeth II Decimal section. Normally the panes comprise one of each design, with additional greetings labels.

1989, January 31. Greetings
Two of each of the five 19p designs as January 31, 1989, plus 12 labels. Cover shows elements of designs   25.00

1990, February 6. Smiles
One each of ten 20p designs as February 6, 1990, plus 12 labels. Cover shows stamps within smiling lips   15.00

1991, February 5. Good Luck
One each of ten 1st class designs as February 5, 1991, plus 12 labels. Cover shows good luck charms   10.00

1991, March 26. Smiles
One each of ten 1st class designs as March 26, 1991, plus 12 labels. Cover shows a happy pillar box   9.00

1992, January 28. Memories
One each of ten 1st class designs as January 28, 1992, plus 12 labels. Cover shows a label and pressed flowers   9.00

1993, February 2. Gift Giving
One each of ten 1st class designs as February 2, 1993, plus 20 labels. Cover shows Rupert the Bear   9.00

1994, February 1. Messages
One each of ten 1st class designs as February 1, 1994, plus 20 labels. Cover shows Rupert and Paddington   9.00

1995, March 21. Art
One each of ten 1st class designs as March 21, 1995, plus 20 labels. Cover shows a clown
yellow strip at right with the inscription 'Pull Open'   9.00
yellow strip at right with no inscription   9.00

1996, February 26. Cartoons
One each of ten 1st class designs as February 26, 1996, plus 20 labels. Cover shows More! Love design   9.00

1996, November 11. Cartoons
One each of ten 1st class designs as November 11, 1996, plus 20 labels. Cover shows More! Love design   25.00

1997, January 6. Flower Paintings
One each of ten 1st class designs as January 6, 1997, plus 20 labels. Cover shows a flower   9.00

1997, February 3. Flower Paintings
One each of ten 1st class designs as January 6, 1997, plus 20 labels. Cover shows a flower with added inscription 'WIN A BEAUTIFUL BOUQUET INSTANTLY'   9.00

1998, January 5. Flower Paintings
One each of ten 1st class designs as January 6, 1997, plus 20 labels. Cover shows a box of chocolates.   9.00

1998, August 3. Flower Paintings
One each of ten 1st class designs as January 6, 1997, plus 20 labels. Cover inscribed 'Make their post memorable'   9.00

PRESTIGE STAMP BOOKS

In this section, prices are quoted for mint condition only.

Stamps for Cooks, 1969

■ **1969, December 1. £1.00 Stamps for Cooks**

Pane of six 1d, three 4d, three 4d, three 5d (recipe label)	9.00
Pane of fifteen 4d (label 'Stuffed Cucumber')	2.00
Pane of fifteen 4d (label 'Method')	2.00
Pane of fifteen 5d (recipe label)	2.00
Complete book	10.00

(* A stapled version of this stitched book exists that is much rarer. Price: £350.)

The Story of Wedgwood, 1972

■ **1972, May 24. £1.00 The Story of Wedgwood**

Pane of twelve 3p	3.00
Pane of six 2½p, six 3p	6.00
Pane of nine 2½p, one ½p	7.50
Pane of four ½p, two 2½p	40.00
Complete book	45.00

The Story of Wedgwood, 1980

■ **1980, April 16. £3.00 The Story of Wedgwood**

Pane of six 2p	0.50
Pane of nine 10p	2.00
Pane of nine 12p	2.00
Pane of one 2p, four 10p, four 12p	2.00
Complete book	5.00

■ **1982, May 19. £4.00 The Story of Stanley Gibbons**

Pane of six 12½p	1.75
Pane of six 15½p	1.75
Pane of nine15½p	2.50
Pane of one 2p, one 3p, seven 12½p	3.00
Complete book	6.00

■ **1983, September 14. £4.00 The Story of the Royal Mint**

Pane of six 12½p (label 'The Royal Mint & America')	1.75
Pane of six 12½p (label 'Maundy Money')	1.75
Pane of nine 16p	2.50
Pane of one 3p, two 3½p, six 16p	3.00
Complete book	6.00

The Story of our Christian Heritage, 1984

■ **1984, September 4. £4.00 The Story of Our Christian Heritage**

Pane of six 17p	2.25
Pane of six 13p (label 'William Wilberforce')	2.00
Pane of six 13p (label 'Lillian Bayliss')	2.00
Pane of one 10p, one 13p, seven 17p	14.00
Complete book	17.00

■ **1985, January 8. £5.00 The Story of The Times**

Pane of six 17p	2.50
Pane of nine 13p	2.50
Pane of nine 17p	3.00
Pane of two 4p, four 13p, two 17p, one 34p	9.00
Complete book	12.00

■ **1986, March 18. £5.00 The Story of British Rail**

Pane of six 17p	2.50
Pane of nine 12p	3.00
Pane of nine 17p	3.00
Pane of six 12p, two 17p, one 31p	12.00
Complete book	16.00

■ 1987, March 3. £5.00 The Story of P&O

Pane of six 13p	2.00
Pane of nine 13p	2.75
Pane of nine 18p	3.00
Pane of one 1p, two 13p, five 18p, one 26p	9.00
Complete book	12.50

■ 1988, March 3. £5.00 FT100 (Financial Times)

Pane of nine 18p	4.50
Pane of six 13p	2.50
Pane of six 13p, one 18p, one 22p, one 34p	16.00
Pane of six 18p	2.50
Complete book	19.00

■ 1989, March 21. £5.00 The Scots Connection

Pane of nine 19p Scotland	2.75
Pane of six 14p Scotland	2.50
Pane of five 14p, two 19p, one 23p, all Scotland	11.00
Pane of six 19p Scotland	2.50
Complete book	12.00

■ 1990, March 20. £5.00 London Life

Pane of four 20p Alexandra Palace	2.50
Pane of six 20p Penny Black Anniversary (label 'Eros')	2.50
Pane of six 20p Penny Black Anniversary (label 'Street Signs')	2.50
Pane of one 15p, one 20p, one 29p all Penny Black Anniversary, plus one 2nd, one 1st, one 15p, one 20p, one 50p	12.00
Complete book	15.00

■ 1991, March 19. £6.00 Alias Agatha Christie

Pane of six 17p (label 'Styles')	2.25
Pane of six 17p (label 'Mousetrap')	2.25
Pane of nine 22p	4.50
Pane of six 22p, two 33p	5.50
Complete book	11.00

■ 1992, February 25. £6.00 Cymru Wales

Pane of four 39p Wintertime	2.50
Pane of six 18p Wales	2.25
Pane of two 18p, two 24p, all Wales, plus one 2nd, one 1st, two 33p	8.00
Pane of six 24p Wales	2.25
Complete book	11.00

Tolkien: The Centenary, 1992

■ 1992, October 27. £6.00 Tolkien: The Centenary

Pane of six 24p (label 'Runes')	2.50
Pane of six 24p (label 'Hobbit')	2.50
Pane of six 18p	2.00
Pane of one 2nd, one 1st, two 18p, two 24p, two 39p	7.50
Complete book	11.00

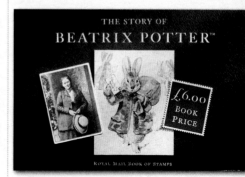

The Story of Beatrix Potter, 1992

■ 1993, August 10. £5.64 The Story of Beatrix Potter

Pane of four 1st Beatrix Potter	3.00
Pane of one 24p of each of Scotland, Wales and Northern Ireland, one 18p of each of Scotland, Wales and Northern Ireland	7.50
Pane of three 1st, three 2nd	6.50
Pane of two 2nd, two 18p, two 33p, two 39p	7.50
Complete book	12.00

■ 1994, July 26. £6.04 Northern Ireland

Pane of four 30p Prince of Wales Paintings	2.50
Pane of one 6p, one 19p, four 25p	9.00
Pane of two 19p, four 25p, one 30p, one 41p, all Northern Ireland	5.00
Pane of one 19p, one 25p, one 30p, one 41p, all Northern Ireland	5.00
Complete book	14.00

■ 1995, April 25. £6.00 The National Trust

Pane of six 25p National Trust	2.00
Pane of two 19p, two 25p, one 10p, one 30p, one 35p, one 41p	11.00
Pane of one 19p of each of Scotland, Wales and Northern Ireland, plus one 25p of each of Scotland, Wales and Northern Ireland	5.50
Pane of six 19p	7.50
Complete book	13.00

■ 1996, May 14. £6.48 European Football Championships

Pane of four 19p Football Legends	1.75
Pane of four 25p Football Legends	2.00
Pane of two 35p, two 41p, two 60p Football Legends	4.50
Pane of two 25p, two 25p Scotland, two 25p Wales, two 25p Northern Ireland	3.50
Complete book	10.00

■ 1997, September 23. £6.15 Celebrating 75 Years of the BBC

Pane of one 26p, one 37p Scotland, one 26p, one 37p Wales, one 26p, one 37p Northern Ireland	4.00
Pane of four 26p gold, four 1st gold	4.50
Pane of three 20p, three 26p	4.00
Pane of four 20p Children's Television	4.50
Complete book	11.00

■ 1998, March 10. £7.49 The Definitive Portrait

Pane of nine 26p Wilding	4.50
Pane of six 20p Wilding	3.00
Pane of four 20p, two 26p, two 37p Wilding	5.50
Pane of three 26p, three 37p Wilding	5.50
Complete book	13.00

Breaking Barriers, 1998

■ 1998, October 13. £6.16 Breaking Barriers

Pane of four 20p Land Speed Records	4.00
Pane of one 20p Scotland, one 20p Wales, one 20p Northern Ireland, three 43p	6.00
Pane of three 2nd, one 26p Scotland, one 26p Wales, one 26p Northern Ireland	5.00
Pane of three 43p, two 10p, three 2nd	6.50
Complete book	16.00

Profile on Print, 1999

■ 1999, February 16. £7.54 Profile on Print

Pane of eight 1st orange-red	7.00
Pane of four 1st Machin large format embossed	7.00
Pane of four 1st Machin large format intaglio	7.00
Pane of four Machin large format typographed	7.00
Pane of nine 1st orange-red	9.00
Complete book	19.00

■ 1999, September 21. £6.99 World Changers

Pane of four 20p Millennium Jenner's vaccination	2.00
Pane of four 44p Millennium Faraday's electricity	6.00
Pane of four 26p Millennium Darwin's theory	7.50
Pane of four 63p Millennium Computers in brain	8.00
Pane of four 1p, three 19p, one 26p	3.00
Complete book	17.00

Special by Design, 2000

■ 2000, February 15. £7.50 Special by Design

Pane of eight 1st Millennium definitive	5.50
Pane of three 1st Scotland, three 1st Wales, three 1st Northern Ireland	8.00
Pane of four 19p, olive-green, two 38p	12.50
Pane of six 1st Penny Black Anniversary	7.50
Complete book	30.00

■ 2000, August 4. £7.03 HM Queen Elizabeth, The Queen Mother

Pane of six 2nd Scotland, two 65p Scotland	5.00
Pane of nine 1st olive brown	5.00
Queen Mother's Century miniature sheet	7.00
Pane of four 27p Queen Mother	6.00
Complete book	17.00

■ 2000, September 18. £7.00 A Treasury of Trees

Pane of two 65p Millennium Doire Dach forest	3.50
Pane of four 45p Millennium Sycamore seeds,	4.00
Pane of two 65p Millennium Bluebell wood	3.50
Pane of four 1st Millennium definitives, four 2nd Wales	9.00
Pane of four 2nd Millennium Roots of trees	2.50
Complete book	20.00

■ 2001, October 21. £6.76 Unseen and Unheard

Pane of two 1st, two 65p Submarines	8.00
Pane of two 2nd, two 45p Submarines	8.00
Pane of four Flags and Ensigns	5.50
Pane of four 1st Scotland, four E Scotland	5.50
Complete book	22.00

■ 2002, February 6. £7.29 A Gracious Accession

Pane of four 2nd, four E	6.50
Pane of one 2nd, one 1st, one E, one 45p Golden Jubilee	9.00
Pane of one 1st, one E, one 45p, one 65p Golden Jubilee	9.00
Pane of four 1st Wilding, five 2nd Wilding (one tilted)	9.50
Complete book	24.00

■ 2002, September 24. £6.83 Across the Universe

Pane of four 1st England, four 2nd England, one 1st Scotland	5.50
Pane of four 1st Millennium National Space Centre	8.50
Pane of four 1st gold, four E	6.00
Astronomy miniature sheet	4.00
Complete book	20.00

■ 2003, February 25. £6.99 Microcosmos

Pane of four 1st Northern Ireland, five 2nd Northern Ireland	6.00
Pane of four 1st gold, four E	6.00
Pane of two 1st and two 2nd Discovery of DNA	2.75
Pane of four E Discovery of DNA	5.00
Complete book	18.00

■ 2003, June 2. £7.46 A Perfect Coronation

Pane of four 1st gold, four 2nd	4.75
Pane of four 1st 50th Anniversary of Coronation	3.25
Pane of four (different) 1st 50th Anniversary of Coronation	2.75
Pane of two 47p Wilding, two 68p Wilding, one £1 Coronation	30.00
Complete book	37.00

Letters by Night, 2004

■ 2004, March 16. £7.44 Letters by Night

Pane of three 2nd Scotland, three 68p Scotland	4.50
Pane of one 28p, one E, one 42p Classic Locomotives	4.50
Pane of four 1st Pub Signs	3.50
Pane of four 1st gold, four 37p	6.00
Complete book	16.00

The Glory of the Garden, 2004

■ 2004, May 25. £7.23 The Glory of the Garden

Pane of four 1st gold, two 42p, two 47p	5.00
Pane of one 2nd, one E, one 68p, one 42p RHS	5.00
Pane of one 1st Iris latifolia, two 1st Tulipa, one 1st Gentiana acaulis	6.00
Pane of two 1st, two 47p RHS	6.00
Complete book	19.00

■ 2005, February 24. £7.43 The Brontë Sisters

Pane of four 2nd, two 39p, two 42p	4.50
Pane of two 2nd England, two 40p England	3.00
Pane of two 1st Brontë, two 1st Bronté	4.00
Pane of one 40p, one 57p, one 68p, one £1.12 Brontë	5.50
Complete book	16.00

■ 2005, October 4. £7.26 Bicentenary of the Battle of Trafalgar

Pane of four 1st, two 50p, two 68p	6.00
Pane of three 1st White Ensign	5.50
Pane of one 1st, one 42p, one 68p Trafalgar (first designs)	3.00
Pane of one 1st, one 42p, one 68p Trafalgar (second designs)	3.00
Complete book	16.00

■ 2006, February 23. £7.40 Brunel

Pane of one 40p, one 60p, one 47p all Brunel	3.50
Pane of one 1st, one 42p, one 68p all Brunel	3.00
Pane of four 1st, two 35p, two 40p	5.50
Pane of two 68p Ocean Liners, one 47p Brunel	11.00
Complete book	18.00

Victoria Cross, 2006

■ 2006, September 21. £7.41 Victoria Cross

Pane of first 1st, 64p and 72p Victoria Cross	3.50
Pane of second 1st, 64p and 72p Victoria Cross	3.50
Pane of four 20p Gallantry Awards	10.00
Pane of four 1st, four 50p	6.00
Complete book	18.00

■ 2007, March 1. £7.68 World of Invention

Pane of three 2nd Scotland and three 44p Wales	5.00
Pane of four 1st revised style and four 5p definitives	3.25
Pane of two 1st and two 64p World of Invention	6.50
Pane of two 1st and two 72p World of Invention	6.00
Complete book	15.00

■ 2007, June 5. £7.66 The Machin: The Making of a Masterpiece

Pane of four 2p, two 46p, two 48p definitives	3.50
Pane of two £1 ruby definitives	4.00
Pane of two 1st Arnold Machin and two 1st 4d deep olive-sepia definitives	4.00
Pane of one 2nd and one 1st revised style, and two 2nd and two 1st Large definitives	4.50
Complete book	15.00

■ 2007, September 20. £7.49 British Army Uniforms

Pane of one each of 1st definitives of England, Northern Ireland, Scotland and Wales	5.00
Pane of three (different) 1st British Army Uniforms	4.00
Pane of three (different) 78p British Army Uniforms	5.00
Pane of two 1p, four 46p and two 54p definitives	5.50
Complete book	16.00

Ian Fleming's James Bond, 2008

■ 2008, January 8. £7.40 Ian Fleming's James Bond

Pane of one 1st Casino Royale, one 54p Goldfinger, one 78p For Your Eyes Only	3.75
Pane of one 1st Dr No, one 54p Diamonds Are Forever, one 78p From Russia With Love	3.75
Pane of eight 1st class gold	7.50
Pane of two 1st White Ensign and two 1st Union Jack, as of October 22, 2001	5.50
Complete book	16.00

■ 2008, September 18. £7.15 Pilot to Plane: RAF Uniforms

Pane of three (different) 1st RAF Uniforms	3.50
Pane of three (different) 81p RAF Uniforms	4.50
Pane of four 1st gold and four 2nd definitives	3.50
Pane of two 1st Air Displays design of July 17, 2008, and two 20p Spitfire design of June 10, 1997	6.00
Complete book	16.00

■ 2008, September 29. £9.72 The Regional Definitives: Heraldry and Symbol

Pane of the 1958 3d, 6d and 1s 3d designs of Northern Ireland, Scotland and Wales re-denominated as 1st	7.50
Pane of the 1958 3d, 6d and 1s 3d designs of Northern Ireland, re-denominated as 1st, and three 1st class Northern Ireland of October 14, 2003	5.50
Pane of the 1958 3d, 6d and 1s 3d designs of Scotland, re-denominated as 1st, and three 1st class Scotland of October 14, 2003	5.50
Pane of the 1958 3d, 6d and 1s 3d designs of Wales, re-denominated as 1st, and three 1st class Wales of October 14, 2003	5.50
Complete book	19.00

British Design Classics, 2009

■ 2009, January 13. £7.68 British Design Classics

Pane of four 16p and four 50p definitives	5.50
Pane of one 1st Spitfire, two 1st Routemaster, one 1st Mini	4.50
Pane of one 1st London Underground Map, one 1st Telephone Kiosk, one 1st Penguin Books, one 1st Anglepoise Lamp, one 1st Polypropylene Chair, one 1st Mini Skirt	7.00
Pane of two 1st Concorde, and two 1st Concorde design of May 2, 2002	4.50
Complete book	21.00

■ 2009, February 12. £7.75 Charles Darwin

Pane of the 48p, 50p and 56p Charles Darwin	10.50
Pane comprising the Charles Darwin miniature sheet	4.50
Pane of the 1st, 72p and 81p Charles Darwin	10.00
Pane of two 1st, two 5p, two 10p and two 48p definitives	5.50
Complete book	32.00

Treasures of the Archive, 2009

■ 2009, August 18. £8.18 Treasures of the Archive

Pane of four 1st Penny Black Anniversary and four 20p Penny Black Anniversary	6.50
Pane of four 20p Royal Mail coach design of October 17, 1989	4.00
Pane of four (different) 1st Post Boxes	6.00
Pane of four 17p, two 22p and two 62p definitives	7.00
Complete book	17.00

■ 2009, September 17. £7.93 Royal Navy Uniforms

Pane of the three (different) 90p Naval Uniforms	4.50
Pane of the three (different) 1st Naval Uniforms	3.50
Pane of two 1st White Ensign and two 1st Jolly Roger designs of October 22, 2001	6.00
Pane of two 1p, four 17p, and two 90p definitives	10.50
Complete book	16.00

■ 2010, January 7. £8.06 Classic Album Covers

Pane of four 20p, two 54p (wrong font), two 62p definitives	6.00
Pane of six (different) 1st Classic Album Covers	9.00
Pane of four (different) 1st Classic Album Covers	8.50
Pane of two 5p (wrong font), five 10p, two 22p definitives	6.00
Complete book	29.00

■ 2010, February 25. £7.72 The Royal Society

Pane of four (different) 1st Royal Society	4.00
Pane of four 22p and four 54p definitives (the 54p stamps with wrong font in error)	7.00
Pane of four (different) 1st Royal Society	4.00
Pane of four (different) 1st Royal Society	4.00
Complete book	19.00

■ 2010, May 8. £11.15 King George V

Pane of three 1st, three £1 Centenary of Accession	8.00
Pane of two (different) £1 Seahorses	5.00
Pane of four 1st British Empire Exhibition	5.00
Pane of four 1st, two 2nd, two 50p definitives, self-adhesive	8.00
Complete book	24.00

Britain Alone, 2010

■ 2010, May 13. £9.76 Britain Alone

Pane of four 5p, two 10p, two 60p definitives	4.00
Pane of four (different) Britain Alone	6.00
Pane of four (different) Britain Alone	7.00
Pane of four (different) Dunkirk	5.00
Complete book	23.00

■ 2011, March 11. £9.05 WWF

Pane of six (different) 1st WWF	7.00
Pane of four (different) 1st WWF	3.50
Pane of WWF miniature sheet	4.00
Pane of three 5p, three 10p, one 67p and one 97p definitives	8.00
Complete book	20.00

Morris & Co, 2011

■ 2011, May 5. £9.99 Morris & Co

Pane of two 1st, two £1.10 Morris & Co	6.00
Pane of one 1st, two 76p, one £1.10 Morris & Co	9.00
Pane of four 2nd Christmas designs of 2009	4.00
Pane of four 5p, two 10p, two 50p definitives, self-adhesive	6.00
Complete book	20.00

■ 2011, September 9. £9.97 First UK Aerial Post

Pane of one £1.10 Aerial Post and two 1st Aerial Post	7.00
Pane of one £1 Aerial Post and two 68p Aerial Post	6.00
Pane of four 50p Windsor Castle designs of 2005	10.00
Pane of four 5p, two 1st, two 76p definitives	20.00
Complete book	40.00

Roald Dahl, 2012

■ 2012, January 10. £11.47 Roald Dahl: Master Storyteller

Pane of two 2p, two 10p and four 68p definitives	9.50
Pane of 1st, 68p and 76p Roald Dahl	5.00
Pane of 66p, £1 and £1.10 Roald Dahl	6.50
Pane of 1st, 68p, 76p, £1 from Roald Dahl miniature sheet	5.00
Complete book	21.00

■ 2012, May 31. £12.77 Diamond Jubilee

Pane of four 1st Wilding, four 1st diamond blue definitives	10.00
Pane of 1st Trooping the Colour and 77p Royal Welsh	3.00
Pane of 1st Golden Jubilee, £1.26 United Nations Address, 87p Silver Jubilee and 87p Garter Ceremony	8.50
Pane of 77p First Christmas TV Broadcast and £1.28 Commonwealth Games	4.50
Complete book	22.00

■ 2012, July 27. £10.71 Keeping The Flame Alive

Pane of three 1st Olympics, three 1st Paralympics, one Worldwide Olympics and one Worldwide Paralympics definitives	32.00
Pane of 1st Aquatics, 1st Field Athletics	3.00
Pane of 1st Paralympic Archery, 1st Equestrian	3.00
Pane of 1st Football, 1st Track athletics	3.00
Complete book	37.00

■ 2013, March 26. £13.77 50 Years of Doctor Who

Pane of four 1st Tardis, one 5p, one 10p, one 20p and one 87p definitives	10.50
Pane of four (different) 1st Doctor Who	5.50
Pane of four (different) 1st Doctor Who	5.50
Pane of three (different) 1st Doctor Who	5.50
Pane of Doctor Who miniature sheet	5.50
Complete book	25.00

(* This book was designed with one half upside–down, so it can be read from either end.)

Football Heroes, 2013

■ 2013, May 9. £11.85 Football Heroes

Pane of five (different) 1st Football Heroes	17.00
Pane of six (different) 1st Football Heroes	17.00
Pane of two 2p, two 5p and two 10p definitives	2.50
Pane of two 1st red, two 1p definitives, one 1st England flag, one 1st Northern Ireland, one 1st Scotland flag and one 1st Wales flag	10.00
Complete book	38.00

(* This book was issued in a sealed plastic wrapper.)

■ 2013, September 19. £11.19 Merchant Navy

Pane of three (different) 1st Merchant Navy	3.75
Pane of three (different) £1.28 Merchant Navy	6.50
Pane of four (different) 1st Atlantic and Arctic Convoys	7.00
Pane of four 5p, four 50p definitives	8.00
Complete book	23.00

■ 2014, February 20. £13.97 Locomotives of the United Kingdom

Pane of two 1st and two 60p Classic Locos of England	11.00
Pane of two 1st and two 68p Classic Locos of Scotland	5.50
Pane of two 1st and two 78p Classic Locos of Northern Ireland	7.50
Pane of two 1st and two 78p Classic Locos of Wales	7.50
Pane of two 2p, two 5p, 1st Northern Ireland, 1st English flag, 1st Scottish flag and 1st Welsh flag	6.00
Complete book	26.00

Buckingham Palace, 2014

■ 2014, April 15. £11.39 Buckingham Palace

Pane of four 1st Buckingham Palace (exterior)	7.00
Pane of two 1st Buckingham Palace (exterior)	4.00
Pane of four 1st Buckingham Palace (interior)	7.00
Pane of two 10p, four 20p and two £1 definitives	7.00
Complete book	23.00

■ 2014, July 28. £11.30 The Great War, 1914

Pane of three (different) 1st First World War	4.50
Pane of three (different) £1.47 First World War	10.00
Pane of two 10p, two 20p, 1st England, 1st Northern Ireland, 1st Scotland and 1st Wales	6.50
Pane of one £1 definitive	2.00
Complete book	22.00

■ 2015, February 19. £14.65 Inventive Britain

Pane of two 1p, two 2p, one 81p and two 97p definitives	14.00
Pane of one 1st Station X, (2012) two 1st Bombe (2012) and one 1st Colossus	5.50
Pane of two (different) 81p, one £1.28 and one £1.47 Inventive Britain	8.00
Pane of two (different) 1st, one £1.28 and one £1.47 Inventive Britain	7.50
Complete book	28.00

■ 2015, May 14. £13.96 The Great War, 1915

Pane of four 1st Observer Royal Field Artillery (2007)	5.00
Pane of three (different) 1st First World War 2015	4.00
Pane of three (different) £1.52 First World War 2015	8.00
Pane of two 1p, two 5p and two £1.33 definitives, and two 1st Poppies	7.00
Complete book	22.00

Battle of Waterloo, 2015

■ 2015, June 18. £14.47 Battle of Waterloo

Pane of Battle of Waterloo miniature sheet	7.50
Pane of one 1st, two (different) £1.00, one £1.52 Battle of Waterloo	8.50
Pane of one 1st and one £1.52 Battle of Waterloo	5.50
Pane of two 5p, two 10p, two 50p and two £1 definitives	7.50
Complete book	25.00

The Making of Star Wars, 2015

■ 2015, December 17. £16.99 The Making of Star Wars

Pane of six (different) 1st Star Wars	6.00
Pane of six (different) 1st Star Wars	6.00
Double pane of Star Wars miniature sheet. Self-adhesive	8.00
Pane of four 1st Union Flag, two 1st red and two 2nd blue definitives	8.00
Complete book	26.00

(* A limited edition of this book was produced with silver-foil printing, sold at £127.)

■ 2016, February 24. £16.36 Royal Mail 500

Pane of two (different) 1st, one £1.52 Royal Mail 500	5.00
Pane of one 1st, two (different) £1.52 Royal Mail 500	8.50
Pane of two (different) 1st, two (different) £1.33 Classic GPO Posters	8.50
Pane of two 1st Penny Black, three 1st Twopenny Blue, three 1st Penny Red	7.50
Complete book	26.00

The Queen's 90th Birthday, 2016

■ 2016, April 21. £15.11 The Queen's 90th Birthday

Pane of two (different) £1.52 Queen's Birthday	4.50
Pane of three (different) 1st, one £1.52 Queen's Birthday	5.00
Pane of Queen's Birthday miniature sheet	4.00

Pane of 1st England, 1st Northern Ireland, 1st Wales, 1st Scotland, two 1st red and two 1st amethyst definitives	7.50
Complete book	21.00

(* A limited edition of this book was produced with gold-foil printing, sold at £59.95.)

■ 2016, June 21. £16.49 The Great War, 1916

Pane of three 1st First World War 2016	3.00
Pane of three £1.52 First World War 2016	7.00
Pane of two 1st, two £1.33 Post Office at War	6.00
Pane of four 1st Poppy, one 1st Northern Ireland, one 1st English flag, one 1st Scottish flag, one 1st Welsh flag	7.50
Complete book	23.00

The Tale of Beatrix Potter, 2016

■ 2016, July 28. £15.37 The Tale of Beatrix Potter

Pane of 1st, £1.33, £1.52 Beatrix Potter	5.00
Pane of 1st, £1.33, £1.52 Beatrix Potter (different)	5.00
Pane of two 1st, two £1.33 Tale of Peter Rabbit	6.00
Pane of three 5p, two 10p, three £1.05 definitives	6.00
Complete book	22.00

(* A limited edition of this book was produced with extra pages, sold at £59.99.)

OFFICIAL STAMPS

During the reigns of Queen Victoria and King Edward VII stamps were overprinted for use by Government Departments. The prices in this section are quoted in two columns: mint (left) and fine used (right).

QUEEN VICTORIA, 1840–1901

■ **Penny Black 'VR'**
Printed by Perkins Bacon. Design as the standard stamp but with the stars in the top corners replaced by the letters 'V' and 'R'. Not officially issued.

1d black (1840 issue) with gum	£30,000	–
1d black (1840 issue) without gum	£15,000	–
1d black (1840 issue) with trial cancel	–	£40,000

■ **Overprinted 'I.R. OFFICIAL' for use by the Inland Revenue**
Printed by De La Rue.

½d green (1880 issue)	80.00	15.00
½d blue (1884 issue)	45.00	13.00
½d orange (1887 issue)	6.00	1.00
½d green (1900 issue)	8.00	3.50
1d lilac (1881 issue)	2.75	1.40
2½d lilac (1884 issue)	£350	50.00
2½d purple on blue paper (1887 issue)	£100	6.00
6d grey (1881 issue)	£350	50.00
6d purple on red paper (1887 issue)	£300	45.00
1/– green (1884 issue)	£6,000	£1,600
1/– green (1887 issue)	£900	95.00
1/– green, red (1900 issue)	£4,000	£1,100
5/– red (1884 issue)	£9,000	£2,000

10/– blue (1884 issue)	£10,000	£3,000
£1 brown (1884 issue)	£65,000	£26,000
£1 brown (1888 issue)	£90,000	£35,000
£1 green (1891 issue)	£10,000	£2,200

■ **Overprinted 'O.W. OFFICIAL' for use by the Office of Works**
Printed by De La Rue.

½d orange (1887 issue)	£200	£100
½d green (1900 issue)	£300	£150
1d lilac (1881 issue)	£350	£100
5d purple and blue (1887 issue)	£3,000	£900
10d purple and red (1887 issue)	£6,500	£2,000

■ **Overprinted 'ARMY OFFICIAL'**
Printed by De La Rue.

½d orange (1887 issue)	2.75	1.25
½d green (1900 issue)	3.00	5.00
1d lilac (1881 issue)	2.50	2.00
2½d purple on blue paper (1887 issue)	25.00	10.00
6d purple on red paper (1887 issue)	60.00	30.00

■ **Overprinted 'GOVT PARCELS' for use by the Government**
Printed by De La Rue.

1d lilac (1881 issue)	70.00	10.00
1½d lilac (1884 issue)	£300	40.00
1½d purple and green (1887 issue)	£100	4.00
2d green and red (1887 issue)	£150	14.00
4½d green and red (1887 issue)	£260	£110
6d green (1884 issue)	£2,400	£900
6d purple on red paper (1887 issue)	£200	40.00
9d green (1884 issue)	£2,000	£700
9d purple and blue (1887 issue)	£275	60.00
1/– brown (1881 issue)	£1,200	£200
1/– green (1887 issue)	£500	£110
1/– green, red (1887 issue)	£500	£125

Overprinted 'BOARD OF EDUCATION'
Printed by De La Rue.

5d purple and blue (1887 issue)	£4,500	£800
1/– green and red (1887 issue)	£10,000	£5,000

KING EDWARD VII, 1902–1904

Overprinted 'I.R OFFICIAL' for use by the Inland Revenue
Printed by De La Rue.

½d blue-green	20.00	2.00
1d red	15.00	1.25
2½d blue	£900	£200
6d purple	–	–
1/– green and red	£3,500	£600
5/– red	£40,000	£10,000
10/– blue	£90,000	£45,000
£1 green	£60,000	£22,000

Overprinted 'O.W. OFFICIAL' for use by the Office of Works
Printed by De La Rue.

½d blue-green	£400	£110
1d red	£400	£100
2d green and red	£1,500	£400
2½d blue	£2,500	£500
10d purple and red	£42,000	£6,000

Overprinted 'ARMY OFFICIAL'
Printed by De La Rue.

½d blue-green	4.00	1.25
1d red	4.00	1.25
6d purple	£130	45.00

Overprinted 'GOVT PARCELS' for use by the Government
Printed by De La Rue.

1d red	30.00	10.00
2d green and red	£150	25.00
6d purple	£240	20.00
9d purple and blue	£550	85.00
1/– green and red	£1,200	£250

Overprinted 'BOARD OF EDUCATION'
Printed by De La Rue.

½d blue-green	£150	20.00
1d red	£150	20.00
2½d blue	£4,000	£275
5d purple and blue	£32,000	£9,000
1/– green and red	£200,000	–

Overprinted 'R.H. OFFICIAL' for use by the Royal Household
Printed by De La Rue.

½d blue-green	£300	£200
1d red	£275	£150

Overprinted 'ADMIRALTY OFFICIAL' for use by the Royal Navy
Printed by De La Rue.

½d blue-green	20.00	10.00
1d red	12.00	4.00
1½d purple and green	£275	70.00
2d green and red	£300	80.00
2½d blue	£425	75.00
3d purple on yellow paper	£375	70.00

POSTAGE DUES

From 1914 until they were withdrawn from service in 2000, postage dues were affixed to covers by the postal service to denote postage unpaid or underpaid.

Up to 1936, prices are quoted in three columns: unmounted mint (left), mounted mint (centre) and used (right), After 1936, they are quoted for mint (left) and fine used (right).

PRE-DECIMAL ISSUES 1914–70

½d to 1/–

2/6 to £1

■ 1914–1923

Des: G. Eve. Printed in typography by Harrison (all values except 1/–) or Somerset House (½d, 1d, 5d, 1/–). Wmk: Simple Royal Cypher GVR. Perf 14x15.

A) Wmk sideways; crown faces left when viewed from front.

½d green	1.25	0.40	0.35
1d red on ordinary paper	1.25	0.50	0.25
1d red on chalky paper	7.50	4.00	4.00
1½d brown	95.00	35.00	13.00
2d black	1.25	0.80	0.30
3d violet	25.00	4.00	0.60
4d green	£300	£150	40.00
5d brown	11.00	4.00	2.00
1/– blue	90.00	19.00	3.00
Set	£400	95.00	22.00

B) Wmk inverted; crown faces right.

½d green	1.50	1.00	1.00
1d red	2.00	1.00	1.00
1½d brown	£120	50.00	15.00
2d black	3.00	1.00	1.00
3d violet	25.00	6.50	2.50
4d green	£110	35.00	5.00
5d brown	32.00	12.00	4.00
1/– blue	90.00	20.00	15.00

■ 1924–1935

Printed in typography by Waterlow and (from 1934) Harrison. Wmk: Multiple Crowns and Block GVR. Perf 14x15.

A) Wmk sideways; crown faces left when viewed from front.

½d green	1.25	0.50	0.30
1d red	1.25	0.50	0.10
1½d brown	90.00	27.00	9.00
2d black	6.00	1.25	0.20
3d violet	6.00	1.75	0.20
4d green	40.00	5.00	0.85
5d brown	110.00	35.00	17.00
1/– blue	25.00	4.00	0.25
2/6 purple (yellow paper)	190.00	50.00	0.80
Set	£450	£120	24.50

B) Wmk inverted; crown faces right.

½d green	4.50	2.00	1.50
1d red	–	–	8.50
1½d brown	–	–	25.00
2d black	–	–	8.50
3d violet	60.00	20.00	20.00
4d green	£125	40.00	40.00
1/– blue	–	–	–
2/6 purple (yellow paper)	–	–	–

■ 1936–1937

Printed in typography by Harrison. Wmk: Multiple Crowns and E8R, sideways. Perf 14x15.

½d green	7.00	6.50
1d red	1.00	1.50
2d black	6.00	6.00
3d violet	1.50	1.50
4d green	60.00	22.00
5d brown	40.00	18.00
1/– blue	20.00	6.50
2/6 purple on yellow paper	£300	10.00
Set	£425	65.00

■ 1937–1938

Printed in typography by Harrison. Wmk: Multiple Crowns and GVIR. Perf 14x15.

A) Wmk sideways; crown faces left when viewed from front.

½d green	8.50	4.50
1d red	2.00	0.20
2d black	1.25	0.30
3d violet	7.00	0.30
4d green	60.00	7.00
5d brown	7.00	0.80
1/– blue	45.00	0.90
2/6 purple on yellow paper	50.00	2.00
Set	£160	12.00

B) Wmk inverted; crown faces right.

1d red	£170	–
2d black	£170	–
3d violet	£170	–
4d green	£300	–
5d brown	£170	–
1/– blue	£170	–

■ 1951–1952

Printed in typography by Harrison. Wmk: Multiple Crowns and

GVIR. Perf 14x15.

A) Wmk sideways; crown faces left when viewed from front.

½d orange	3.50	3.50
1d blue	1.25	0.50
1½d green	1.25	1.50
4d blue	30.00	12.00
1/- brown	22.00	4.00
Set	45.00	18.00

B) Wmk inverted; crown faces right.

1d blue	–	–
1½d green	£110	–
1/- brown	£2,000	–

■ 1954–1955

Printed in typography by Harrison. Wmk: Tudor Crown and E2R. Perf 14x15.

A) Wmk sideways; crown faces left when viewed from front.

½d orange	8.00	8.50
2d black	25.00	16.00
3d violet	70.00	30.00
4d blue	20.00	16.00
5d brown	15.00	10.00
2/6 purple on yellow paper	£150	8.00
Set	£220	85.00

B) Wmk inverted; crown faces right.

½d orange	£150	–

■ 1955–1957

Printed in typography by Harrison. Wmk: St Edward's Crown and E2R. Perf 14x15.

A) Wmk sideways; crown faces left when viewed from front.

½d orange	4.00	4.00
1d blue	3.00	1.25
1½d green	7.00	4.50
2d black	25.00	5.25
3d violet	3.50	1.25
4d blue	16.00	2.00
5d brown	20.00	1.75
1/- brown	40.00	2.00
2/6 purple on yellow paper	£115	10.00
5/- red on yellow paper	60.00	18.00
Set	£240	40.00

B) Wmk inverted; crown faces right.

½d orange	60.00	–
1½d green	60.00	–
3d violet	90.00	–
4d blue	£125	–
1/- brown	–	–
2/6 purple on yellow paper	–	–
5/- red on yellow paper	–	£175

■ 1959–1963

Printed in typography by Harrison. Wmk: Multiple St Edward's Crown. Perf 14x15.

A) Wmk sideways; crown faces left when viewed from front.

½d orange	0.15	0.25
1d blue	0.15	0.10
1½d green	1.50	2.00
2d black	1.00	0.30
3d violet	0.35	0.15

4d blue	0.35	0.15
5d brown	0.35	0.30
6d purple	0.50	0.15
1/- brown	1.00	0.15
2/6 purple on yellow paper	1.50	0.20
5/- red on yellow paper	4.00	0.50
10/- blue on yellow paper	10.00	3.00
£1 black on yellow paper	30.00	4.50
Set	45.00	9.50

B) Wmk inverted; crown faces right.

½d orange	1.25	–
1d blue	90.00	–
2d black	£150	–
3d violet	60.00	–
4d blue	£225	–
5d brown	4.00	–
6d purple	£225	–
1/- brown	75.00	–
2/6 purple on yellow paper	15.00	–
5/- red on yellow paper	25.00	–
10/- blue on yellow paper	50.00	–

■ 1968–1969

Printed in typography by Harrison. No watermark. Perf 14x15. Chalky paper.

A) Gum Arabic.

2d black	0.50	0.50
4d blue	0.40	0.20

B) PVA gum.

2d black	1.50	1.00
3d violet	0.50	0.50
5d brown	5.00	5.00
6d purple	1.00	1.25
1/- brown	3.00	2.00

■ 1968–1969

Printed in gravure by Harrison. No watermark. Perf 14x15. Chalky paper. PVA gum.

4d blue	4.50	5.00
8d red	0.50	1.00

DECIMAL ISSUES 1970–2000

½p to 7p

10p to £5

1p to 5p

10p to £5

■ 1970–1975

Des: J. Matthews. Printed in gravure by Harrison. No watermark. Chalky paper. Perf: 14x15.

A) PVA gum. Original coated paper.

½p turquoise	0.10	0.25
1p purple	0.50	0.10
2p green	0.25	0.10
3p blue	0.75	0.20
4p sepia	0.25	0.10
5p violet	1.00	0.30
10p carmine	0.80	0.30
20p deep green	1.10	0.50
50p blue	2.25	1.00
£1 black	4.00	0.25

B) PVA gum. Fluorescent coated paper.

1p purple	0.50	–
3p blue	1.75	–
5p violet	2.25	–
10p carmine	45.00	–
20p deep green	45.00	–
£5 orange and black	15.00	1.00

C) PVAD gum (blue-tinged).

1p purple	0.10	–
2p green	0.10	–
3p blue	0.15	–
4p sepia	0.15	–
5p violet	0.15	–
7p red-brown	0.25	0.25
10p carmine	0.25	–
11p green	0.40	0.35
20p deep green	0.50	–
50p blue	1.00	–
£1 black	2.00	–
£5 orange and black	18.00	1.00
Set (one of each value)	20.00	10.00

D) PVAD gum. Phosphor coated paper).

10p carmine	0.70	0.50
20p deep green	1.00	0.75

■ 1982, June 9

Des: Sedley Place. Printed in gravure by Harrisons. No watermark. Perf: 14x15.

1p crimson	0.15	0.10
2p bright blue	0.15	0.10
3p purple	0.15	0.15
4p blue	0.15	0.10
5p brown	0.15	0.10
10p light brown	0.20	0.10
20p sage green	0.40	0.30
25p blue–grey	0.60	0.60
50p charcoal	1.00	1.50
£1 red	2.00	0.50
£2 turquoise	4.00	2.50
£5 dull orange	8.50	1.25
Set	14.00	5.00
Gutter pairs	30.00	–

1p to £5

■ 1994, February 15

Des: Sedley Place. Printed in lithography by Questa. No watermark. Perf: 15x14.

1p yellow, orange-red and black	0.15	0.30
2p magenta, purple and black	0.15	0.30
5p yellow, brown and black	0.20	0.30
10p yellow, green and black	0.30	0.40
20p violet, emerald–green and black	1.00	1.00
25p magenta, claret and black	1.50	1.50
£1 pink, violet and black	6.00	6.00
£1.20 green, blue and black	7.50	7.50
£5 green, charcoal and black	17.50	17.50
Set	27.00	28.00
First day cover	–	35.00

3). No, the answer is that Stamp Collecting is alive and well – stamps shops are all but defunct – but 'underground' – on-line, by mail-order and at auction things are still 'humming' depending upon whom you are dealing with. So, let's look at potentially / probably the biggest sourcing area of the hobby apart from retail which is fairly self-explanatory … and that is bidding / buying at Stamp Auction.

4). **Nowadays there are three types of stamp auction:** – Pure Internet / Public - (including on-line bidding) / Postal (Mail-Bid Sales – including on-line). Each has its strengths and weaknesses. Let's start with Pure Internet live auctions, I won't mention names but in some senses these are today's equivalent of the 'Wild West'. As fast as these internet Giants catch up with the some of the crooks using them, the crooks move a step ahead … many internet bidders using them are 'hooked'.

TIP 4a). They have become 'live auction obsessed' unwilling / not capable of looking elsewhere – thinking that bidding / buying this way guarantees value which it does not. What happens when they come to sell?

Perhaps then they realise that _only_ some of what they may have glistening is 'gold'. Indiscriminate internet auction bidders buying 1,000's of low price items … may have spent large sums IN TOTAL … but may not have created desirable collections. The cost of a low priced item is the labour and cost of selling it. Nothing changes when that item comes to being re-sold.

TIP 5). **Now let's look at Public Auction.** Yes – you will be hard pressed to find a Public Stamp Auction that does not accept on-line / live internet bidding. As with 'Pure Internet' stamp sales – and perhaps even more so – 'Caveat Emptor' (buyer beware becomes even more the mantra. Generally individual lots may have higher average values so that lots offered are often higher value collections, accumulations or higher value sets / singles / rarities. Such auctions are the 'haunts' of dealers and astute buyers … but risk is attached, plus

the absence of guarantees and the pernicious unpleasant buyer's premium + other charges which at certain auctions can convert a £1000 stamp purchase into as much as an invoice for £1,300.

TIP 5a).There are bargains to be had – but it is very much a 'big boys' playing field. Some of these auctions deliberately under-estimate lots that they know are worth far more … so that they can then have the dubious pleasure of publicising that a £1,000 estimated lot realised £10,000, when perhaps their knowledge suggested it should have been estimated at upwards of £5,000 in the first place … (hence – how wonderful they are).

TIP 5b). For certain types of lots such as actual Collections offered fairly intact the absence of guarantee combined with unreliable estimate means that for those who do not physically view a Public Stamp Auction and bid 'blind' – this is a dangerous place to be. Of course this may work to the advantage of an astute bidder who is actually present to physically view lots in the auction room. Historically that person was usually a Dealer. Perhaps less so these days.

TIP 6). **Finally we come to look at Postal Auctions/Mail-Bid Sales.** First I must profess that I have an interest in a Mail-Bid / Postal Auction Sale. My company U P A conducts the largest postal auctions in the U K … What should the Collector or Dealer be looking for here?

TIP 6a). Most good Postal Auctions including U P A offer Collectors a No Quibble Refund Guarantee (NQRG) … and by 'No Quibble' I mean NO QUIBBLE. Look for this – it is crucial. You are probably not actually seeing the stamps before bidding … so no guarantee would mean unacceptable risk.

TIP 6b). Unlike Public Auctions most Postal Auctions 'break' many collections into smaller 'collector-sized' units so that you may find what you seek without having to purchase what you do

Please turn to page 277 ☛

FRAMA LABELS

In this section, prices are quoted in two columns: mint (left) and fine used (right).

From May 1984 until April 1985, Frama machines were installed at five locations, printing labels to order for any value from ½p (until withdrawn in January 1985) to 16p (17p from August 28, 1984).

■ **1984, May 1**
Machine-printed in red on phosphor-coated security paper with a grey-green background pattern. Gummed and imperforate.

Set (½p to 17p)	18.00	19.00
Pack (all values from ½p to 16p)	25.00	–
Pack (16½p, 17p)	4.00	–
Pack (3½p, 12½p, 16p)	4.00	–
First day cover (3½p, 12½p, 16p)	–	2.50

POST & GO STAMPS

In most of this section, prices are quoted in two columns: mint on backing paper (left) and fine used (right). Where there is only one column, this is for mint stamps on backing paper, except in the case of first day covers.

This listing is limited to labels dispensed from self-service machines, with the value printed at point of sale and no restrictions on date of use.

Post office machines

Since October 2008, automated kiosks have been installed at an increasing number of post offices, vending self-adhesive stamps to order.

Besides a 'Post It Now' service with labels meeting a wide range of postage rates (which are outside the scope of this publication), they offer a 'Buy A Stamp' service in which a pre-printed base design is overprinted at the time of the transaction with details of one of a limited selection of postage rates, along with a code which identifies the post office and machine number.

The machines installed in post offices from 2008 were manufactured by Wincor Nixdorf, and could print the stamps in strips of up to five. Between February 2014 and March 2015, these were gradually replaced by machines manufactured by NCR, which can print in strips of up to six.

Royal Mail machines

Since 2011, Royal Mail has also had its own range of machines, initially referred to as Hytech but upgraded to Series B in 2014.

These have been used to print the strips and packs which are available from the philatelic service. They have also been temporarily installed at various philatelic events in Britain and abroad, in 'pop up' post shops, and permanently installed at a growing range of museums, in many cases dispensing stamps with an additional commemorative or location-identifying inscription. Machines at Royal Mail enquiry offices also had location-identifiers in 2014–15, but this practice was then discontinued.

Some machines, such as those at the Royal Mail Engineering Department at Wheatstone House, Swindon, and at RAF Hortholt, are accessible only to people working on the premises.

As the use of Post & Go has extended to other stamp-issuing countries, machines installed at Broad Street in Jersey, Envoy House in Guernsey and Gibraltar House in London have also dispensed stamps with UK postage rates and location-identifying overprints.

When machines are installed at exhibitions beyond Europe, strips with the same event inscription are also made available from Tallents House in Edinburgh.

Postage rates

From 2008, the five rates available were 1st class, 1st Large, Europe up to 20g, Worldwide up to 10g and Worldwide up to 20g. Towards the end of 2011, Worldwide up to 40g was added to offer a sixth option.

From 2011, vending machines have offered a 'collector's strip' comprising one of each of the six standard rates (although in the case of Wincor Nixdorf machines these were vended as two strips of three).

A 2nd class rate was introduced in 2013, although it was not made widely available until 2014 and is not included in standard collector's strips.

With tariff changes in 2014, the Worldwide up to 10g and Worldwide up to 20g rates were replaced by Europe up to 60g and Worldwide up to 60g, and after a short delay the Europe up to 20g rate was changed to Europe up to 20g/Worldwide up to 10g (expressed on the stamps as 'Euro 20g/World 10g'). In 2015, both 60g rates were uprated to 100g.

Although pictorial sets are regularly superseded by new designs, none has formally been withdrawn from use, with the result that new rates have been reported machine-printed on old designs. Examples have also been found of the 2nd class design printed with 1st class rates, and vice versa.

Printing

It is possible to distinguish the type of machine used to print a stamp from its typeface. In most cases the differences are slight, but two exceptions are '60g' and 'Euro 20g/World 10g', where there are clear differences between different machines.

Starting in September 2015, some rolls of stamps required in limited quantities were printed digitally. These have a shinier appearance than gravure printings.

Stamps printed in corrupted typefaces, with misplaced inscriptions and with incorrect values also exist, especially from the 2010–12 period, but they are are outside the scope of this publication.

Phosphor

All the stamps have two phosphor bands, except the 2nd class Machin, which has one phosphor band.

DEFINITIVE ISSUES

Machin portrait (1st, 1st L, E20g, W10g, W20g)

■ **2008, October 8. Machin Portrait**
Printed in gravure by Walsall. Self-adhesive. Olive-brown security overlay with no year code. Machine-printed in black.

Strip of five (one of each value)	60.00
Philatelic pack (one of each value)	75.00

Machin portrait (1st, 1st L, E20g, E20/W10, E60g, E100g, W10g, W20g, W40g, W60g, W100g)

■ **2010, September. Machin Portrait**
Printed in gravure by Walsall. Self-adhesive. Olive-brown security overlay with no year code, or year code '13' or '14'. Machine-printed in black, in a new typeface suitable for use with pictorial designs.

Collector's strips

1st, 1st L, E20, W10, W20, W40	14.00
1st, 1st L, E20, E60, W40, W60 (Wincor)	14.00
1st, 1st L, E20, E60, W40, W60 (NCR)	18.00
1st, 1st L, E20/W10, E60, W40, W60 (NCR)	14.00
1st, 1st L, E20/W10, E60, W40, W60 (RM)	14.00
1st, 1st L, E20/W10, E60, W20, W60 (Wincor)	12.00
1st, 1st L, E20/W10, E100, W20, W100 (NCR)	12.00
1st, 1st L, E20/W10, E100, W20, W100 (RM)	12.00
'The B.P.M.A.' (1st, 1st L, E20, W10, W20, W40)	12.00
'The B.P.M.A.' (1st, 1st L, E20/W10, E60, W40, W60)	12.00
'The B.P.M.A.' (1st, 1st L, E20/W10, E100, W20, W100)	12.00
'Arnold Machin/1911–1999' (Autumn Stampex 2011)	20.00
'Diamond Jubilee/1952–2012' (Spring Stampex 2012)	20.00
'Perth 2012/19–22 October' (ABPS Exhibition 2012)	20.00
'The Coronation/60th Anniversary' (Spring Stampex 2013)	15.00
'84th Scottish/Congress 2013' (ASPS Congress 2013)	15.00
'Australia 2013/Stamp Expo' (Australia 2013)	30.00
'Australia 2013/World Stamp Expo' (Tallents House 2013)	15.00
'Stampex 2014/19–22 February' (Spring Stampex 2014)	12.00
'Stampex Spring/19–22 February' (Spring Stampex 2014)	12.00
'The B.P.M.A./Postage Due 1914' (BPMA 2014)	

(1st, 1st L, E20, W10, W20, W40)	12.00
(1st , 1st L, E20, E60, W40, W60)	12.00
'85th Scottish/Congress 2014' (ASPS Congress 2014)	12.00
'The B.P.M.A./Inland Airmail 1934' (BPMA 2014)	12.00
'The NMRN' (National Museum of the Royal Navy 2014)	
(1st, 1st L, E20/W10, E60, W20, W60)	13.00
(1st, 1st L, E20/W10, E100, W20, W100)	12.00
'PhilaKorea 2014/World Stamp Expo' (PhilaKorea 2014)	12.00
'The RMM' (Royal Marines Museum 2014)	
(1st, 1st L, E20/W10, E60, W20, W60)	13.00
(1st, 1st L, E20/W10, E100, W20, W100)	12.00
'Crewe' (Royal Mail Enquiry Office 2014)	12.00
'Bradford N' (Royal Mail Enquiry Office 2014)	12.00
'The B.P.M.A./Trollope 200' (BPMA 2015)	
(1st, 1st L, E20/W10, E60, W20, W60)	12.00
(1st, 1st L, E20/W10, E100, W20, W100)	12.00
'The FAAM' (Fleet Air Arm Museum 2015)	12.00
'86th Scottish Congress' (ASPS Congress 2015)	12.00
'86th Scottish Congress 2015' (ASPS Congress 2015)	12.00
'Messe Essen/7–9 May 2015' (Essen Stamp Fair 2015)	12.00
'The B.P.M.A./Penny Black 175' (BPMA 2015)	12.00
'Europhilex London/Penny Black 175' (London 2015)	12.00
'Wheatstone House' (Royal Mail Engineering Dept 2015)	–
'Steam GWR' (Museum of the Great Western Railway 2015)	15.00
'The RNSM' (Royal Navy Submarine Museum 2015)	15.00
'Singpex 2015 World Stamp Expo' (Singpex 2015)	15.00
'Queen Elizabeth II Longest Reign' (Autumn Stampex 2015)	15.00
'Sindelfingen October 2015' (Sindelfingen Stamp Fair 2015)	15.00
'Paris November 2015' (Paris Autumn Stamp Fair 2015)	15.00
'RN Submarine' (Royal Navy Submarine Museum 2015)	14.00
'Royal Navy' (National Museum of the Royal Navy 2015)	14.00
'Royal Marines' (Royal Marines Museum 2015)	14.00
'Fleet Air Arm' (Fleet Air Arm Museum 2015)	14.00
'The Postal Museum' (The Postal Museum 2016)	13.00
'500 Years of Royal Mail' (Spring Stampex 2016)	12.00
'500 Years of Royal Mail' (Guildhall, June 2016)	12.00
'87th Scottish Congress' (ASPS Congress 2016)	15.00
'RN Submarine/Battle of Jutland' (RNSM June 2016)	15.00
'Royal Navy/Battle of Jutland' (RNM June 2016)	15.00
'Royal Marines/Battle of Jutland' (RMM June 2016)	15.00
'Fleet Air Arm/Battle of Jutland' (FAAM June 2016)	15.00

Union flag (1st, 1st L, E20g, E20/W10, E60g, E100g, W10g, W20g, W40g, W60g, W100g)

■ **2012, May 21. Union Flag**
Des: Dick Davis, from illustration by Anton Morris. Printed in gravure by Walsall. Self-adhesive. Blue security overlay with no year code or year code '13'. Machine-printed in black.

Single (1st)	1.70
Philatelic pack (1st only)	2.00

First day cover	3.00	'RN Submarine/Battle of Jutland' (RNSM June 2016)	15.00
Collector's strips		'Royal Marines/Battle of Jutland' (RMM June 2016)	15.00
1st, 1st L, E20, W10, W20, W40	14.00	'Fleet Air Arm/Battle of Jutland' (FAAM June 2016)	15.00
1st, 1st L, E20, E60, W40, W60 (Wincor)	14.00	'World Stamp Show NY2016' (New York 2016)	15.00
1st, 1st L, E20/W10, E60, W40, W60 (RM)	14.00		
1st, 1st L, E20/W10, E100, W20, W100 (RM)	12.00		
'The B.P.M.A.' (1st, 1st L, E20, W10, W20, W40)	12.00		
'The B.P.M.A.' (1st, 1st L, E20/W10, E60, W40, W60)	12.00		
'Diamond Jubilee/1952–2012' (Autumn Stampex 2012)	20.00		
'Perth 2012/19–22 October' (ABPS Exhibition 2012)	20.00		
'84th Scottish/Congress 2013' (ASPS Congress 2013)	15.00		
'Australia 2013/Stamp Expo' (Australia 2013)	30.00		
'Australia 2013/World Stamp Expo' (Tallents House 2013)	15.00		
'The Coronation/60th Anniversary' (Autumn Stampex 2013)	15.00		
'The B.P.M.A./Postage Due 1914' (BPMA 2014)			
(1st, 1st L, E20, W10, W20, W40)	12.00		
(1st, 1st L, E20, E60, W40, W60)	12.00		
'85th Scottish/Congress 2014' (ASPS Congress 2014)	12.00		
'The NMRN' (National Museum of the Royal Navy 2014)			
(1st, 1st L, E20/W10, E60, W20, W60)	13.00		
(1st, 1st L, E20/W10, E100, W20, W100)	12.00		
'The NMRN/Trafalgar Day' (NMRN October 2014)	13.00		
'The NMRN/V.E. Day 70' (NMRN May 2015)	12.00		
'PhilaKorea 2014/World Stamp Expo' (Philakorea 2014)	12.00		
'The RMM' (Royal Marines Museum 2014)			
(1st, 1st L, E20/W10, E60, W20, W60)	13.00		
(1st, 1st L, E20/W10, E100, W20, W100)	12.00		
'The RMM/V.E. Day 70' (RMM May 2015)	12.00		
'Broad Street' (Jersey 2015)	12.00		
'Spring Stampex/February 2015' (Spring Stampex 2015)	12.00		
'The FAAM' (Fleet Air Arm Museum 2015)	12.00		
'The FAAM/V.E. Day 70' (FAAM May 2015)	12.00		
'86th Scottish Congress' (ASPS Congress 2015)	12.00		
'86th Scottish Congress 2015' (ASPS Congress 2015)	12.00		
'Messe Essen/7–9 May 2015' (Essen Stamp Fair 2015)	12.00		
'Gibraltar House' (Gibraltar Embassy, London 2015)	12.00		
'Steam GWR' (Museum of the Great Western Railway 2015)	15.00		
'The RNSM' (Royal Navy Submarine Museum 2015)	15.00		
'Singpex 2015 World Stamp Expo' (Singpex 2015)	15.00		
'Envoy House' (Guernsey 2015)	15.00		
'Sindelfingen October 2015' (Sindelfingen Stamp Fair 2015)	15.00		
'Hong Kong/November 2015' (Hong Kong 2015)	15.00		
'RN Submarine' (RNSM 2015)	13.00		
'Royal Navy' (NMRN 2015)	13.00		
'Royal Navy/Trafalgar Day' (NMRN October 2015)	15.00		
'Royal Marines' (RMM 2015)	13.00		
'Royal Marines/Trafalgar Day' (RMM October 2015)	15.00		
'Fleet Air Arm' (FAAM 2015)	13.00		
'The Postal Museum' (The Postal Museum 2016)	13.00		
'Steam GWR/Swindon 175' (GWR Museum 2016)	15.00		
'87th Scottish Congress 2016' (ASPS Congress 2016)	15.00		
'Royal Navy/Battle of Jutland' (NMRN June 2016)	15.00		

Machin portrait (2nd, 2nd Large)

■ **2013, February 20. Machin Portrait**
Printed in gravure by Walsall. Self-adhesive. Blue security overlay with year code '12', '13' or '14'. Machine-printed in black.

Pair (2nd, 2nd L)	2.50
Philatelic pack (2nd, 2nd L)	3.50
First day cover	4.00
Collector's strips	
'The B.P.M.A.'	2.50
'The B.P.M.A./Inland Airmail 1934' (BPMA 2014)	3.00
'The B.P.M.A./Trollope 200' (BPMA 2015)	2.50
'The B.P.M.A./Penny Black 175' (BPMA 2015)	2.50
'Crewe'	2.50
'Bradford N'	2.50
'Wheatstone House' (Royal Mail Engineering Dept 2015)	–
'The Postal Museum' (The Postal Museum 2016)	5.00
statue image (RAF Northolt 2016)	60.00

Machin portrait (wide range of values available)

■ **2014, February 28. Machin Portrait. New Service Indicia**
Printed in gravure by Walsall. Self-adhesive. Olive-brown or blue security overlay with year code '12', '13' or '14'. Machine-printed in black with new service indicia of NCR machines.

Collector's pack (2L, 1L, 2LG, 1LG, A)	8.00

(* The collector's pack was issued in July 7.)

Keep up with the latest Post & Go developments through the news pages of Stamp Magazine

PICTORIAL ISSUES

The values noted for each design are those which appertained when they were first issued, and should be expected in collector's strips. They may also exist with values which were introduced later.

```
002010 9 51840 01    Blue Tit
```

Blue tit (1st, 1st L, E20g, W10g, W20g)
Goldfinch (1st, 1st L, E20g, W10g, W20g)
House sparrow (1st, 1st L, E20g, W10g, W20g)
Robin (1st, 1st L, E20g, W10g, W20g)
Starling (1st, 1st L, E20g, W10g, W20g)
Wood pigeon (1st, 1st L, E20g, W10g, W20g)

■ 2010, September 17. Birds of Britain, series 1
Des: Kate Stephens, from illustrations by Robert Gillmor. Printed in gravure by Walsall. Self-adhesive. Machine-printed in black.

Set of 6 (all 1st class)	12.50	–
Collector's strip (one of each value)	17.00	–
Philatelic pack (all 1st class)	15.00	–
First day cover	–	25.00

```
002011 1 51840 02
```

Blackbird (1st, 1st L, E20g, W10g, W20g)
Chaffinch (1st, 1st L, E20g, W10g, W20g)
Collared dove (1st, 1st L, E20g, W10g, W20g)
Greenfinch (1st, 1st L, E20g, W10g, W20g)
Long-tailed tit (1st, 1st L, E20g, W10g, W20g)
Magpie (1st, 1st L, E20g, W10g, W20g)

■ 2011, January 24. Birds of Britain, series 2
Des: Kate Stephens, from illustrations by Robert Gillmor. Printed in gravure by Walsall. Self-adhesive. Machine-printed in black.

Set of 6 (all 1st class)	11.50	–
Collector's strip (one of each value)	17.00	–
Philatelic pack (all 1st class)	30.00	–
First day cover	–	30.00

```
002011 5 51840 03    Kingfisher
```

Great crested grebe (1st, 1st L, E20g, W10g, W20g)
Greylag goose (1st, 1st L, E20g, W10g, W20g)
Kingfisher (1st, 1st L, E20g, W10g, W20g)
Mallard (1st, 1st L, E20g, W10g, W20g)
Moorhen (1st, 1st L, E20g, W10g, W20g)
Mute swan (1st, 1st L, E20g, W10g, W20g)

■ 2011, May 19. Birds of Britain, series 3
Des: Kate Stephens, from illustrations by Robert Gillmor. Printed in gravure by Walsall. Self-adhesive. Machine-printed in black.

Set of 6 (all 1st class)	7.00	–
Collector's strip (one of each value)	17.00	–
Philatelic pack (all 1st class)	8.00	–
First day cover	–	15.00

```
002011 9 51840 04    Arctic Tern
```

Arctic tern (1st, 1st L, E20g, W10g, W20g, W40g)
Cormorant (1st, 1st L, E20g, W10g, W20g, W40g)
Gannet (1st, 1st L, E20g, W10g, W20g, W40g)
Oystercatcher (1st, 1st L, E20g, W10g, W20g, W40g)
Puffin (1st, 1st L, E20g, W10g, W20g, W40g)
Ringed plover (1st, 1st L, E20g, W10g, W20g, W40g)

■ 2011, September 16. Birds of Britain, series 4
Des: Kate Stephens, from illustrations by Robert Gillmor. Printed in gravure by Walsall. Self-adhesive. Machine-printed in black.

Set of 6 (all 1st class)	7.00	–
Collector's strip (one of each value)	17.00	–
Philatelic pack (all 1st class)	8.00	–
First day cover	–	16.00

Dalesbred (1st, 1st L, E20g, W10g, W20g, W40g)
Jacob (1st, 1st L, E20g, W10g, W20g, W40g)
Leicester longwool (1st, 1st L, E20g, W10g, W20g, W40g)
Soay (1st, 1st L, E20g, W10g, W20g, W40g)
Suffolk (1st, 1st L, E20g, W10g, W20g, W40g)
Welsh mountain badger face (1st, 1st L, E20g, W10g, W20g, W40g)

■ 2012, February 24. Sheep
Des: Kate Stephens, from illustrations by Robert Gillmor. Printed in gravure by Walsall. Self-adhesive. Machine-printed in black.

Set of 6 (all 1st class)	7.00	–
Collector's strip (one of each value)	17.00	–
Philatelic pack (all 1st class)	7.00	–
First day cover	–	16.00

1st Class
up to 100g

Berkshire

Berkshire (1st, 1st L, E20g, W10g, W20g, W40g)
British saddleback (1st, 1st L, E20g, W10g, W20g, W40g)
Gloucestershire old spots (1st, 1st L, E20g, W10g, W20g, W40g)
Oxford sandy and black (1st, 1st L, E20g, W10g, W20g, W40g)
Tamworth (1st, 1st L, E20g, W10g, W20g, W40g)
Welsh (1st, 1st L, E20g, W10g, W20g, W40g)

■ **2012, April 24. Pigs**
Des: Kate Stephens, from illustrations by Robert Gillmor. Printed in gravure by Walsall. Self-adhesive. Machine-printed in black.

Set of 6 (all 1st class)	7.00	–
Collector's strip (one of each value)	17.00	–
Philatelic pack (all 1st class)	15.00	–
First day cover	–	15.00

1st Class
up to 100g

Highland

Aberdeen Angus (1st, 1st L, E20g, W10g, W20g, W40g)
Highland (1st, 1st L, E20g, W10g, W20g, W40g)
Irish moiled (1st, 1st L, E20g, W10g, W20g, W40g)
Red poll (1st, 1st L, E20g, W10g, W20g, W40g)
Welsh black (1st, 1st L, E20g, W10g, W20g, W40g)
White park (1st, 1st L, E20g, W10g, W20g, W40g)

■ **2012, September 28. Cattle**
Des: Kate Stephens, from illustrations by Robert Gillmor. Printed in gravure by Walsall. Self-adhesive. Machine-printed in black.

Set of 6 (all 1st class)	9.00	–
Collector's strip (one of each value)	17.00	–
Philatelic pack (all 1st class)	7.00	–
First day cover	–	16.00

1st Class
up to 100g

002010 9 51840 01

Robin

Robin (1st, 1st L, E20g, W10g, W20g, W40g)

■ **2012, November 6. Christmas Robin**
Des: Kate Stephens, from illustration by Robert Gillmor (as the Robin design from Birds of Britain series I, but with year code). Printed in gravure by Walsall. Self-adhesive. Year code '12' or '13' in security overlay. Machine-printed in black.

Single (1st)	2.50	–
Collector's strip (up to W40)	15.00	–
Collector's strip ('The B.P.M.A.')	20.00	–
First day cover	–	3.00

1st Class
up to 100g

Emperor Dragonfly

Emperor dragonfly (1st, 1st L, E20g, W10g, W20g, W40g)
Fairy shrimp (1st, 1st L, E20g, W10g, W20g, W40g)
Glutinous snail (1st, 1st L, E20g, W10g, W20g, W40g)
Lesser silver water beetle (1st, 1st L, E20g, W10g, W20g, W40g)
Smooth newt (1st, 1st L, E20g, W10g, W20g, W40g)
Three-spined stickleback (1st, 1st L, E20g, W10g, W20g, W40g)

■ **2013, February 22. Pond Life**
Des: Kate Stephens, from illustrations by Chris Wormell. Printed in gravure by Walsall. Self-adhesive. Machine-printed in black.

Set of 6 (all 1st class)	7.00	–
Collector's strip (one of each value)	15.00	–
Philatelic pack (all 1st class)	7.00	–
First day cover	–	10.00

1st Class
up to 100g

Arctic Char

Arctic char (1st, 1st L, E20g, W10g, W20g, W40g)
Caddis fly larvae (1st, 1st L, E20g, W10g, W20g, W40g)
Common toad (1st, 1st L, E20g, W10g, W20g, W40g)
Crucian carp (1st, 1st L, E20g, W10g, W20g, W40g)
European eel (1st, 1st L, E20g, W10g, W20g, W40g)
Perch (1st, 1st L, E20g, W10g, W20g, W40g)

■ **2013, June 25. Lake Life**
Des: Kate Stephens, from illustrations by Chris Wormell. Printed in gravure by Walsall. Self-adhesive. Machine-printed in black.

Set of 6 (all 1st class)	7.00	–
Collector's strip (one of each value)	17.00	–
Philatelic pack (all 1st class)	7.00	–
First day cover	–	10.00

1st Class
up to 100g

Atlantic salmon (1st, 1st L, E20g, W10g, W20g W40g)
Blue–winged olive mayfly larva (1st, 1st L, E20g, W10g, W20g, W40g)
Brown trout (1st, 1st L, E20g, W10g, W20g, W40g)
Minnow (1st, 1st L, E20g, W10g, W20g, W40g)
River lamprey (1st, 1st L, E20g, W10g, W20g, W40g)
White–clawed crayfish (1st, 1st L, E20g, W10g, W20g, W40g)

■ 2013, September 20. River Life
Des: Kate Stephens, from illustrations by Chris Wormell. Printed in gravure by Walsall. Self–adhesive. Machine–printed in black.

Set of 6 (all 1st class)	7.00	–
Collector's strip (one of each value)	17.00	–
Philatelic pack (all 1st class)	7.00	–
First day cover	–	10.00

1st Class
up to 100g

Blackthorn (1st, 1st L, E20g, W10g, W20g, W40g)
Dog violet (1st, 1st L, E20g, W10g, W20g, W40g)
Lesser celandine (1st, 1st L, E20g, W10g, W20g, W40g)
Primrose (1st, 1st L, E20g, W10g, W20g, W40g)
Snowdrop (1st, 1st L, E20g, W10g, W20g, W40g)
Wild daffodil (1st, 1st L, E20g, W10g, W20g, W40g)

■ 2014, February, 19. Spring Blooms
Des: Kate Stephens, from illustrations by Julia Trickey. Printed in gravure by ISP. Self–adhesive. Year code '14' in security overlay. Machine–printed in black.

Set of 6 (all 1st class)	7.00	–
Collector's strip (up to W40)	17.00	–
Philatelic pack (all 1st class)	7.00	–
First day cover	–	10.00

1st Class
up to 100g

Forget–me–not (1st, 1st L, E20/W10, E60g, W20g, W60g)
Common poppy (1st, 1st L, E20/W10, E60g, W20g, W60g)
Dog rose (1st, 1st L, E20/W10, E60g, W20g, W60g)
Spear thistle (1st, 1st L, E20/W10, E60g, W20,g W60g)
Heather (1st, 1st L, E20/W10, E60g, W20g, W60g)
Cultivated flax (1st, 1st L, E20/W10, E60g, W20g, W60g)

■ 2014, September 17. Symbolic Flowers
Des: Kate Stevens, from illustrations by Julia Trickey. Printed in gravure by ISP. Self–adhesive. Year code '14' in security overlay. Machine–printed in black.

Set of 6 (all 1st class)	7.00	–
Collector's strip (one of each value)	12.00	–
Philatelic pack (all 1st class)	7.00	–
First day cover	–	10.00

■ 2014, October 21. Poppy
Des: Kate Stevens, from illustrations by Julia Trickey (as the Common Poppy design from the Symbolic Flowers set). Printed in gravure by ISP. Self–adhesive. Year code '14' or '15' in security overlay. Machine–printed in black.

Single (1st)	1.50	
Collector's strips		
1st, 1st L, E20/W10, E60, W20, W60 (2014)	12.00	–
1st, 1st L, E20/W10, E100, W20, W100 (2015)	14.00	–
'First World War/Centenary' (Sep 2014)	12.00	–
'The B.P.M.A.' (Oct 2014)	12.00	–
'The NMRM/Remembrance' (Oct 2014)	12.00	–
'The B.P.M.A.' (Oct 2015)	14.00	–
'Sindelfingen October 2015' (Oct 2015)	15.00	–
'Paris November 2015' (Nov 2015)	15.00	–
'RN Submarine' (Nov 2015)	14.00	–
'Royal Navy' (Nov 2015)	14.00	–
'Royal Marines' (Nov 2015)	14.00	–
'Fleet Air Arm' (Nov 2015)	14.00	–
First day cover	–	3.00

(* The collector's strip with the First World War commemorative inscription was available at Autumn Stampex from September 17, before the nationwide release of rolls of the single stamp.)

1st Large
up to 100g

Common ivy (2nd, 2nd L)
Mistletoe (2nd, 2nd L)
Butcher's broom (1st, 1st L, E20/W10, E60g, W20g, W60g)
Holly (1st, 1st L, E20/W10, E60g, W20g, W60g)

■ 2014, November 13. Winter Greenery
Des: Kate Stevens, from illustrations by Julia Trickey. Printed in gravure by ISP. Self–adhesive. One phosphor band (2nd), two phosphor bands (1st). Year code '14' in security overlay. Machine–printed in black.

Set of 4 (2nd, 2nd, 1st, 1st L)	6.50	–
Collector's strips		
2nd, 2nd L	2.50	–
1st, 1st L, E20/W10, E60, W20, W60	12.00	–
'The B.P.M.A.' (2nd, 2nd L)	2.50	–
'The B.P.M.A.' (all other values)	12.00	–
Philatelic pack (2nd, 2nd,1st, 1st L)	5.00	–
First day cover	–	7.00

1st Class
up to 100g

'Falcon' (1st, 1st L, E20/W10, E60g, W20g, W60g)
'Briar' (1st, 1st L, E20/W10, E60g, W20g, W60g)
'Harry' (1st, 1st L, E20/W10, E60g, W20g, W60g)
'Margaret' (1st, 1st L, E20/W10, E60g, W20g, W60g)
'Stag' (1st, 1st L, E20/W10, E60g, W20g, W60g)
'Nell Morgan' (1st, 1st L, E20/W10, E60g, W20g, W60g)

■ 2015, February 18. Working Sail

Des: Osborne Ross. Printed in gravure by ISP. Self-adhesive. Year code '15' in security overlay. Machine-printed in black.

Set of 6 (all 1st class)	7.00	–
Collector's strip (one of each value)	12.00	–
Philatelic pack (all 1st class)	7.00	–
First day cover	–	10.00

1st Class
up to 100g

Lion (1st, 1st L, E20/W10, E100g, W20g, W100g)
Unicorn (1st, 1st L, E20/W10, E100g, W20g, W100g)
Yale (1st, 1st L, E20/W10, E100g, W20g, W100g)
Dragon (1st, 1st L, E20/W10, E100g, W20g, W100g)
Falcon (1st, 1st L, E20/W10, E100g, W20g, W100g)
Griffin (1st, 1st L, E20/W10, E100g, W20g, W100g)

■ 2015, May 13. Heraldic Beasts

Des: Osborne Ross. Printed in gravure by ISP. Self-adhesive. Year code '15' in security overlay. Machine-printed in black.

Set of 6 (all 1st class)	7.00	–
Collector's strip (one of each value)	13.00	–
Philatelic pack (all 1st class)	7.00	–
First day cover	–	10.00
Collector's strip (Lion only, BPMA)	15.00	–
Collector's strip (Lion only, Sindelfingen)	15.00	–
Collector's strip (Lion only, Postal Museum)	13.00	–
Collector's strip (Lion only, Scottish Congress)	15.00	–

1st Class
up to 100g

White Cliffs of Dover (1st, 1st L, E20/W10, E100g, W20g, W100g)
Hong Kong Harbour (1st, 1st L, E20/W10, E100g, W20g, W100g)
Sydney Opera House (1st, 1st L, E20/W10, E100g, W20g, W100g)
Ha Long Bay (1st, 1st L, E20/W10, E100g, W20g, W100g)
New York Harbour (1st, 1st L, E20/W10, E100g, W20g, W100g)
Venice (1st, 1st L, E20/W10, E100g, W20g, W100g)

■ 2015, September 16. Sea Travel

Des: Osborne Ross, from illustrations by Andy Tuohy. Printed in gravure by ISP. Self-adhesive. Year code '15' in security overlay. Machine-printed in black.

Set of 6 (all 1st class)	7.00	–
Collector's strip (one of each value)	13.00	–
Philatelic pack (all 1st class)	7.00	–
First day cover	–	10.00
Collector's strip (Hong Kong only, HK 2015)	15.00	–
Collector's strip (New York only, NY 2015)	15.00	–

(* The Hong Kong exhibition strip was digitally printed.)

1st Class
up to 100g

Mountain hare (2nd, 2nd L)
Redwing (2nd, 2nd L)
Red fox (1st, 1st L, E20/W10, E100g, W20g, W100g)
Red squirrel (1st, 1st L, E20/W10, E100g, W20g, W100g)

■ 2015, November 16. Winter Fur and Feathers

Des: Osborne Ross. Printed in gravure by ISP. Self-adhesive. One phosphor band (2nd), two phosphor bands (1st). Year code '15' in security overlay. Machine-printed in black.

Set of 4 (2nd, 2nd L, 1st, 1st L)	5.00	–
Philatelic pack (2nd, 2nd L, 1st, 1st L)	5.00	–
First day cover	–	7.00
Collector's strip (2nd, 2nd L)	3.00	–
Collector's strip (higher values)	14.00	–
Collector's strip (2nd, 2nd L, BPMA)	3.00	–
Collector's strip (higher values, BPMA)	14.00	–

1st Class
up to 100g

Post boy 1640s (1st, 1st L, E20/W10, E100g, W20g, W100g)
Mail coach 1790s (1st, 1st L, E20/W10, E100g, W20g, W100g)
Falmouth packet ship 1820s (1st, 1st L, E20/W10, E100, W20, W100)
Travelling post office 1890s (1st, 1st L, E20/W10, E100, W20, W100)
Airmail 1930s (1st, 1st L, E20/W10, E100g, W20g, W100g)
Minivan 1970s (1st, 1st L, E20/W10, E100g, W20g, W100g)

■ 2016, February 17. Royal Mail Heritage: Transport

Des: Howard Brown, from illustrations by Andrew Davidson. Printed in gravure by ISP. Self-adhesive. Year code '16' in security overlay. Machine-printed in black.

Set of 6 (all 1st class)	7.00	–
Collector's strip (one of each value)	14.00	–
Philatelic pack (all 1st class)	7.00	–
First day cover	–	10.00
Collector's strip (Mail Coach, Postal Museum)	13.00	–
Collector's strip (TPO, Spring Stampex 2016)	15.00	–
Collector's strip (TPO, Steam GWR Swindon)	14.00	–

(* The Mail Coach collector's strip was digitally printed.)

SMILERS GENERIC SHEETS

Smilers sheets are personalisable, by way of having a photograph or other supplied image printed on labels alongside conventional stamps. Listed here are Royal Mail's generic sheets for each available issue, which have decorative labels instead of customers' photographs.

Smilers

THE STAMP SHOW 2000

The Stamp Show, 2000

■ **2000, May 22. The Stamp Show 2000**
Sheet of 10 1st class Smiles as March 26, 1991   20.00

■ **2000, October 3. Christmas: Robin in Letterbox**
Sheet of 20 19p Robin in pillar box as October 30,
1995, inscribed copyright 'Post Office 2000'   £125

■ **2000, October 3. Christmas: Father Christmas**
Sheet of 10 1st class Father Christmas as October 27,
1997, inscribed copyright 'Post Office 2000'   £125

■ **2001, June 5. Occasions: Hallmarks**
Sheets of 20 1st class as February 6, 2001   £150

■ **2001, July 3. Smiles**
Sheet of 10 1st class Smiles as May 22, 2000,
but with revised labels and border   £150

■ **2001, October 9. Christmas: Robin in Letterbox**
Sheet of 20 19p Robin in pillar box as
October 30, 1995, inscribed copyright 'Consignia 2001'   £500

■ **2001, October 9. Christmas: Father Christmas**
Sheet of 10 1st class Father Christmas as October 27,
1997, inscribed copyright 'Consignia 2001'   £500

■ **2001, December 18. Cartoons**
Sheet of 10 1st class as February 26, 1996   35.00

■ **2002, April 23. Occasions: Pictorial Messages**
Sheet of 20 1st class as March 5, 2002   55.00

■ **2002, May 21. Football World Cup**
Sheet of 20 1st class Flag as May 21, 2002   25.00

■ **2002, October 1. Smiles**
Sheet of 10 1st class Teddy Bear and 10 1st class
Dennis the Menace as March 26, 1991   27.00

■ **2002, October 1. Christmas: Father Christmas**
Sheet of 20 1st class as October 27, 1997   30.00

■ **2003, January 21. Flowers**
Sheet of 20 1st class Flower Paintings as January 6, 1997   30.00

Occasions, 2003

■ **2003, February 4. Occasions: Multiple Choice**
Sheet of 20 1st class as February 4, 2003   25.00

■ **2003, July 29. Cartoons Crossword**
Sheet of 20 1st class as February 26, 1996   21.00

■ **2003, September 30. Christmas: Winter Robins**
Sheet of 20 1st class as November 6, 2001. Self-adhesive 22.00

■ **2003, November 4. Christmas: Ice Sculptures**
Sheet of 20 2nd class Ice Sculptures as November 4,
2003. Self-adhesive   16.00
Sheet of 20 1st class Ice Sculptures as November 4,
2003. Self-adhesive   25.00

■ **2004, January 30. Hong Kong Stamp Exhibition**
Sheet of 20 1st class Hello as March 5, 2002   17.50

■ **2004, February 3. Occasions: Entertaining Envelopes**
Sheet of 20 1st class as February 3, 2004   17.50

■ **2004, May 25. Royal Horticultural Society**
Sheet of 20 1st class as May 25, 2004   17.50

Rule Britannia, 2004

■ 2004, July 27. Rule Britannia
Sheet of 20 1st class Union Flag as October 22, 2001   17.50

■ 2004, November 2. Christmas: Father Christmas
Sheet of 10 1st class and 10 2nd class. Self-adhesive   20.00

■ 2005, January 11. Farm Animals
Sheet of 20 1st class as January 11, 2005   20.00

■ 2005, March 15. Magic
Sheet of 20 1st class as March 15, 2005   20.00

■ 2005, April 21. Pacific Explorer Stamp Exhibition
Sheet of 20 1st class Hello as March 5, 2002   19.00

■ 2005, June 21. White Ensign
Sheet of 20 1st class White Ensign as October 22, 2001   18.00

■ 2005, September 15. Classic ITV
Sheet of 20 1st class as September 15, 2005   18.00

■ 2005, November 1. Christmas: Winter Robins
Sheet of 10 1st class and 10 2nd class as November 6,
2001. Self-adhesive   18.00

A Bear Called Paddington, 2006

■ 2006, January 10. A Bear Called Paddington
Sheet of 20 1st class Paddington Bear as January 10,
2006. Self-adhesive
18.00

■ 2006, March 7. Fun Fruit and Veg
Sheet of 20 1st class as March 7, 2006. Self-adhesive   18.00

■ 2006, May 25. Washington Stamp Exhibition
Sheet of 20 1st class Hello as March 5, 2002   18.00

■ 2006, June 6. World Cup Winners
Sheets of 20 1st class as June 6, 2006   18.00

■ 2006, July 4. For Life's Special Moments
Sheet of 20 1st class as October 4, 2005. Self-adhesive   18.00

■ 2006, October 17. For Life's Extra Special Moments
Sheet of 20 1st class as October 17, 2006 Self-adhesive   18.00

■ 2006, November 7. Christmas
Sheet of 10 1st class and 10 2nd class as November 7,
2006 Self-adhesive   18.00

■ 2006, November 9. We Will Remember Them, issue 1
Sheet of 20 1st class Poppies as November 6, 2006   18.00

■ 2006, November 14. Belgica Stamp Exhibition
Sheet of 20 1st class Hello as March 5, 2002   18.00

Glorious Wales, 2007

■ 2007, March 1. Glorious Wales
Sheet of 20 1st class Wales as October 14, 2003.
Self-adhesive   18.00

■ 2007, April 23. Glorious England
Sheet of 20 1st class England as October 14, 2003.
Self-adhesive   18.00

■ 2007, May 17. Wembley Stadium
Sheet of 20 1st class Lion & Shield of St George
as May 17, 2007   18.00

■ 2007, June 5. 40th Anniversary of the Machin Definitive
Sheet of 20 1st class Arnold Machin as June 5, 2007   18.00

■ **2007, July 17. Harry Potter**
Sheet of 20 1st class Crest of Hogwarts School as
July 17, 2007. Self-adhesive   17.00

Christmas, 2007

■ **2007, November 6. Christmas**
Sheet of 20 2nd class, 1st class and 78p as
November 6, 2007. Self-adhesive   17.50

■ **2007, November 8. We Will Remember Them, issue 2**
Sheet of 20 1st class Poppy as November 8, 2007   17.00

■ **2007, November 30. Glorious Scotland**
Sheet of 20 1st class Scotland as October 14, 2003.
Self-adhesive   17.00

■ **2008, January 15. I Wrote To Say ...**
Sheet of 20 1st class as October 4, 2005, with
circular labels. Self-adhesive   21.00

■ **2008, March 11. Glorious Northern Ireland**
Sheet of 20 1st class Northern Ireland as October
14, 2003. Self-adhesive   17.00

■ **2008, July 17. 100 Years of Aviation**
Sheet of 20 1st class as July 17, 2008   17.00

■ **2008, August 5. Beijing 2008 Olympic Expo**
Sheet of 20 1st class Hello as March 5, 2002   17.00

■ **2008, September 29. Glorious United Kingdom**
Sheet of 20 1st class England, Northern Ireland, Scotland
and Wales as as October 14, 2003. Self-adhesive   17.00

■ **2008, November 4. Christmas**
Sheet of 20 2nd class, 1st class and 81p as
November 4, 2008. Self-adhesive   17.00

■ **2008, November 6. We Will Remember Them, issue 3**
Sheet of 20 1st class Poppy as November 6, 2008   17.00

■ **2009, January 13. The Mini**
Sheet of 20 1st class Mini as January 13, 2009   17.00

Concorde, 2009

■ **2009, March 2. Concorde**
Sheet of 20 1st class Concorde as January 13, 2009   17.00

■ **2009, March 17. Castles of Northern Ireland**
Sheet of 20 1st class Northern Ireland as
October 14, 2003. Self-adhesive   17.00

■ **2009, April 23. Castles of England**
Sheet of 20 1st class English flag as April 23, 2007.
Self-adhesive   17.00

■ **2009, August 3. Thaipex 2009 Exhibition**
Sheet of 20 1st class Hello as March 5, 2002   17.00
(* Panes of 10 were sold separately at the exhibition.)

Post Boxes, 2009

■ **2009, August 18. Post Boxes**
Sheet of 20 1st class as August 18, 2009   17.00

■ **2009, October 21. Italia 2009 Exhibition**
Sheet of 20 1st class Hello as March 5, 2002   17.00

■ **2009, November 3. Christmas**
Sheet of 20 2nd class, 1st class, 56p and 90p
as November 3, 2009. Self-adhesive   17.00

■ 2009, November 30. Castles of Scotland
Sheet of 20 1st class Scotland as October 14, 2003.
Self-adhesive 18.00

■ 2009, December 4. MonacoPhil 2009 Exhibition
Sheet of 20 1st class Hello as March 5, 2002 .... 18.00

■ 2010, January 26. For All Occasions
Sheet of 20 1st class, Europe and Worldwide
as January 26, 2010. Self-adhesive 32.00

■ 2010, March 1. Castles of Wales
Sheet of 20 1st class Wales as October 14, 2003.
Self-adhesive 26.00

■ 2010, May 8. 10th Anniversary of Smilers
Sheet of 20 1st class, Europe and Worldwide
as January 26, 2010. Self-adhesive 35.00

■ 2010, May 8. London 2010 Stamp Exhibition
Sheet of 20 1st class Hello as October 4, 2005.
Self-adhesive 27.00

■ 2010, September 15. Battle of Britain
Sheet of 20 1st class Spitfire as January 13, 2009 ... 20.00

■ 2010, November 2. Christmas
Sheet of 20 2nd class, 1st class, 60p and 97p
as November 2, 2010. Self-adhesive 20.00

Indipex, 2011

■ 2011, February 12. Indipex 2011 Exhibition
Sheet of 20 1st class Union Flag as October 4, 2005 ... 20.00

■ 2011, July 28. Philanippon 2011 Exhibition
Sheet of 20 1st class Union Flag as October 4, 2005 ... 20.00

■ 2011, September 15. 350 Years of Postmarks
Sheet of 20 1st class Seal as January 26, 2010 ...... 20.00

■ 2011, November 8. Christmas
Sheet of 20 1st class, 2nd class, 68p, £1.10 as
November 8, 2011. Self-adhesive 32.00

Year of the Dragon, 2012

■ 2012, January 20. Year of the Dragon
Sheet of 20 1st class Firework as October 17, 2006.
Self-adhesive 23.00

■ 2012, June 18. Indonesia 2012 Exhibition
Sheet of 20 1st class Hello as October 4, 2005 ...... 23.00

■ 2012, June 27. Olympic and Paralympic Games Venues
Sheet of 20 1st class and Worldwide Olympic Games and
Paralympic Games as January 5, 2012. Self-adhesive ... 95.00

■ 2012, November 6. Christmas
Sheet of 20 1st class, 2nd class, 87p and £1.28
as November 6, 2012. Self-adhesive 22.00

■ 2013, February 2. Year of the Snake
Sheet of 20 1st class Firework as October 17, 2006.
Self-adhesive 21.00

Doctor Who, 2013

■ 2013, March 26. Doctor Who
Sheet of 20 1st class Tardis as March 26, 2013.
Self-adhesive 21.00

■ 2013, May 10. Australia 2013 Exhibition
Sheet of 20 1st class Hello as October 4, 2005 ...... 21.00

■ **2013, August 2. Bangkok 2013 Exhibition**
Sheet of 20 1st class Hello as October 4, 2005   21.00

■ **2013, November 5. Christmas**
Sheet of 20 1st class, 2nd class, 88p, £1.28 and £1.88
as November 5, 2013. Self-adhesive   23.00

■ **2013, December 10. Year of the Horse**
Sheet of 20 1st class Firework as October 17, 2006.
Self-adhesive   21.00

■ **2014, November 4. Christmas**
Sheet of 20 1st class, 2nd class, £1.28 and £1.47 as
November 4, 2014. Self-adhesive   20.00

■ **2014, November 19. Year of the Sheep**
Sheet of 20 1st class Firework as October 17, 2006.
Self-adhesive   18.00

■ **2014, December 1. Kuala Lumpur 2014 Exhibition**
Sheet of 20 1st class Hello as October 4, 2005.
Self-adhesive.   18.00

■ **2015, January 20. Smilers 2015**
Sheet of 20 1st class Smilers as January 20, 2015.
Self-adhesive   32.00

■ **2015, May 6. 175th Anniversary of the Penny Black**
Sheet of 10 1st class Penny Black and 10 1st class
Twopenny Blue as May 6, 2015. Self-adhesive   32.00

■ **2015, May 13. London 2015 Europhilex Exhibition**
Sheet of 20 1st class Hello as October 4, 2005.
Self-adhesive   20.00

■ **2015, October 20. Heroes and Villains: Star Wars**
Sheet of 10 1st class Yoda, Han Solo, Darth Vader and
Stormtrooper as October 20, 2015. Self-adhesive   11.00

■ **2015, November 3. Christmas**
Sheet of 20 1st class, 2nd class, £1, £1.33, £1.52 and £2.25
as November 3, 2015. Self-adhesive   23.00

■ **2015, November 9. Year of the Monkey**
Sheet of 20 1st class Firework as October 17, 2006.
Self-adhesive   18.00

■ **2016, February 18. 175th Anniversary of the Penny Red**
Sheet of 20 1st class Penny Red as February 18, 2016.
Self-adhesive   18.00

■ **2016, May 26. New York 2016 World Stamp Exhibition**
Sheet of 20 1st class Hello as October 4, 2005.
Self-adhesive   18.00

SMILERS FOR KIDS

Peter Rabbit, 2008

■ **2008, October 28. Mr Happy**
Sheet of 20 1st class Balloons   £100
Sheet of 10 1st class Balloons, and writing pack   60.00

■ **2008, October 28. Almond Blossom**
Sheet of 20 1st class Flower   £100
Sheet of 10 1st class Flower, and writing pack   60.00

■ **2008, October 28. Peter Rabbit**
Sheet of 20 1st class New Baby   £100
Sheet of 10 1st class New Baby, and writing pack   60.00

■ **2008, October 28. Noddy**
Sheets of 20 1st class Balloons   £100
Sheets of 10 1st class Balloons, and writing pack   60.00

■ **2009, April 30. Little Miss Sunshine**
Sheet of 20 1st class Balloons   £100
Sheet of 10 1st class Balloons, and writing pack   60.00

■ **2009, April 30. Wild Cherry**
Sheet of 20 1st class Flower   £100
Sheet of 10 1st class Flower, and writing pack   60.00

■ **2009, April 30. Jeremy Fisher**
Sheet of 20 1st class Hello   £100
Sheet of 10 1st class Hello, and writing pack   60.00

■ **2009, April 30. Big Ears**
Sheets of 20 1st class Balloons   £100
Sheets of 10 1st class Balloons, and writing pack   60.00

not need - it follows that most of the stamps in most postal auctions may be owned by the company presenting the auction. It is not viable to sell low priced lots on a commission basis. Ask yourself why you may be asked to pay a buyer's premium? Is it actually a Vendor's lot or owned by 'The House'?

TIP 6c). The Buyer's Premium was introduced to 'split' cost between buyer and seller so that a 'low' seller's commission looks attractive (if you forget about the premium the buyer is paying for the seller's stamps). Be aware of this or deal with auctions not charging a buyer's premium. You are in control. You can bid anywhere that you fi nd what you seek – but it is good to be aware and informed.

TIP 6d). Prices Realised are IMPORTANT. For some unknown reason – even some larger Postal / Mail-Bid Auctions still do not produce lists of what their lots sold for after the auction. Look for auctions providing this feature – it provides reassurance combined with a trackable 'snapshot' of current market values *PLUS* what is selling and what is not selling. You can learn such a lot from 'Prices Realised' – I study them each day.

TIP 7). Credit Cards. 75% of some auction sales are settled by credit / debit card. The Biggest in the land has no need to charge you for use of them … Sheer volume of business accesses lowest rates. Why are you paying a premium to use your card? Is the supplier making a profi t upon the extra % you are charged to use your card?

TIP 8). Look for unique 'Collector friendly' benefi ts that turn the disadvantage of lots not being sold to your advantage. U P A, for example, has for the past 15 years offered their Unique Reducing Estimate System (**URES**) whereby lots are increasingly reduced in estimate price till sold – some have reached one penny and then sold. Approaching one million lots have been offered through this system.

TIP 9). Cost of Delivery is one of the most annoying hidden costs that collectors absolutely abhor. Look for transparency in this area.

TIP 10). Beware the Seller / Auction NOT including Insurance when sending your winnings.

And Finally We Come to C H O I C E... and Mind-Set?

TIP Without Choice we have nothing. So it follows that you need substantial choice to form a good, even great, stamp collection. You cannot do business when each time you 'visit' all you see is what you have seen before – stagnating stocks offered at prices that ensure continued stagnation. If choice is limited you'll never fi nd philatelic items you need – or even that you were unaware of their existence. That's the joy of collecting. The thrill of the unexpected, the chance fi nd. You need dealers that want to help and auctions that wish to serve – so, in stamps 'attitude is all'.

So when you're searching for a stamp auction compare it against your list above of what to look for and if and when you're offered a 'No Risk Free Trial' … please consider – take it Now ◆

So if you're new to my company, while you are thinking about it, please turn to the OUTSIDE BACK COVER Now to take YOUR 1st £55 FREE TRIAL Introductory Offer →

COMMEMORATIVE SHEETS

In this section, prices are quoted for complete mint sheets only.

Commemorative sheets are an evolution of Smilers sheets. They are not personalisable but are customised as a souvenir product by Royal Mail.

Early issues had normal gum, but most subsequent issues have been self-adhesive.

GUMMED SHEETS

Centenary of the Territorial Army, 2008

■ **2008, April 1. Centenary of the Territorial Army**
Sheet of 10 1st class Union Flag as October 22, 2001   20.00

■ **2008, July 24. London 1908 Olympic Games**
Sheet of 10 1st class Union Flag as October 22, 2001   20.00

■ **2009, October 22. Olympic and Paralympic Games**
Sheet of 10 1st class as October 22, 2009   20.00

■ **2010, July 27. Olympic and Paralympic Games**
Sheet of 10 1st class as July 27, 2010   20.00

■ **2011, July 27. Olympic and Paralympic Games**
Sheet of 10 1st class as July 27, 2011   20.00

SELF-ADHESIVE SHEETS

■ **2008, November 14. 60th Birthday of Prince Charles**
Sheet of 10 1st class Wales   20.00

■ **2009, July 21. 40th Anniversary of the First Moon Landing**
Sheet of 10 1st class Union Flag as February 28, 2008   20.00

■ **2009, September 18. 150th Anniversary of Big Ben**
Sheet of 10 1st class Union Flag as February 28, 2008   20.00

■ **2009, October 7. 800th Anniversary of the University of Cambridge**
Sheet of 10 1st class Firework as February 28, 2008   20.00

■ **2010, May 18. Halley's Comet**
Sheet of 10 1st class Union Flag as February 28, 2008   20.00

■ **2010, July 8. British World Champion Grand Prix Drivers**
Sheet of 10 1st class Union Flag as February 28, 2008   20.00

■ **2010, August 10. 10th Anniversary of the London Eye**
Sheet of 10 1st class Union Flag as February 28, 2008   20.00

■ **2010, October 28. National Memorial Arboretum**
Sheet of 10 1st class Poppies as January 26, 2010   20.00

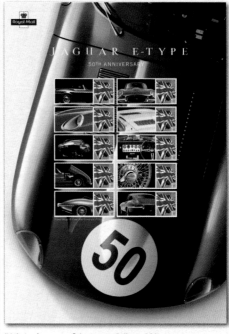

50th Anniversary of the Jaguar E-Type, 2011

■ **2011, March 30. 50th Anniversary of the Jaguar E-Type**
Sheet of 10 1st class Union Flag as February 28, 2008   20.00

90th Birthday of Prince Philip, 2011

■ **2011, June 10. 90th Birthday of Prince Philip, Duke of Edinburgh**
Sheet of 10 1st class Union Flag as February 28, 2008   20.00

■ **2012, April 10. 100th Anniversary of the RMS Titanic**
Sheet of 10 1st class Seal as January 26, 2010   20.00

■ **2012, May 1. 50th Anniversary of James Bond**
Sheet of 10 1st class Union Flag as February 28, 2008   20.00

■ **2012, October 5. 40th Anniversary of the Last Goon Show**
Sheet of 10 1st class Union Flag as February 28, 2008   20.00

■ **2012, November 8. 150th Anniversary of Notts County Football Club**
Sheet of 10 1st class Firework as February 28, 2008   20.00

■ **2013, April 16. 60th Anniversary of the Launch of HMY Britannia**
Sheet of 10 1st class Union Flag as February 28, 2008   20.00

■ **2013, May 1. Bicentenary of the Birth of David Livingstone**
Sheet of 10 1st class Scottish Flag as November 30, 2006   20.00

■ **2013, September 19. 150th Anniversary of the Birth of Bertram Mackennel**
Sheet of 10 1st class Seal as January 26, 2010   22.00

■ **2014, February 25. 150th Anniversary of Middlesex County Cricket Club**
Sheet of 10 1st class Firework as February 28, 2008   22.00

■ **2014, March 26. 350th Anniversary of the Royal Marines**
Sheet of 10 1st class Union Flag as February 28, 2008   22.00

■ **2014, October 16. Donald Campbell**
Sheet of 20 1st class Union Flag as February 28, 2008   20.00

■ **2014, November 11. 100th Anniversary of the Christmas Truce**
Sheet of 20 1st class Poppies as January 26, 2010   20.00

■ **2015, March 18. The Post Office Rifles**
Sheet of 20 1st class Union Flag as February 28, 2008   20.00

■ **2015, April 24. Bicentenary of the Birth of Anthony Trollope**
Sheet of 20 1st class Union Flag as February 28, 2008   20.00

■ **2015, August 20. Bicentenary of the Gurkhas' Service to the Crown**
Sheet of 20 1st class Union Flag as February 28, 2008   20.00

■ **2015, September 17. Animals of the First World War**
Sheet of 20 1st class Union Flag as February 28, 2008   20.00

■ **2015, September 25. 3oth Anniversary of Danger Mouse**
Sheet of 20 1st class Union Flag as February 28, 2008   26.00

■ **2016, January 12. 6oth Anniversary of The Duke of Edinburgh's Award**
Sheet of 20 1st class Union Flag as February 28, 2008   20.00

■ **2016, March 8. 8oth Anniversary of Oor Wullie**
Sheet of 20 1st class Scottish Flag as November 30, 2006   20.00

■ **2016, March 8. 8oth Anniversary of The Broons**
Sheet of 20 1st class Scottish Flag as November 30, 2006   20.00

■ **2016, April 25. Australian and New Zealand Army Corps (ANZAC)**
Sheet of 20 1st class Poppies as January 26, 2010   20.00

■ **2016, May 18. Farewell Boleyn (West Ham United FC)**
Sheet of 20 1st class Union Flag as February 28, 2008   20.00

PRESENTATION PACKS

In this section, prices are quoted for packs in mint condition only.

Presentation packs have been issued regularly for special stamp issues since 1964, and definitives since 1967, but many collectors regard the packs sold in 1960 (which were also marketed in the USA and therefore also found priced in US dollars) as the forerunners of these collectables.

Packs issued by Royal Mail in foreign language and other special versions are listed in this section, but those produced privately, commercially sponsored or not placed on general sale are outside the scope of this publication.

'FORERUNNERS'

Wilding definitives 'forerunner' pack, 1960

■ 1960

Wilding definitives (priced in Sterling)	£275
Wilding definitives (priced in Dollars)	£375
Phosphor–graphite definitives (priced in Sterling)	£250
Phosphor–graphite definitives (priced in Dollars)	£350
Regional definitives (priced in Sterling)	£275
Regional definitives (priced in Dollars)	£375
Castle high values (priced in Sterling)	£1,500
Castle high values (priced in Dollars)	£1,750
Castle high values (unpriced)	£1,750

SPECIAL ISSUES

Shakespeare Festival, 1964

■ 1964

Shakespeare Festival	15.00
Geographical Congress	£110
Botanical Congress	£125
Forth Road Bridge	£350

■ 1965

Churchill Commemoration	40.00
700th Anniversary of Parliament	50.00
Battle of Britain	55.00
Post Office Tower	12.00

World Cup, 1966

■ 1966

Robert Burns	42.00
Westminster Abbey	38.00
World Cup	22.00
British Birds	13.00
British Technology	12.00
Battle of Hastings	12.00
Christmas	12.50

■ 1967

EFTA	35.00
British Wild Flowers	15.00
British Paintings	22.00
British Discovery and Invention	7.00

■ 1968

British Bridges	6.00
Anniversaries	5.00
British Paintings	5.00
British Paintings (German version)	25.00
Christmas	6.50
Christmas (German version)	22.00

■ 1969

British Ships	5.50
British Ships (German version)	42.00
British Ships (Cunard version)*	20.00
Concorde	7.00
Concorde (German version)	85.00
Anniversaries	4.50
Anniversaries (German version)	65.00
British Cathedrals	5.00
British Cathedrals (German version)	50.00

Investiture of the Prince of Wales	3.50
Investiture of the Prince of Wales (German version)	50.00
Investiture of the Prince of Wales (Welsh version)	17.00
Post Office Technology	4.00
Christmas	4.00

(* A version of the British Ships pack with slightly amended text was sold exclusively on the ocean liner QE2.)

General Anniversaries, 1970

1970

Rural Architecture	4.50
General Anniversaries	4.50
Literary Anniversaries	5.00
Commonwealth Games	4.50
Philympia Exhibition	4.50
Christmas	5.00

1971

Ulster Paintings	4.50
Literary Anniversaries	4.50
General Anniversaries	4.50
Modern University Buildings	5.50
Christmas	4.00

1972

Polar Explorers	5.50
General Anniversaries	3.50
Village Churches	5.50
Village Churches (Belgica version)	7.00
BBC*	4.00
Christmas	3.00
Royal Silver Wedding	3.00
Royal Silver Wedding (Japanese version)	5.00

(* The BBC produced a souvenir pack in a similar format to the Royal Mail pack, titled '50th Anniversary of the BBC', as a gift to its staff; price £15.00)

1973

European Communities	3.50
British Trees: Oak	3.00
British Explorers	3.00
County Cricket	4.00
British Painters	2.50
Inigo Jones	2.50
Parliamentary Conference	2.50

Royal Wedding	3.00
Christmas	3.00

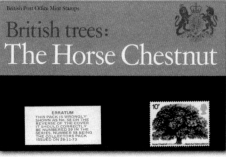

British Trees: Horse Chestnut, 1974

1974

British Trees: Horse Chestnut	2.00
Fire Engines	2.75
UPU	2.75
Medieval Warriorss	2.75
Winston Churchill	2.75
Christmas	2.25

1975

J. M. W. Turner	2.25
Architectural Heritage Year	2.25
Sailing	2.00
Public Railways	3.00
Inter–Parliamentary Union Conference	2.00
Jane Austen	4.00
Christmas	2.75

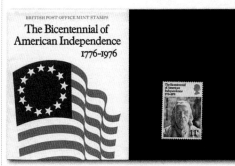

Bicentennial of American Independence, 1976

1976

Telephones	2.00
Social Reformers	2.00
Bicentennial of American Independence	1.75
Cultural Traditions	2.00
Royal National Rose Society	2.00
British Printing	2.00
Christmas	2.00

1977

Racket Sports	3.00
Royal Institute of Chemistry	3.00
Silver Jubilee	2.00
Commonwealth Heads of Government	1.75
British Wildlife	2.00
Christmas	2.50

Energy Resources, 1978

1978

Energy Resources	2.00
Historic Buildings	2.00
25th anniversary of Coronation	2.00
Horses	2.00
Cycling	2.00
Christmas	2.00

1979

British Dogs	2.00
Spring Wild Flowers	2.00
Elections to European Assembly	2.00
Horse Racing Paintings	2.00
Year of the Child	3.00
Rowland Hill	2.00
Metropolitan Police	2.00
Christmas	2.00

1980

Water Birds	2.00
Liverpool & Manchester Railway	2.00
London 1980 Exhibition	2.00
London Landmarks	2.00
Famous Authoresses	2.00
British Conductors	2.00
Sports Centenaries	2.00
Christmas	2.00

1981

Folklore	2.00
Year of the Disabled	2.00
British Butterflies	2.00
British Landscapes	2.00
Royal Wedding	3.50
Duke of Edinburgh Awards	2.00
Fishing Industry	2.00
Christmas	2.00

Charles Darwin, 1982

1982

Charles Darwin	2.00
Youth Organisations	2.00
British Theatre	2.00
Maritime Heritage	2.00
British Textiles	2.00
Information Technology Year	1.75
British Motor Cars	2.50
Christmas	2.00

1983

British River Fish	2.00
Commonwealth Day	2.00
Engineering Achievements	1.75
British Army Uniforms	3.00
British Gardens	2.00
British Fairs	2.00
Christmas	2.00

1984

College of Arms	2.50
British Cattle	2.50
Urban Renewal	2.00
CEPT/Elections to European Parliament	2.00
Greenwich Meridian	2.00
Mail Coaches	2.50
British Council	2.00
Christmas	2.00

1985

Famous Trains	3.50
Insects	2.50
British Composers	2.00
Safety at Sea	2.00
350th Anniversary of Royal Mail	2.00
Arthurian Legend	2.50
British Film Year	2.75
Christmas	2.00

1986

Industry Year	2.00
Halley's Comet	2.75
Queen's 60th Birthday	2.75
Nature Conservation	2.00

Domesday Book	2.00
Commonwealth Games/World Hockey Cup	3.50
Royal Wedding	2.25
Royal Air Force	2.50
Christmas	2.25

■ 1987

Flowers	2.25
Sir Isaac Newton	2.25
British Architects in Europe	2.25
St John Ambulance	2.25
Order of the Thistle	2.25
150th Anniversary of Accession of Queen Victoria	2.25
Studio Pottery	2.25
Christmas	2.25

■ 1988

Linnean Society	2.25
Welsh Bible	2.25
Sports Organisations	2.25
Transport and Mail Services	2.75
Bicentennary of Australian Settlement	2.25
Spanish Armada	2.25
Edward Lear	2.25
Christmas	2.50

Industrial Archaeology, 1989

■ 1989

Royal Society for the Protection of Birds	3.00
Food and Farming Year	2.25
Anniversaries and Events	2.25
Games and Toys	2.75
Industrial Archaeology	2.25
Royal Microscopical Society	2.25
Lord Mayor's Show	2.25
Christmas	2.75

■ 1990

Penny Black Anniversary	4.00
RSPCA	3.50
Stamp World Exhibition and Glasgow	2.25
Queen's Awards for Export and Technology	2.25
Kew Gardens	2.25
Thomas Hardy	1.75
90th Birthday of Queen Mother	3.50

Gallantry Awards	2.25
Astronomy	2.25
Christmas	2.50

■ 1991

Dog Paintings	3.75
Scientific Achievements	2.25
Europe in Space	2.50
World Student Games/Rugby World Cup	2.25
World Congress of Roses	3.75
Identification of Dinosaurs	3.75
Ordnance Survey	2.75
Christmas	2.75

Four Seasons: Wintertime, 1992

■ 1992

Four Seasons: Wintertime	2.40
40th Anniversary of Accession	3.50
Alfred, Lord Tennyson	2.50
International Events	2.75
Civil War	2.40
Gilbert and Sullivan Operas	3.50
Protection of the Environment	2.40
Single European Market	1.75
Christmas	2.75

■ 1993

Abbotsbury Swannery	3.50
John Harrison	2.50
World Orchid Conference	3.00
Contemporary Art	2.50
Roman Britain	2.40
Inland Waterways	2.40
Four Seasons: Autumn	2.75
Sherlock Holmes	5.00
Christmas	5.00

■ 1994

Age of Steam	4.00
25th Anniversary of Investiture of the Prince of Wales	4.00
Picture Postcards	3.50
Channel Tunnel	3.00
D–Day	3.50
Scottish Golf Courses	3.00
Four Seasons: Summertime	3.00
Medical Discoveries	2.50
Christmas	3.00

Cats, 1995

1995
Cats	4.00
Four Seasons: Springtime	2.50
National Trust	2.50
Peace and Freedom	2.50
Novels of H. G. Wells	3.50
Shakespeare' Globe Theatre	3.75
Pioneers of Communications	3.00
Rugby League	3.50
Christmas	3.50

1996
Robert Burns	3.50
Wildfowl and Wetlands Trust	2.50
Cinema	2.50
European Football Championship	4.25
Olympic and Paralympic Games, Atlanta	3.25
Famous Women	2.75
Children's Television	2.75
Classic Sports Cars	4.50
Christmas	4.00

1997
King Henry VIII	6.00
Religious Anniversaries	3.50
Tales of Horror	2.75
British Aircraft Designers	3.25
All The Queen's Horses	3.50
Sub Post Offices	2.75
Enid Blyton	4.00
Christmas	4.00
Royal Golden Wedding Anniversary	4.00

Diana, Princess of Wales, 1998 (Welsh version)

1998
Endangered Species	3.75
Diana, Princess of Wales	4.50
Diana, Princess of Wales (Welsh version)	42.00
The Queen's Beasts	3.50
Lighthouses	4.00
Comedians	4.25
National Health Service	3.00
Children's Fantasy Novels	4.00
Notting Hill Carnival	3.00
British Land Speed Records	3.25
Christmas	3.25

(* The Princess of Wales pack's limited edition Welsh language version was available only at post offices in Wales.)

Inventors' Tale, 1999

1999
Inventors' Tale	3.00
Travellers' Tale	3.00
Patients' Tale	3.00
Settlers' Tale	3.00
Workers' Tale	3.00
Entertainers' Tale	6.00
Royal Wedding	2.50
Citizens' Tale	3.00
Scientists' Tale	3.00
Farmers' Tale	3.00
Soldiers' Tale	3.00
Christians' Tale	3.00
Artists' Tale	3.00
Millennium Timekeeper	9.00

2000
Above and Beyond	3.50
Fire and Light	3.50
Water and Coast	3.50
Life and Earth	4.00
Art and Craft	4.00
Her Majesty's Stamps	30.00
People and Places	4.00
Stone and Soil	4.00
Tree and Leaf	4.00
Queen Mother's 100th Birthday	10.00
Mind and Matter	4.00
Body and Bone	4.00
Spirit and Faith	4.00
Sound and Vision	4.00

Punch and Judy, 2001

2001

Rights of the Child	4.00
Occasions	6.00
Cats and Dogs	11.00
The Weather	5.50
Submarine Service	9.00
Double-Decker Buses	7.00
Fashion Hats	4.50
Pond Life	4.50
Punch and Judy Puppets	7.00
Nobel Prizes	16.00
Flags and Ensigns	12.00
Christmas	6.00

2002

Just So Stories	10.00
Golden Jubilee	7.50
Occasions	5.25
British Coastlines	5.00
Circus	5.50
Queen Mother Memorial	4.75
Airliners	7.00
Football World Cup, Japan and Korea	5.50
Commonwealth Games	5.50
Peter Pan	7.50
Bridges of London	20.00
Astronomy	7.00
Pillar Boxes	5.50
Wilding Definitives, part I	17.00
Christmas	5.50

Rugby World Cup, 2003

2003

Birds of Prey	11.00
Occasions	6.00
Discovery of DNA	5.50
Fruit and Vegetables	11.00
Extreme Endeavours	6.00
Wilding Definitives, part II	6.00
50th Anniversary of Coronation	11.00
21st Birthday of Prince William	8.50
British Journey: Scotland	6.50
Pub Signs	5.25
Classic Transport Toys	5.50
British Museum	6.00
Christmas	7.50
Rugby World Cup	17.00

Classic Locomotives (miniature sheet version), 2004

2004

Classic Locomotives	9.00
Classic Locomotives (miniature sheet version)	12.00
Occasions	4.50
Lord of the Rings	9.00
British Journey: Northern Ireland	6.50
Entente Cordiale	11.00
Ocean Liners	6.50
Royal Horticultural Society	6.50
British Journey: Wales	5.00
Royal Society of Arts	5.50
Woodland Animals	11.00
Crimean War	6.50
Christmas	6.50

2005

Farm Animals	11.00
British Journey: South-West England	5.50
Jane Eyre	6.50
Magic Circle	5.50
Royal Wedding	7.00
World Heritage Sites	7.50
Trooping the Colour	6.50
Motorcycles	6.75
London 2012 Host City	7.00
Changing Tastes in Britain	5.25
Classic ITV Programmes	5.25
The Ashes	4.50
Battle of Trafalgar	6.50
Christmas	6.50

Modern Architecture, 2006

2006

Animal Tales	7.50
British Journey: England	11.00
Isambard Kingdom Brunel	5.00
Ice Age Animals	5.50
Queen's 80th Birthday	7.50
World Cup Winners	6.50
Modern Architecture	6.00
National Portrait Gallery	11.00
Victoria Cross	7.00
Sounds of Britain	6.00
Smilers	11.00
Christmas	8.00
Lest We Forget, part I	6.00
Celebrating Scotland	4.75

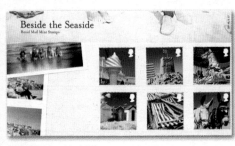

Beside The Seaside, 2007

2007

The Beatles	13.00
Sea Life	11.00
The Sky at Night	6.50
World of Invention	6.50
Abolition of the Slave Trade	6.50
Celebrating England	5.50
Beside the Seaside	6.50
40th Anniversary of Machin Definitives	5.50
Grand Prix	7.00
Harry Potter	13.00
Scouting	6.50
Endangered Species: Birds	12.00
British Army Uniforms	7.00
Royal Diamond Wedding	11.00
Christmas	10.00
Lest We Forget, part II	6.50

2008

Ian Fleming's James Bond	8.50
Working Dogs	7.50
Houses of Lancaster and York	11.00
Celebrating Northern Ireland	5.00
Rescue at Sea	6.00
Endangered Species: Insects	11.00
Cathedrals	11.00
Classic Carry On & Hammer Films	7.00
Air Displays	6.50
Handover of Olympic Flag	20.00
RAF Uniforms	7.00
50th Anniversary of Country Definitives	6.00
Women of Distinction	6.50
Christmas	7.00
Lest We Forget, part III	6.75

Olympic and Paralympic Games, 2009

2009

British Design Classics	11.00
Robert Burns	6.00
Charles Darwin	11.00
Celebrating Wales	5.00
Industrial Revolution	7.50
House of Tudor	11.00
Endangered Species: Plants	15.00
Mythical Creatures	8.00
Post Boxes	6.50
Fire and Rescue Services	9.00
Royal Navy Uniforms	8.00
Eminent Britons	11.00
Olympic and Paralympic Games, part I	11.00
Christmas	10.00

Royal Society, 2010

2010

Classic Album Covers	12.00
Business Customised and Smilers Stamps	12.00
Girlguiding	7.00
The Royal Society	11.00
Battersea Dogs & Cats Home	12.00
House of Stewart	11.00
Endangered Species: Mammals	9.00
Accession of George V/The King's Stamps	10.00
Britain Alone	14.00
House of Stuart	12.50
Olympic and Paralympic Games, part II	10.50
Great British Railways	7.50
Medical Breakthroughs	7.00
Winnie-the-Pooh	12.00
Christmas	14.00

2011

FAB. The Genius of Gerry Anderson	20.00
Classic Locomotives of England	5.50
Musicals	10.50
Magical Realms	9.50
WWF	15.00
Royal Shakespeare Company	13.00
Royal Wedding	9.00
Morris & Co	8.50
Thomas the Tank Engine	12.50
Olympic and Paralympic Games, part III	10.00
Crown Jewels	10.00
First UK Aerial Post	5.50
House of Hanover	12.50
UK A–Z, part 1	12.00
Christmas	10.50

House of Windsor and Saxe–Coburg Gotha, 2012

2012

Roald Dahl	13.00
House of Windsor and Saxe–Coburg Gotha	11.50
Diamond Jubilee (miniature sheet)	6.00
Britons of Distinction	10.50
Classic Locomotives of Scotland	5.50
Comics	10.50
UK A–Z, part 2	14.00
Great British Fashion	10.50
Diamond Jubilee (stamps)	20.00
Charles Dickens	13.50
Welcome to the Olympic Games	22.00
Welcome to the Paralympic Games	8.00
Memories of London 2012	12.50

Space Science	9.00
Christmas	12.00

2013

London Underground	14.00
Jane Austen	9.50
Doctor Who	19.00
Great Britons	11.00
Football Heroes	11.75
Royal Portraits	10.00
Classic Locomotives of Northern Ireland	7.00
Butterflies	11.00
Andy Murray	7.00
British Auto Legends	14.00
Merchant Navy	14.00
Dinosaurs	10.75
Christmas	12.00
Children's Christmas	4.00

2014

Classic Children's TV	12.75
Working Horses	9.50
Classic Locomotives of Wales	6.50
Remarkable Lives	10.50
Buckingham Palace	11.00
Great British Film	14.00
Sustainable Fish	11.00
Commonwealth Games	11.50
First World War 1914	10.50
Seaside Architecture	16.00
Prime Ministers	10.50
Christmas	12.50

2015

Alice's Adventures in Wonderland	16.00
Smilers	8.50
Inventive Britain	13.50
Bridges	10.00
Comedy Greats	10.00
175th anniversary of the Penny Black	5.00
First World War 1915	10.00
Magna Carta	11.00
Battle of Waterloo	16.00
Battle of Britain	9.00
Bees	18.00
Long To Reign Over Us	7.50
Rugby World Cup	10.50
Star Wars	16.50
Christmas	13.00

2016

Shackleton and the Endurance Expedition	13.00
Royal Mail 500	15.00
British Humanitarians	8.50
Shakespeare	9.50
The Queen's 90th Birthday	15.00
Animail	9.00
First World War 1916	12.00
Pink Floyd	12.00
Beatrix Potter	15.00

LOW–VALUE DEFINITIVES

Low–value definitives, 1971

1967	½d to 1/9	7.50
1967	½d to 1/9 (German version)	£110
1971	½p to 9p	6.50
1971	½p to 9p (Scandinavia tour)	18.00
1971	½p to 10p	22.00
1977	½p to 50p	4.50
1981	2½p to 75p (pack No129a)	10.00
1983	½p to 75p (pack No1)	22.00
1984	½p to 75p	19.00
1987	1p to 75p	22.00
1988	14p to 35p	6.25
1989	15p to 37p	5.50
1990	Penny Black Anniversary	4.00
1990	10p to 33p	5.75
1991	1p to 75p	22.00
1991	6p to 39p	6.00
1993	Self-adhesive booklet	17.00
1993	19p to 41p	5.00
1995	1p to £1	29.00
1996	20p to 63p	6.00
1997	2nd and 1st	4.00
1997	26p and 1st	3.50
1998	2nd, 1st, 1p to £1	14.00
1999	7p to 64p	7.50
2000	Millennium 1st	3.50
2000	Jeffery Matthews Colour Palette	80.00
2000	8p to 65p	6.00
2002	2nd, 1st, 1p to £1	14.00
2002	37p to 68p	4.25
2002	Wildings (part 1)	17.00
2002	Definitives Collection folder, containing the low values pack (2002), high values pack (2002) and country packs (2001–02)	32.00
2003	Worldwide and Europe	5.50
2003	Wildings (part 2)	6.00
2004	1st, Worldwide Postcard, 7p to 43p	10.00
2005	Castle definitives	5.00
2005	1p, 2p, 5p, 9p, 10p, 20p, 35p, 40p, 42p, 46p, 47p, 50p, 68p, £1, plus self-adhesive 2nd, 1st, Europe, Worldwide and postcard	50.00
2005	Definitives Collection folder, containing the low values pack (2005), high values pack (2003), country packs (2003) and country 42p values pack (2005)	32.00
2006	37p to 72p	9.50
2006	Pricing in Proportion	9.00

2007	16p to 78p	7.50
2007	1p to £1 ruby	37.50
2008	15p to 81p	4.00
2009	2nd to £1 with security features	7.50
2009	17p to 90p	7.00
2010	Definitives Collection folder, containing 1p to £1.46, plus Europe, Worldwide, Worldwide Postcard and 'Recorded Signed For'	52.00
2010	Low values in current use	23.00
2010	Special Delivery	21.00
2011	1p to £1.65	12.50
2012	Olympic and Paralympic Games definitives	12.00
2012	1st, 1st Large, 87p, £1.28, £1.90	11.00
2013	1p to £1 in new colour palette	8.00
2013	78p to £1.88 and 'Royal Mail Signed For'	13.00
2014	81p to £2.15	9.00
2015	£1.33 to £3.30	21.00
2016	£1.05	2.25

HIGH–VALUE DEFINITIVES

£10 definitive, 1993

1969	2/6 to £1	13.00
1969	2/6 to £1 (German version)	70.00
1970	10p to 50p	7.00
1971	20p to £1	10.00
1977	£1 to £5 (pack no. 91)	13.50
1987	£1 to £5 (pack no. 13)	£120
1987	£1.60	15.00
1988	Castles £1 to £5	16.00
1992	Castles £1 to £5	15.00
1993	£10	18.00
1995	£3	10.00
1997	Castles £1.50 to £5	65.00
1999	£1.50 to £5 (Enschedé)	28.00
2000	£1.50 to £5 (De La Rue)	27.50
2003	£1.50 to £5 (gravure)	19.00
2009	£1.50 to £5 with security features	19.00

COUNTRY DEFINITIVES

Scotland definitives, 1983

England

2001	2nd, 1st, E, 65p	5.00
2003	2nd, 1st, E, 68p	5.00

Northern Ireland

1970	3d, 4d sepia, 4d red, 5d, 9d, 1/3, 1/6	5.50
1971	2½p, 3p, 5p, 7½p	2.50
1974	3p, 3½p, 5½p, 8p	3.00
1974	3p, 3½p, 4½p, 5½p, 8p	3.00
1976	6½p, 8½p, 10p, 11p	2.00
1981	7p, 9p, 10½p, 11½p, 12p, 13½p, 14p, 15p, 18p, 22p	5.00
1983	10p, 12½p, 16p, 20½p, 26p, 28p	10.00
1984	10p, 13p, 16p, 17p, 22p, 26p, 28p, 31p	10.00
1987	12p, 13p, 17p, 18p, 22p, 26p, 28p, 31p	11.00
1999	19p, 25p, 30p, 41p	9.50
2000	1st, 40p, 65p	12.50
2001	2nd, 1st, E, 65p	5.00
2003	2nd, 1st, E, 68p	5.00

Scotland

1970	3d, 4d sepia, 4d red, 5d, 6d, 9d, 1/3, 1/6	5.00
1971	2½p, 3p, 5p, 7½p	2.50
1974	3p, 3½p, 5½p, 8p	3.00
1974	3p, 3½p, 4½p, 5½p, 8p	3.00
1976	6½p, 8½p, 10p, 11p	2.00
1981	7p, 9p, 10½p, 11½p, 12p, 13½p, 14p, 15p, 18p, 22p	6.00
1983	10p, 12½p, 16p, 20½p, 26p, 28p	10.00
1984	10p, 13p, 16p, 17p, 22p, 26p, 28p, 31p	9.00
1987	12p, 13p, 17p, 18p, 22p, 26p, 28p, 31p	10.00
1999	2nd, 1st, E, 64p	7.50
2000	65p	8.00
2002	2nd, 1st, E, 65p	13.00
2003	2nd, 1st, E, 68p	6.00

Wales

1970	3d, 4d sepia, 4d red, 5d, 9d, 1/6	5.00
1971	2½p, 3p, 5p, 7½p	2.50
1974	3p, 3½p, 5½p, 8p	3.00
1974	3p, 3½p, 4½p, 5½p, 8p	3.00
1976	6½p, 8½p, 10p, 11p	2.00
1981	7p, 9p, 10½p, 11½p, 12p, 13½p, 14p, 15p, 18p, 22p	6.00
1983	10p, 12½p, 16p, 20½p, 26p, 28p	10.00
1984	10p, 13p, 16p, 17p, 22p, 26p, 28p, 31p	10.00
1987	12p, 13p, 17p, 18p, 22p, 26p, 28p, 31p	10.00
1997	20p, 26p, 37p, 63p	10.50
1999	2nd, 1st, E, 64p	7.50
2000	65p	8.50
2002	2nd, 1st, E, 65p	13.00
2003	2nd, 1st, E, 68p	6.00

All Countries

(comprising the stamps of Northern Ireland, Scotland and Wales up to 1998, and additionally England from 2002)

1988	14p, 19p, 23p, 32p (x 3 countries)	9.00
1989	15p, 20p, 24p, 34p (x 3 countries)	9.00
1990	17p, 22p, 26p, 37p (x 3 countries)	9.00
1991	18p, 24p, 28p, 39p (x 3 countries)	9.00
1993	19p, 25p, 30p, 41p (x 3 countries)	9.00
1996	20p, 26p, 37p, 63p (x 3 countries)	14.00
1998	20p (centre band), 26p, 37p, 63p (x 3 countries)	15.00

2002	68p (x 4 countries)	5.00
2004	40p (x 4 countries)	6.00
2005	42p (x 4 countries)	6.00
2006	44p, 72p (x 4 countries)	10.00
2007	48p, 78p (x 4 countries)	8.50
2008	50p, 81p (x 4 countries)	9.00
2008	2nd, 1st, 50p, 81p (x 4 countries)	32.00
2008	50th anniversary of Country Definitives	10.00
2009	56p, 90p (x 4 countries)	11.00
2010	60p, 97p (x 4 countries)	11.00
2011	68p, £1.10 (x 4 countries)	14.00
2012	87p, £1.28 (x 4 countries)	22.00
2013	88p (x 4 countries)	7.00
2014	97p (x 4 countries)	6.50
2015	£1, £1.33 (x 4 countries)	15.00
2016	£1.05 (x 4 countries)	6.50

Isle of Man

1971	2½p, 3p, 5p, 7½p	2.50

POSTAGE DUES

Postage dues, 1977

1971	½p to 5p, 10p, 20p, 50p, £1	35.00
1977	½p to £1	10.00
1982	1p to £5	26.00
1994	1p to £5	32.00

GREETINGS STAMPS

Memories, 1992

1992	Memories	10.00
1993	Gift giving	10.00
1994	Messages	10.00
1995	Art	10.00
1996	Cartoons	10.00
1997	Flowers	10.00

SPECIAL PACKS

British Films, 1985

1971	NABA Exhibition	
	(definitives ½p to £1 and postage dues)	85.00
1972	Belgica Exhibition	
	(1971 Christmas and 1972 Village Churches sets)	7.00
1972	Royal Silver Wedding	3.50
1973	County Cricket	4.00
1973	Palace of Westminster	
	(Parliamentary Conference set)	4.00
1974	Winston Churchill	3.50
1975	Railways	3.50
1977	Silver Jubilee	2.50
1978	25th Anniversary of Coronation	2.50
1981	Royal Wedding	3.00
1981	Royal Wedding (Japanese version)	5.00
1982	Electronic Post (Information Technology set)	£175
1984	Royal Mail (Mail Coaches set)	4.50
1985	British Films	5.00
1986	The Queen's Birthday	7.50
1988	Australian Bicentennary	7.50
1990	Penny Black Anniversary	
	(set of five stamps and miniature sheet)	10.50
1994	Channel Tunnel (joint issue with France)	15.00
1997	Royal Golden Wedding	
	(Queen's Horses and Golden Wedding sets)	20.00
2000	Stamp Show 2000	
	(mint and cancelled miniature sheets)	£100
2000	Stamp Show 2000	
	(The Definitive Portrait, Profile On Print and	
	Special By Design prestige stamp books)	50.00
2004	Entente Cordiale (joint issue with France)	12.00
2005	World Heritage (joint issue with Australia)	35.00
2008	Lest We Forget collection	
	(2006, 2007 and 2008 miniature sheets)	35.00
2009	Brilliant Britain collection	
	(2006 Celebrating Scotland, 2007 Celebrating	
	England, 2008 Celebrating Northern Ireland	
	and 2009 Celebrating Wales miniature sheets)	30.00
2009	Military Uniforms collection	
	(2007, 2008, and 2009 miniature sheets)	30.00
2011	Harry Potter Heroes and Villains	
	(Magical Realms block of 10)	12.00

CHRISTMAS PACKS

Christmas, 1985

1985	Christmas stamps (50 x 12p)	20.00
1986	Christmas stamps (36 x 13p)	9.00
1987	Christmas stamps (36 x 13p)	9.00

FACSIMILE PACKS

Penny Black, 2000

2000	1840 Penny Black (Stamp Show 2000)	70.00
2010	1929 PUC £1 (London 2010)	8.50
2011	1841 Penny Red (170th anniversary)	8.50
2012	1948 Olympic Games set (London Olympics)	35.00
2013	1913 Seahorses set (100th anniversary)	15.00
2014	Festival of Britain 2½d	9.00

MINIATURE SHEET PACKS

Miniature Sheets, 2005

2005	Miniature Sheets collection	65.00
2006	Miniature Sheets collection	80.00
2007	Miniature Sheets collection	60.00
2008	Miniature Sheets collection	60.00
2009	Miniature Sheets collection	60.00
2010	Miniature Sheets collection	55.00
2011	Miniature Sheets collection	£130
2012	Miniature Sheets collection	60.00
2013	Miniature Sheets collection	60.00
2014	Miniature Sheets collection	50.00
2015	Miniature Sheets collection	45.00

YEAR BOOKS & PACKS

In this section, prices are quoted for packs in mint condition only.

YEAR PACKS

Year Pack, 1967

1967 year pack	5.50
1968 year pack (blue cover)	3.50
1968 year pack (red cover)	3.50
1968 year pack (German version)	£100
1969 year pack	10.00
1970 year pack	15.00
1971 year pack	17.50
1972 year pack	17.50
1973 year pack	12.50
1974 year pack	8.00
1975 year pack	6.00
1976 year pack	7.50
1977 year pack	6.00
1978 year pack	4.50
1979 year pack	6.00
1980 year pack	7.00
1981 year pack	8.50
1982 year pack	12.50
1983 year pack	12.50
1984 year pack	15.00
1985 year pack	15.00
1986 year pack	16.00
1987 year pack	15.00
1988 year pack	15.00
1989 year pack	15.00
1990 year pack	15.00
1991 year pack	17.00
1992 year pack	17.00
1993 year pack	18.00
1994 year pack	28.00
1995 year pack	25.00
1996 year pack	30.00
1997 year pack	25.00

1998 year pack	30.00
1999 year pack	45.00
2000 year pack	45.00
2001 year pack	55.00
2002 year pack	70.00
2003 year pack	76.00
2004 year pack	70.00
2005 year pack	70.00
2006 year pack	85.00
2007 year pack	£115
2008 year pack	90.00

Year Pack, 2009

2009 year pack	£110
2010 year pack	£140
2011 year pack	£140
2012 year pack	£120
2013 year pack	£140
2014 year pack	£125
2015 year pack	£155

YEAR BOOKS

Year Book, 1984

1984 year book	45.00
1985 year book	30.00
1986 year book	25.00
1987 year book	15.00
1988 year book	16.00
1989 year book	17.00
1990 year book	17.00
1991 year book	18.50
1992 year book	21.00
1993 year book	23.00
1994 year book	23.00
1995 year book	23.00
1996 year book	28.00
1997 year book	26.00
1998 year book	30.00
1999 year book	45.00
2000 year book	50.00
2001 year book	60.00
2002 year book	70.00
2003 year book	80.00
2004 year book	70.00
2005 year book	70.00
2006 year book	80.00
2007 year book	£120
2008 year book	£100

Year Book, 2009

2009 year book	£110
2010 year book	£140
2011 year book	£140
2012 year book	£300
2013 year book	£140
2014 year book	£140
2015 year book	£180

STAMP POSTAL AUCTIONS

held every few months with good selection of GB, Commonwealth and World, also Cigarette Cards. Suit both collectors and dealers. Keen estimates and no buyer premiums.

Free catalogue from:

G Sharples, 32 Carr Gate,

Thornton Cleveleys, Lancashire, FY5 1LB

Tel: 01253 825464

email:sharples601@btinternet.com

You won't regret it!

Use these pages to compile a 'wants' list or make notes

....

....

....

....

....

....

....

....

....

....

....

....

....

....

....

....

....

....

....

....

....

....

....

....

....

....

....

....

....

....

....

....

....

....

....

....

....

....

....

....

....

KEY CONTACTS

To help you find your way around the hobby, here are contact details for the major players in the world of British stamps

ROYAL MAIL
■ **Philatelic Bureau**
Tallents House, 21 South Gyle Crescent,
Edinburgh EH12 9PB.
Tel: 08457 641641 (orders)
www.royalmail.com/stamps
■ **London Special Handstamp Centre**
Royal Mail, Mount Pleasant, Farringdon Road,
London EC1A 1BB.
■ **Midlands Special Handstamp Centre**
Royal Mail, St Stephen's Street, Birmingham B6 4AA.
■ **Northern England Special Handstamp Centre**
Royal Mail, South Shields DO, Keppell
Street, South Shields, Tyne & Wear
NE33 1AA.
■ **Scotland & Northern Ireland Special
Handstamp Centre**
Royal Mail, Tallents House, 21 South Gyle Crescent,
Edinburgh EH12 9PB.
■ **Wales & The West Special Handstamp Centre**
Royal Mail, 220 Penarth Road, Cardiff CF11 8TA.

PHILATELIC COLLECTIONS
■ **British Library**
96 Euston Road, London NW1 2DB.
Tel: 020 7412 7635
www.collectbritain.co.uk
■ **The Postal Museum**
Freeling House, Phoenix Place, London WC1X 0DL.
Tel: 020 7239 2570
www.postalheritage.org.uk
■ **Royal Philatelic Collection**
www.royal.gov.uk

SOCIETIES
■ **Royal Philatelic Society London**
41 Devonshire Place, London W1N 1PE.
www.rpsl.org.uk
■ **National Philatelic Society**
www.ukphilately.org.uk/nps
■ **Great Britain Philatelic Society**
www.gbps.org.uk
■ **Association of British Philatelic Societies**
www.abps.org.uk
■ **British Philatelic Trust**
Suite 101, Business Design Centre,
52 Upper Street, London N1 0QH.
www.ukphilately.org.uk/bpt
■ **Machin Collectors Club**
www.machins.org
■ **Modern British Philatelic Circle**
www.mbp-circle.co.uk
■ **Association of Great Britain
First Day Cover Collectors**
www.gbfdc.co.uk
■ **British Thematic Association**
www.brit-thematic-assoc.com
■ **Philatelic Traders Society**
PO Box 290, Lingfield, Surrey RH7 9AX.
www.thephilatelictraderssociety.co.uk

EXHIBITIONS
■ **Stampex**
www.stampex.ltd.uk

STAMP MAGAZINE
www.stampmagazine.co.uk

ADVERTISING INDEX